INSPIRE MATHS

TEACHER'S GUIDE 5A

Noogol

Googol

Ooogol

Koogol

Toogol

Zoogol

Consultant and author
Dr Fong Ho Kheong

Authors
Gan Kee Soon and Chelvi Ramakrishnan

UK consultants
Carole Skinner, Simon d'Angelo and Elizabeth Gibbs

OXFORD
UNIVERSITY PRESS

© 2015 Marshall Cavendish Education Pte Ltd

Published by Marshall Cavendish Education
Times Centre, 1 New Industrial Road, Singapore 536196
Customer Service Hotline: (65) 6213 9444
Email: tmesales@mceducation.com
Website: www.mceducation.com

Distributed by
Oxford University Press
Great Clarendon Street, Oxford,
OX2 6DP, United Kingdom
www.oxfordprimary.co.uk
www.oxfordowl.co.uk

First published 2015
Reprinted 2015

ISBN 978-981-01-8901-3

Printed in the United Kingdom

Acknowledgements
Written by Dr Fong Ho Kheong, Gan Kee Soon and Chelvi Ramakrishnan

UK consultants: Carole Skinner, Simon d'Angelo and Elizabeth Gibbs

Cover artwork by Daron Parton

The authors and publisher would like to thank all schools and individuals who helped to trial and review Inspire Maths resources.

Contents

The background to *Inspire Maths*   iv

What is *Inspire Maths?*   vi

The concrete-pictorial-abstract approach   vii

The bar model   viii

Heuristics for problem solving   ix

Making use of variation   x

The *Inspire Maths* teaching pathway   xi

Using the Teacher's Guide   xvi

Long-term planning   xviii

Unit 1 Whole Numbers (1)

   Medium-term plan   2

   Teaching sequences   6

Unit 2 Whole Numbers (2)

   Medium-term plan   45

   Teaching sequences   49

Unit 3 Fractions (1)

   Medium-term plan   112

   Teaching sequences   116

Unit 4 Fractions (2)

   Medium-term plan   164

   Teaching sequences   168

Unit 5 Area of a Triangle

   Medium-term plan   219

   Teaching sequences   221

Unit 6 Ratio

   Medium-term plan   242

   Teaching sequences   246

Heuristics-based questions   302

Photocopy masters   318

The background to *Inspire Maths*

A letter from Dr Fong Ho Kheong

Dear Colleague,

I am both humbled and proud to see that my work has now been adapted for use in many countries. *My Pals are Here!*, the series from which *Inspire Maths* is adapted, has been translated into languages including Spanish, Indonesian, Dutch and Arabic, and the books are used by millions of children all over the world.

International surveys show that children taught with the series score higher than their peers in standardised tests, and also that it helps young children to become more confident with maths. The 2012 PISA survey again placed Singapore's children at the top of international rankings for mathematics; the country also had the highest percentage of top achievers. In the USA, it was reported in 2013 that schools in the Fayette County, West Virginia who had adopted the programme had made impressive progress in their mathematics results, including a 12 per cent improvement among third graders in one school and a 20 per cent improvement among fourth graders in another.

Why does *Inspire Maths* work? A major strength of *Inspire Maths* is its robust structure, based on best-practice principles and methods of teaching and learning mathematics, including the concrete-pictorial-abstract (CPA) and scaffolding approaches, and a systematic teaching pathway. This comprehensive pathway emphasises mastery – with continuous, active reinforcement of concepts to help children assimilate and accommodate their learning – followed by extension, challenging children to develop and practise the thinking skills that will enable them to become confident, critically aware and independent learners. The textbooks from which *Inspire Maths* is adapted have also been informed by continuous evaluation of their success in the classroom, through a process of school visits, classroom observation and programme review. Because of this, *Inspire Maths* gives you a proven framework for supporting children of all abilities to achieve success.

Inspire Maths is based on well-established constructivist ideas of learning, and the views of internationally-renowned educationalists including Jerome Bruner, Jean Piaget, Lev Vygotsky, Richard Skemp and David Ausubel. Constructivism underpins the programme's approach to learning mathematical concepts and skills through assimilation and accommodation, and their reinforcement through reflective activities such as journal writing and error correction. This perspective is also reflected in the programme's emphasis on mastery learning and building children's confidence.

More particularly, Bruner's three modes of representation are mirrored by the concrete–pictorial–abstract learning progression which is central to *Inspire Maths*. Bruner's ideas parallel Piaget's stages of development; essentially, children's understanding of mathematical concepts depends on their stage of development. Learning in the early stages is achieved through concrete representation. Then, when ready, children can move on to pictorial representations – such as the bar model – which in turn provide them with a bridge to the abstract stage, and a flexible, fully independent understanding of the abstract, symbolic language of maths. Though it cannot be used to tackle every problem, the bar model has a particularly significant role in helping children at the concrete and semi-concrete operational stage (Piaget's developmental theory) to approach and solve problems successfully.

Skemp's ideas about instrumental and relational understanding are also an important part of the pedagogy underpinning *Inspire Maths*. Skemp suggests that learning mathematics by relating ideas to each other (relational understanding) is more meaningful, and therefore more effective, than memorising facts and procedures (instrumental understanding). Building on these ideas, *Inspire Maths* is designed to develop children's lasting and profound mathematical understanding which they will continue to extend and apply.

I would like to congratulate the UK schools and teachers who have made the choice to use *Inspire Maths*. I am confident that your children will experience similar success to that seen in other countries who have adopted this approach.

Dr Fong achieved a PhD in Mathematics Education from King's College London before teaching mathematics in the National Institute of Education, Nanyang Technological University, for over 24 years. He is currently a senior Mathematics Specialist with the Regional Centre for Education in Science and Mathematics (RECSAM) in Penang, Malaysia. He has published more than 100 journal articles, research reports, and primary and secondary mathematics books, and his research work includes diagnosing children with mathematical difficulties and teaching thinking skills to solve mathematical problems.

What is *Inspire Maths*?

Inspire Maths is the UK edition of *My Pals are Here!*, the internationally renowned approach used to teach maths in Singapore, which was heavily influenced by the Cockroft report of 1982[1]. Singapore's Ministry of Education drew on leading international research on effective teaching and learning of mathematics to meet the challenge of raising primary mathematics attainment within Singapore's schools.

The approach to mathematics teaching and learning that was developed was further refined over subsequent decades and it is this approach that is central to *My Pals are Here!* Authored by Dr Fong Ho Kheong and first published in 2001, *My Pals are Here!* is used by almost 100% of State Primary schools and over 80% of Primary schools in Singapore.

Dr Fong's overarching aim in developing *My Pals are Here!* was to help all children understand and use mathematics confidently and competently, and to support non-specialist maths teachers to deliver this. The programme's success in achieving this aim is reflected in the high levels of mathematics attainment by Singapore's pupils, who are consistently ranked among the very top in international comparison studies such as PISA and TIMSS. It is also reflected in the results of schools outside Singapore that have adopted the series, for example, in the USA and South Africa.

Inspire Maths provides a highly scaffolded learning framework with problem solving at its heart. It is built on a focused, coherent and cumulative spiral curriculum that continuously builds and consolidates knowledge to reach deep understanding. The programme encourages extensive practice to develop fluency and mastery, so that every child – across all abilities – can succeed at mathematics.

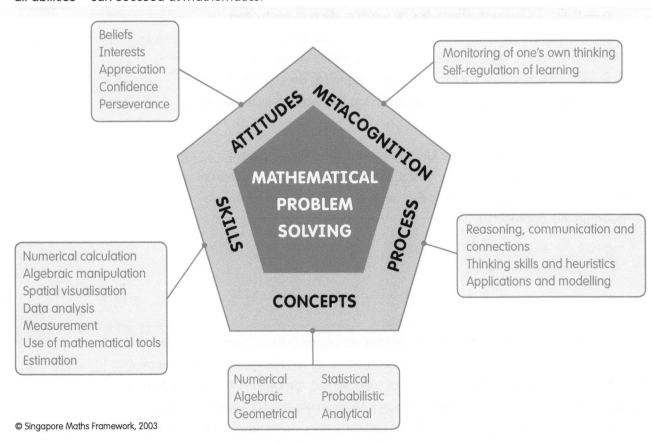

© Singapore Maths Framework, 2003

The principles that underpin *Inspire Maths*

---

[1] Mathematics Counts, Dr W.H.Cockroft, 1982

The concrete-pictorial-abstract approach

Inspire Maths emphasises the development of critical thinking and problem solving skills, which help children make connections to develop deeper understanding. The powerful concrete–pictorial–abstract (CPA) approach, including the bar model method, is central to this.

Why is the CPA approach so powerful? From very early on in their school life, we expect children to use and understand numbers, which are abstract concepts. Many children struggle with this and so their first experiences of mathematics can be confusing, leaving them with no solid foundation to build on for later learning. The CPA approach helps children achieve secure number sense – that is, a sense of what numbers really represent and how to use them mathematically. This is done through a series of carefully structured representations – first using physical objects (concrete), then diagrams or pictures (pictorial), and ultimately using representations such as numerals (abstract).

In the example below from *Inspire Maths* Pupil Textbook 5A, children are building their understanding of place value and numbers up to 10 million. Using the CPA approach, the learning is first introduced using counters on place value charts, this is then presented in pictorial forms and finally words and numerals.

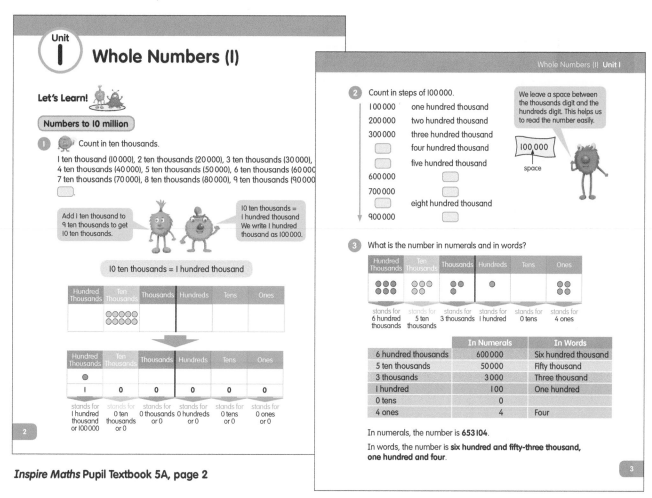

Inspire Maths Pupil Textbook 5A, page 2

Inspire Maths Pupil Textbook 5A, page 3

The bar model

The bar model is a step-by-step method that helps children to understand and extract the information within a calculation or word problem. By drawing a bar model, children translate a calculation or word problem into a picture. The approach helps children process the information given in the problem, visualise the structure, make connections and solve the problem.

The bar model is first introduced in *Inspire Maths* 2. In the following activity, children explore addition and subtraction initially with concrete apparatus before moving on to using a pictorial representation – the bar model.

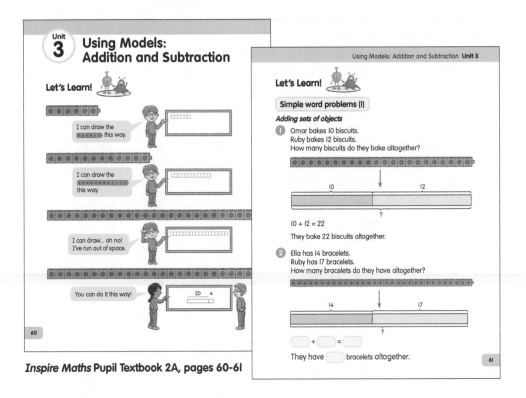

Inspire Maths Pupil Textbook 2A, pages 60-61

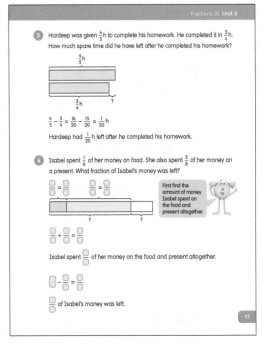

Inspire Maths Pupil Textbook 5A, page 97

In *Inspire Maths* 5 and 6, bar models are applied to increasingly complex situations. Children are encouraged to draw and interpret bar models to solve a wide variety of problems. In this example, use of bar models helps children realise what strategy they need to adopt to solve word problems involving fractions.

Heuristics for problem solving

Inspire Maths helps children learn to use *heuristics* to solve problems. *Heuristics* refers to the different strategies that children can adopt to solve unfamiliar or non-routine problems. These strategies include drawing the bar model, pattern-spotting, using diagrams and estimating or 'guess and check'.

In this *Let's Explore!* activity from *Inspire Maths* Pupil Textbook 5A, children are encouraged to use the strategy of 'guess and check' to find equivalent ratios.

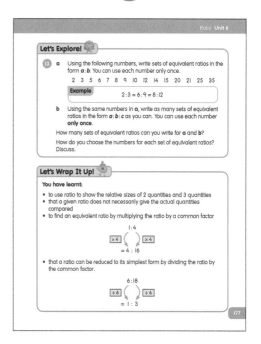

Inspire Maths **Pupil Textbook 5A, page 177**

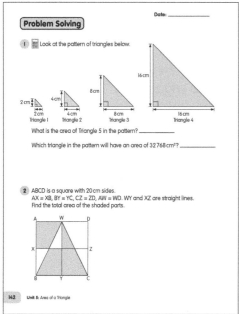

Inspire Maths **Practice Book 5A, page 142**

The *Inspire Maths* Practice Books reinforce concepts introduced in the Pupil Textbooks and provide varied, frequent practice to develop fluency. As they practise, children begin to self-select the appropriate strategy for each problem, helping them to become confident problem solvers.

Higher-order questioning

Inspire Maths is designed to stimulate thinking beyond the activities from the Pupil Textbooks. The activities should kick-start mathematically meaningful conversations through questioning, giving children opportunities to think mathematically, discover connections and be creative.

You can use written problems as a starting point for further questioning by asking open-ended questions. For example, 'Can you see a pattern? Why does it work? Does it always work? What happens if …?'

Modelling higher-order questioning at every opportunity will encourage children to use this strategy to explore and solve problems for themselves.

A heuristics-based question section at the end of this book contains additional questions to supplement your resources for developing pupils' higher-order thinking skills and skills in solving non-routine questions.

Making use of variation

Research shows that mathematical and perceptual variation deepens understanding as it constantly challenges children to develop their existing understanding by looking at questions from different perspectives and adapting to new situations. The numbers and problems in *Inspire Maths* activities have been specifically selected on this basis to challenge children as the questions progress and lead them towards mastery.

Mathematical variation

With mathematical variation, the mathematical concept, for example addition, stays the same but the variation is in the mathematics. For example, addition *without* regrouping and addition *with* regrouping. The variation challenges children to use their mathematical skills flexibly to suit the situation, deepening understanding.

Perceptual variation

With perceptual variation, the mathematical concept is the same throughout the sequence of questions but is presented in different ways. In this example from *Inspire Maths* Pupil Textbook 5A, a variety of models and diagrams are used to demonstrate like and unlike fractions. This use of perceptual variation helps to a deeper understanding.

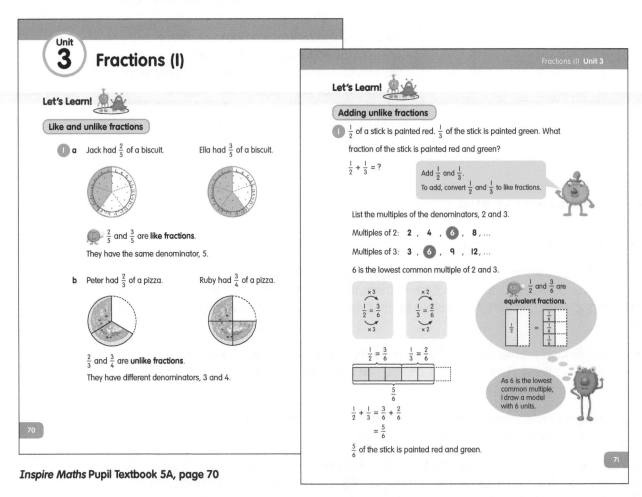

Inspire Maths Pupil Textbook 5A, page 70

Inspire Maths Pupil Textbook 5A, page 71

The *Inspire Maths* teaching pathway

Inspire Maths is a programme that teaches to mastery. It is built on a cumulative spiral curriculum, focusing on core topics to build deep understanding. The *Inspire Maths* teaching pathway scaffolds in-depth learning of key mathematical concepts through the development of problem-solving and critical thinking skills, and extensive opportunities for practice.

Pupil Textbooks to scaffold new learning

Inspire Maths Pupil Textbooks present new learning clearly and consistently, providing a highly scaffolded framework to support all children. Mathematical concepts are presented visually, with specific and structured activities, to build firm foundations. There are two Pupil Textbooks for each level.

Let's Learn! to build firm foundations

Carefully scaffolded learning through *Let's Learn!* activities in the *Inspire Maths* Pupil Textbooks promotes deep mathematical understanding through:

- clearly presented pages to illustrate how the CPA approach can be used to build firm foundations

- careful questioning to support the use of concrete apparatus

- opportunities for higher-order questioning (see page ix) to help children become confident and competent problem solvers

- opportunities to assess each child's understanding and prior knowledge through observing their use of concrete apparatus and how they approach the activity

- use of mathematical talk to explore and develop reasoning skills.

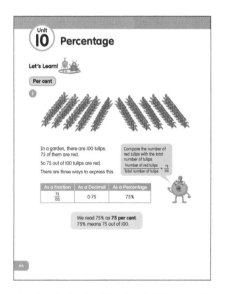

Inspire Maths Pupil Textbook 5B, page 64

Guided practice to develop deep understanding

After a concept has been introduced in *Let's Learn!*, guided practice develops the deep understanding required for mastery. Support and guide children as they work collaboratively in pairs or small groups through the guided practice activities indicated by empty coloured boxes in the Pupil Textbook.

Frequent opportunities for guided practice:

- help children develop deep understanding

- develop mathematical language and reasoning through collaborative work

- provide further opportunities to check children's understanding by observing their use of concrete apparatus and listening to their discussions

- help you to provide appropriate intervention – guiding those who need extra support and challenging those who are ready for the next step.

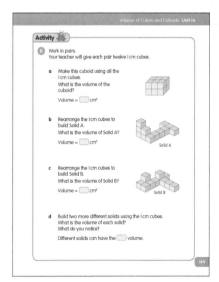

Inspire Maths Pupil Textbook 5B, page 169

Let's Explore! to investigate and apply learning

Engaging and investigative *Let's Explore!* activities in the *Inspire Maths* Pupil Textbooks encourage children to apply concepts they have been learning and provide an opportunity to assess their reasoning skills by observing how they approach the tasks. Children work collaboratively in small groups or pairs:

- *Let's Explore!* activities encourage children to investigate connections through mathematical reasoning

- meaningful discussion and conversation develops mathematical language.

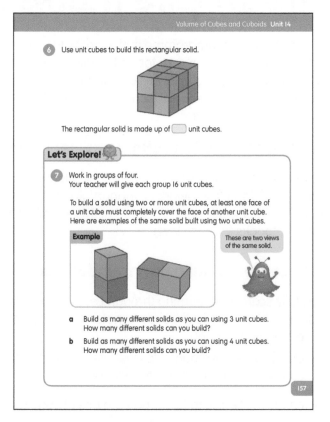

Inspire Maths **Pupil Textbook 5B, Page 157**

Maths Journal to reflect

The *Maths Journal* is where each child records their mathematical thinking and reflects on their learning. The typical *Maths Journal* would be a child's own exercise book or notebook – something that the child 'owns', can share with you, with parents or carers, and that builds up over time.

Children reflect on their learning through their *Maths Journal*:

- giving both the child and you a valuable assessment tool, showing progress over time

- providing opportunities for children to discuss their thinking with each other, parents or carers, and with you, helping to establish next steps and giving a sense of pride in their achievements.

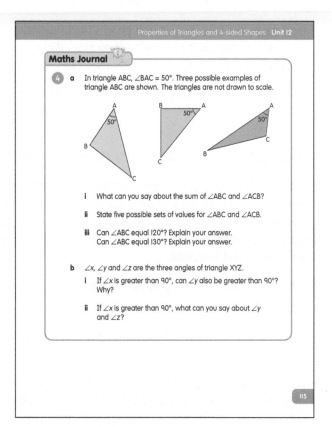

Inspire Maths **Pupil Textbook 5B, Page 115**

Let's Wrap It Up! and *Let's Revise!* to consolidate learning

The key concepts covered are summarised in *Let's Wrap It Up!* at the end of each unit. Worked examples provided in *Let's Revise!* allow children to explore their own understanding of those key concepts and reinforce strategies learnt.

Learning is consolidated through:

- emphasising key concepts

- discussion and exploration of the strategies used in worked examples

- enabling children to reflect on their own learning.

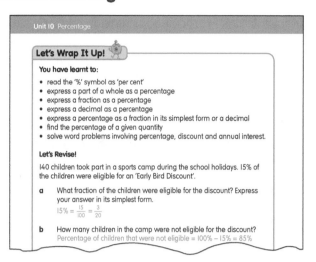

Inspire Maths **Pupil Textbook 5B, page 90**

Put On Your Thinking Caps! to challenge

Each unit concludes with a *Put On Your Thinking Caps!* activity in the Pupil Textbook which challenges children to solve non-routine problems.

Challenging activities:

- ask children to draw on prior knowledge as well as newly learned concepts

- ask children to use problem solving strategies and critical thinking skills, for example sequencing or comparing

- provide valuable opportunities to assess whether children have developed a deep understanding of a concept by listening to their explanations of their mathematical thinking and looking at how they model the problem, for example using concrete apparatus and pictorial representations.

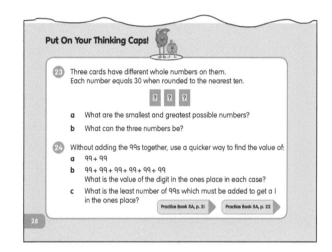

Inspire Maths **Pupil Textbook 5A, page 28**

Home Maths to encourage mathematical conversations

Home Maths activities in the Pupil Textbooks are engaging, hands-on suggestions that parents and carers can use with children to explore maths further outside the classroom, for example through finding shapes in pictures and around the house.

Engaging home activities:

- help you to involve parents and carers in their child's mathematical learning

- help children to see maths in the world around them.

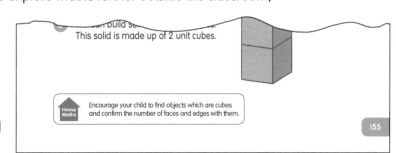

Inspire Maths **Pupil Textbook 5B, page 155**

Practice Books to develop fluency and consolidate

Inspire Maths Practice Books provide carefully structured questions to reinforce concepts introduced in the Pupil Textbooks and to provide varied, frequent practice. A wealth of activities develop fluency, build mathematical confidence and lead towards mastery. The Practice Books are also a valuable record of individual progress. There are four Practice Books for *Inspire Maths* 1-3 and two Practice Books for *Inspire Maths* 4-6.

Each Practice Book includes:

- **Challenging Practice** and **Problem Solving** activities to develop children's critical thinking skills

- **Reviews** after every two or three units, to reinforce learning

- **Revisions** that draw from a range of preceding topics, concepts and strands, for more complete consolidation.

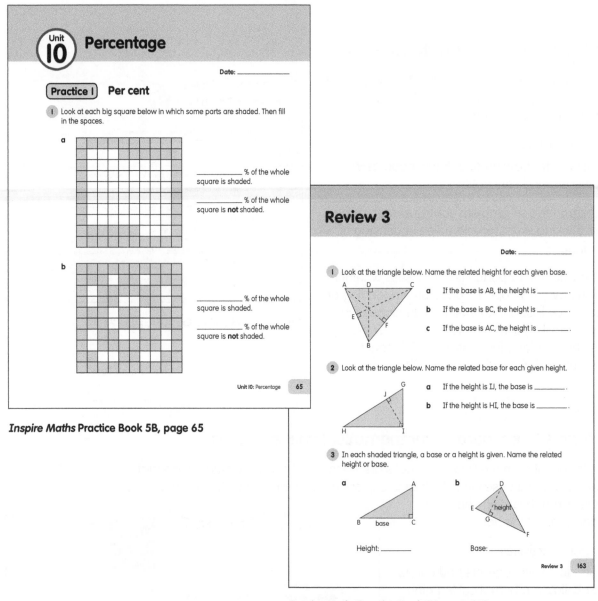

Inspire Maths **Practice Book 5B, page 65**

Inspire Maths **Practice Book 5A, page 163**

Assessment Books to create a record of progress

Inspire Maths provides comprehensive Assessment Books with regular summative assessments to create a record of progress for each child, as well as giving children opportunities to reflect on their own learning. The wraparound assessment provided through the *Inspire Maths* teaching pathway in combination with the *Inspire Maths* Assessment Books enables rapid, appropriate intervention as soon as a child needs it, before they fall behind and when they are ready to be challenged. Topics and concepts are frequently revisited in the assessments, helping to build mastery.

There is one Assessment Book for each level, providing complete coverage of the key concepts across a year. Each assessment is divided into sections so you can easily break them down into appropriate chunks to suit your class. For the early levels, you may choose to assess in small groups, reading out the questions and scribing answers. Encourage children to use concrete apparatus when they need support to help them work through the questions.

There are three types of assessment within each Assessment Book:

1. **Main assessments:** The main assessments cover the key learning objectives from the preceding two or three units of the Pupil Textbooks. Through the main assessments, children are given opportunities to apply their learning in a variety of different contexts, helping you to quickly identify which children are ready to move on and which need further support. Children may self-mark to reflect on their progress.

2. **Check-ups:** There are four check-ups in Year 5 which revisit the previous units, drawing on prior knowledge to encourage children to make connections and apply their learning to solve problems. These assessments give you valuable opportunities to check children's understanding through observing how they approach questions, use and interpret mathematical language and use heuristics.

3. **Challenging Problems:** These assessments make use of non-routine and unfamiliar questions to see how children use their repertoire of strategies to tackle more challenging problems. Use this as an opportunity to assess children's mathematical thinking, reasoning and problem solving skills by looking at their methods and how they approach the problem. They are particularly suitable for extension and assessing a child's level of mastery.

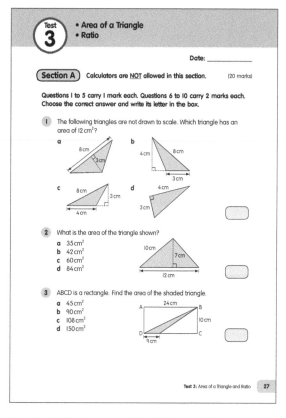

Inspire Maths Assessment Book 5, page 27

Using the Teacher's Guide

There are two *Inspire Maths* Teacher's Guides for each level, one per Pupil Textbook. Each Teacher's Guide contains:

- information on how to get started
- long-term planning support
- medium-term planning support
- suggested teaching sequence for each pupil textbook page
- answers
- photocopiable activities.

Opportunities are flagged for children to work independently in their **Maths Journal**, to record and reflect on their learning, leading towards mastery.

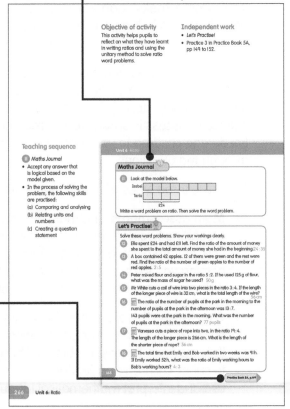

Inspire Maths Teacher's Guide 5A, page 266

Links to the Practice Books provide opportunities for **independent work** when children are ready, to develop fluency and lead towards mastery.

Equipment needed for each Pupil Textbook page is listed to help you prepare for the activities.

 This icon is used to indicate where children recall skills from earlier years and link them to new concepts in the current unit.

 This icon indicates that appropriate use of calculators is encouraged for the activities and practices to extend problem-solving skills.

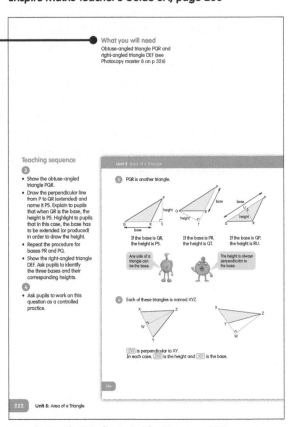

Inspire Maths Teacher's Guide 5A, page 222

Key concepts
clearly outline the important ideas children will be introduced to within each unit.

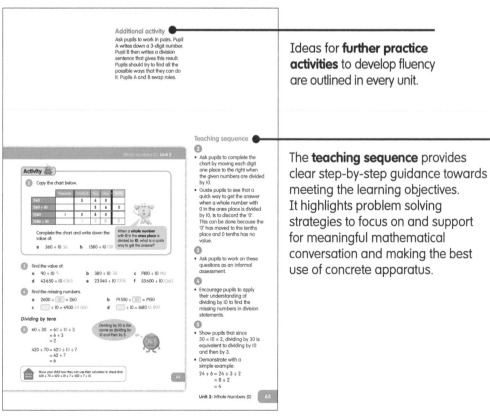

Inspire Maths Teacher's Guide 5A, page 267

Key thinking skills and problem solving strategies to look for and encourage are clearly highlighted, helping you to make meaningful assessments of children's understanding.

Learning objectives clearly signal the aims of the unit, which are designed to help children develop their understanding of the unit's key concepts. Children are introduced to the learning objectives in the Pupil Textbook. The Practice Book provides opportunities to practise and consolidate for mastery.

Ideas for **further practice activities** to develop fluency are outlined in every unit.

The **teaching sequence** provides clear step-by-step guidance towards meeting the learning objectives. It highlights problem solving strategies to focus on and support for meaningful mathematical conversation and making the best use of concrete apparatus.

Inspire Maths Teacher's Guide 5A, page 63

Long-term planning

Unit title	Key concepts
1 Whole Numbers (1)	
Numbers to 10 million	• The next place after the ten thousands place is the hundred thousands place • 10 ten thousands = 1 hundred thousand
Place and value	• The actual value of a digit in a number is equal to the digit multiplied by the place value. E.g. the value of the digit 5 in the number 4 657 809 is 5 ten thousands, i.e. $5 \times 10\,000 = 50\,000$ • The value of a number is the sum of the values of each digit in the number
Comparing numbers within 10 million	• In a number, e.g. 1999, the value of the first digit (1000) is always greater than the sum of the values of the remaining digits (999)
Rounding to the nearest thousand and estimating	• There are 10 hundreds between two consecutive thousands
2 Whole Numbers (2)	
Using a calculator	• Understanding the concepts of place value and the four operations
Multiplying by tens, hundreds or thousands	In the base ten number system: • Ones × 10 = tens, Tens × 10 = hundreds, Hundreds × 10 = thousands • Ones × 100 = hundreds, Tens × 100 = thousands, Hundreds × 100 = ten thousands • Ones × 1000 = thousands, Tens × 1000 = ten thousands, Hundreds × 1000 = hundred thousands
Dividing by tens, hundreds or thousands	In the base ten number system: • Thousands ÷ 10 = hundreds, Hundreds ÷ 10 = tens, Tens ÷ 10 = ones, Ones ÷ 10 = tenths • Ten thousands ÷ 100 = hundreds, Thousands ÷ 100 = tens, Hundreds ÷ 100 = ones, Tens ÷ 100 = tenths, Ones ÷ 100 = hundredths • Hundred thousands ÷ 1000 = hundreds, Ten thousands ÷ 1000 = tens, Thousands ÷ 1000 = ones, Hundreds ÷ 1000 = tenths, Tens ÷ 1000 = hundredths, Ones ÷ 1000 = thousandths
Order of operations	• In number sentences with only addition and subtraction or only multiplication and division, the order of operations is from left to right • In number sentences with multiplication and/or division together with addition and/or subtraction, the order of operations is from left to right with multiplication and/or division carried out first • In number sentences with brackets, the order of operations is from left to right with the operations in the brackets carried out first
Word problems (1)	• Application of concepts and skills of the four operations to solving word problems

Unit title	Key concepts
Word problems (2)	• Application of concepts and skills of the four operations and various strategies to solving word problems
Practice Book – Review I	
Assessment Book – Test I	
3 Fractions (I)	
Like and unlike fractions	• A fraction refers to a part of a whole • Like fractions are fractions with the same denominator • Unlike fractions are fractions with different denominators
Adding unlike fractions	• Fractions are equivalent when they show the same parts of the whole • Fractions can be added when they are expressed as like fractions
Subtracting unlike fractions	• Two fractions can be subtracted if they come from the same whole or from identical wholes
Fractions and division	• A whole number when divided by another whole number can result in: (a) a whole number with or without remainder (b) a proper fraction (c) a mixed number
Converting fractions to decimals	• Fractions and decimals are interchangeable • Decimals are a special type of fractions with denominators in tens, hundreds and thousands
Adding mixed numbers	• A mixed number comprises a whole number and a proper fraction • Mixed numbers can be added like adding proper and improper fractions
Subtracting mixed numbers	• A mixed number comprises a whole number and a proper fraction • Mixed numbers can be subtracted like subtracting proper and improper fractions
Word problems	• The following concepts are applied to fractions: part-whole concepts in addition and subtraction, comparison concept, adding-on in addition, taking-away in subtraction and division concept
4 Fractions (2)	
Product of proper fractions	• Multiplying two fractions is the same as finding the fractional part of another fraction
Word problems (I)	• The product of two proper fractions is the fractional part of another fraction
Product of an improper fraction and a proper or improper fraction	• Multiplying a fraction and another fraction is the same as finding the fractional part of another fraction
Product of a mixed number and a whole number	• The product of a whole and a mixed number refers to the group and item multiplication concept

Unit title	Key concepts
Word problems (2)	• Use the group and item multiplication concept to find the product of a whole number and a mixed number
Dividing a fraction by a whole number	• Division in fractions is dividing each fractional part into smaller equal parts/units
Word problems (3)	• The concepts of the four operations and division of a fraction are applied

Practice Book – Review 2

Assessment Book – Test 2, Challenging Problems I, Check-up I

5 Area of a Triangle

Base and height of a triangle	• Any side of a triangle can be the base and for each base, there is a corresponding height
Finding the area of a triangle	• The area of a triangle is half that of its related rectangle • Area of a triangle = $\frac{1}{2}$ × base × height

6 Ratio

Finding ratio	• Ratio is a way of comparing the relative sizes of two quantities or sets of items
Equivalent ratios	• Finding the common factor of the terms of the ratio of two quantities • Dividing the terms of a ratio of two quantities by the common factor to express a ratio in its simplest form
Word problems (I)	• Applying equivalent ratio concept, part-whole concept, taking away concept and comparison concept to solve up to 2-step word problems involving ratio of two quantities
Comparing three quantities	• Ratio is a way of comparing the relative sizes of three quantities or sets of items
Word problems (2)	• Applying the equivalent ratio concept, part-whole concept and comparison concept to solve up to 2-step word problems involving ratio of three quantities

Practice Book – Review 3

Practice Book – Revision I

Assessment Book – Test 3, Challenging Problems 2, Check-up 2

7 Decimals

Converting decimals to fractions	• Decimals are an extension of the representation of fractions • Decimals can be converted to fractions, and vice versa
Multiplying by tens, hundreds and thousands	• When a number is multiplied by 10, 100 or 1000, each digit in the number moves I, 2 or 3 places respectively to the left in the place value chart • When a number is multiplied by 10, 100 or 1000, the decimal place shifts I, 2 or 3 places respectively to the right

Unit title	Key concepts
Dividing by tens, hundreds and thousands	• When a number is divided by 10, 100 or 1000, each digit in the number moves 1, 2 or 3 places respectively to the right in the place value chart • When a number is divided by 10, 100 or 1000, the decimal place shifts 1, 2 or 3 places respectively to the left • Dividing by 10 is the same as multiplying by $\frac{1}{10}$
Using a calculator	• Understanding the concepts of place value and the four arithmetical operations
Word problems	• Application of concepts and skills of the four operations to solving word problems
8 Measurements	
Converting a measurement from a larger unit to a smaller unit	• Understanding direct proportion
Converting a measurement from a smaller unit to a larger unit	• Understanding direct proportion
Practice Book – Review 4	
Assessment Book – Test 4	
9 Mean (average)	
Understanding mean (average)	• The total amount or sum of the data is found by multiplication: Total = Mean × Number of data or items
Word problems	• Applying the mean concept and part-whole concept to solve problems involving more than one set of items
10 Percentage	
Per cent	• 5% means 5 out of 100 • Percentage is a specific fraction where the denominator is 100
Converting more fractions to percentages	• Fractions and percentages are two representations for comparison of numbers • Percentage is a specific fraction where the denominator is 100
Percentage of a quantity	• Percentage of a quantity refers to part of a whole where the whole is equivalent to 100 units
Word problems	• 100 parts = the whole = 100%
Practice Book – Review 5	
Assessment Book – Test 5, Challenging Problems 3, Check-up 3	

Unit title	Key concepts
11 Angles	
Angles on a straight line	• An angle is made when two straight lines meet at a point • A unit of measurement of angles is the degree • The sum of angles on a straight line is 180°
Angles at a point	• The sum of angles at a point is 360°
Vertically opposite angles	• Vertically opposite angles are made by two intersecting straight lines • Vertically opposite angles are equal
12 Properties of Triangles and 4-sided Shapes	
Angles of a triangle	• Sum of angles in a triangle = 180°
Right-angled, isosceles and equilateral triangles (Right-angled triangles)	• A right-angled triangle has an angle equal to 90°
Right-angled, isosceles and equilateral triangles (Isosceles triangles)	• An isosceles triangle has two equal sides
Right-angled, isosceles and equilateral triangles (Equilateral triangles)	• An equilateral triangle has three equal sides
Parallelograms, rhombuses and trapeziums (Parallelograms)	A parallelogram is a 4-sided shape in which: • the opposite sides are parallel • the opposite angles are equal • each pair of angles between parallel sides add up to 180°
Parallelograms, rhombuses and trapeziums (Rhombuses)	• A rhombus is a parallelogram with four equal sides where the opposite angles are equal and each pair of angles between parallel sides add up to 180°
Parallelograms, rhombuses and trapeziums (Trapeziums)	• A trapezium is a 4-sided shape in which only one pair of opposite sides is parallel and each pair of angles between parallel sides add up to 180°
Practice Book - Review 6	
Assessment Book – Test 6	

Unit title	Key concepts
I3 Geometrical Construction	
Drawing triangles	• Given two angles and the side adjacent to the given angles or two sides and the included angle, only one triangle can be drawn
Drawing 4-sided shapes	• Given the side of a square, only one square can be drawn • Given the length and width of a rectangle, only one rectangle can be drawn • Given one side and one angle of a rhombus, only one rhombus can be drawn • Given two adjacent sides and one angle of a parallelogram, only one parallelogram can be drawn • Given two adjacent sides, the included angle and the angle adjacent to the included angle of a trapezium with the parallel sides indicated, only one trapezium can be drawn
I4 Volume of Cubes and Cuboids	
Building solids using unit cubes	• A cube is a solid which has 6 square faces • A unit cube means a single cube
Drawing cubes and cuboids	• On isometric dotty paper, only two views of a unit cube can be drawn
Understanding and measuring volume	• Volume is the amount of space an object occupies • Volume is measured in cubic units • Volume can be measured in different units, including cm^3 and m^3
Volume of a cuboid and of liquid	• Volume of a cube = Edge × Edge × Edge • Volume of a cuboid = Length × Width × Height • Volume of liquid in a container that is completely filled is equal to the capacity of the container
Practice Book - Review 7	
Practice Book - Revision 2	
Assessment Book – Test 7, Challenging Problems 4, Check-up 4	

Unit I: Whole Numbers (I)

Week	Learning Objectives	Thinking Skills	Resources
I	**(I) Numbers to I0 million** Pupils will be able to: • count on in ten thousands to I hundred thousand • count on in hundred thousands to I million • state that I0 ten thousands = I hundred thousand and that I0 hundred thousands = I million • translate place value models of numbers up to I0 million into numerals and words • read and write 6- and 7-digit numbers up to I0 million in numerals and words • use a calculator to type in 6- and 7-digit numbers	• Comparing • Identifying relationships	• Pupil Textbook 5A, pp 2 to II • Practice Book 5A, pp I to 6 • Teacher's Guide 5A, pp 6 to I5

Unit 1: Whole Numbers (1)

Week	Learning Objectives	Thinking Skills	Resources
1	**(2) Place and value** Pupils will be able to: • identify the value and place of each digit in a 6- and 7-digit number • represent a number as the sum of the values of each digit in the number	• Comparing • Identifying relationships	• Pupil Textbook 5A, pp 12 to 15 • Practice Book 5A, pp 7 to 10 • Teacher's Guide 5A, pp 16 to 19
1	**(3) Comparing numbers within 10 million** Pupils will be able to: • state which number is greater or smaller using the strategy of comparing the values of their digits from the left • arrange a set of numbers in order • identify the pattern in a number sequence	• Comparing • Sequencing • Identifying patterns and relationships	• Pupil Textbook 5A, pp 16 to 19 • Practice Book 5A, pp 11 to 14 • Teacher's Guide 5A, pp 20 to 23

Unit 1: Whole Numbers (1)

Week	Learning Objectives	Thinking Skills	Resources
2	**(4) Rounding to the nearest thousand and estimating** Pupils will be able to: • round numbers to the nearest thousand • recognise and use the symbol '≈' • mark the approximate position of a number on a given number line • use rounding to estimate answers in addition, subtraction, multiplication and division *Maths Journal* These questions require pupils to: • explain why a 6-digit number is greater than a 5-digit number • explain the errors made in rounding numbers to the nearest hundred and thousand.	• Comparing • Identifying patterns and relationships • Analysing • Evaluating	• Pupil Textbook 5A, pp 20 to 26 • Practice Book 5A, pp 15 to 20 • Teacher's Guide 5A, pp 24 to 30

Unit 1: Whole Numbers (1)

Week	Learning Objectives	Thinking Skills	Resources
2	*Let's Wrap It Up!* Emphasise the key concepts, skills and processes that have been taught in the unit. Discuss the worked example with pupils to assess whether they have mastered these concepts, skills and processes. *Put On Your Thinking Caps!* These questions require pupils to list the possible whole numbers that round to 30.	• Comparing • Identifying patterns and relationships Heuristics for problem solving: • Guess and check • Look for a pattern	• Pupil Textbook 5A, pp 27 to 28 • Practice Book 5A, pp 21 to 22 • Teacher's Guide 5A, pp 31 to 32

Whole Numbers (I)

Learning objectives:
Numbers to I0 million
Pupils will be able to:
- count on in ten thousands to I hundred thousand
- count on in hundred thousands to I million
- state that I0 ten thousands = I hundred thousand and that

I0 hundred thousands = I million
- translate place value models of numbers up to I0 million to numerals and words
- read and write 6- and 7-digit numbers up to I0 million in numerals and words
- use a calculator to type in 6- and 7-digit numbers

Key concepts
- The next place after the ten thousands place is the hundred thousands place.
- I0 ten thousands = I hundred thousand

Thinking skills
- Comparing
- Identifying relationships

Teaching sequence

- Show a place value chart. One at a time, place counters into the ten thousands place of the place value chart and ask pupils to count in ten thousands: I ten thousand, 2 ten thousands, … up to 9 ten thousands. Highlight to pupils that I ten thousand = I0 000, 2 ten thousands = 20 000, … and 9 ten thousands = 90 000.
- Add one more counter and ask pupils: *"What do you get when you add another I ten thousand to 9 ten thousands?"* (I0 ten thousands)
- Help pupils to notice that I ten thousand + 9 ten thousands is equal to I0 000 + 90 000, i.e. I00 000. Ask pupils: *"What is I0 ten thousands equal to?"* (I00 000)
- Write the number 'I00 000' and the words 'I hundred thousand' on the board.
- Explain to pupils that the ten counters in the ten thousands place can be exchanged for one counter in the hundred thousands place to the left.
- Emphasise to pupils that I0 ten thousands = I hundred thousand.

Unit I

Whole Numbers (I)

Let's Learn!

Numbers to I0 million

I Count in ten thousands.

I ten thousand (I0 000), 2 ten thousands (20 000), 3 ten thousands (30 000), 4 ten thousands (40 000), 5 ten thousands (50 000), 6 ten thousands (60 000), 7 ten thousands (70 000), 8 ten thousands (80 000), 9 ten thousands (90 000),
[   ]. I0 ten thousands (I00 000)

Add I ten thousand to 9 ten thousands to get I0 ten thousands.

I0 ten thousands = I hundred thousand We write I hundred thousand as I00 000.

I0 ten thousands = I hundred thousand

Hundred Thousands	Ten Thousands	Thousands	Hundreds	Tens	Ones
	⊙⊙⊙⊙⊙ ⊙⊙⊙⊙⊙				

↓

Hundred Thousands	Ten Thousands	Thousands	Hundreds	Tens	Ones
⊙					
I	0	0	0	0	0
stands for I hundred thousand or I00 000	stands for 0 ten thousands or 0	stands for 0 thousands or 0	stands for 0 hundreds or 0	stands for 0 tens or 0	stands for 0 ones or 0

2

What you will need
- Place value chart (see Photocopy master I on p 318)
- Counters

Additional activities
- Ask pupils to work in pairs and give each pair a copy of the place value chart provided on Photocopy master I. Pupil A places some counters on the place value chart. Pupil B studies the chart and writes the numeral that represents the value.
- Pupil A writes a number up to I million. Pupil B places the counters on the place value chart that represent the value of the number.

---

2 Count in steps of 100 000.

100 000	one hundred thousand
200 000	two hundred thousand
300 000	three hundred thousand
400 000	four hundred thousand
500 000	five hundred thousand
600 000	☐ six hundred thousand
700 000	☐ seven hundred thousand
800 000	eight hundred thousand
900 000	☐ nine hundred thousand

> We leave a space between the thousands digit and the hundreds digit. This helps us to read the number easily.

100 000

space

3 What is the number in numerals and in words?

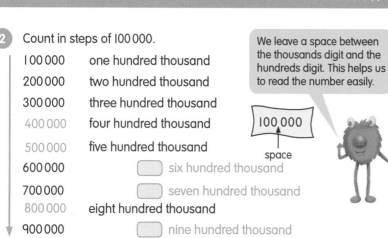

Hundred Thousands	Ten Thousands	Thousands	Hundreds	Tens	Ones
stands for 6 hundred thousands	stands for 5 ten thousands	stands for 3 thousands	stands for I hundred	stands for 0 tens	stands for 4 ones

	In Numerals	In Words
6 hundred thousands	600 000	Six hundred thousand
5 ten thousands	50 000	Fifty thousand
3 thousands	3 000	Three thousand
I hundred	100	One hundred
0 tens	0	
4 ones	4	Four

In numerals, the number is **653 104**.

In words, the number is **six hundred and fifty-three thousand, one hundred and four**.

3

Teaching sequence

2
- Put the counters one at a time in the hundred thousands place, and guide pupils to count in steps of 100 000 from 100 000 to 900 000. Ask pupils to state the missing numbers in numerals or words.

3
- Encourage pupils to notice that in numerals, the digits are written from left to right, starting with the digit in the hundred thousands place.
- Guide pupils to notice that, stated in words, six hundred thousand, fifty thousand and three thousand are added together to give six hundred and fifty-three thousand.
- Highlight to pupils that a place value with zero need not be stated when the number is written in words.

Additional activity

Ask pupils to work in pairs.
Pupil A places some counters on the place value chart. Pupil B then looks at the chart and writes the value in numerals and words.

• Ask pupils to work on this exercise as an informal assessment.

Unit I Whole Numbers (I)

 a What is the number in numerals and in words?

Hundred Thousands	Ten Thousands	Thousands	Hundreds	Tens	Ones
●●●● ●●	●●● ●●	●●●● ●●●	●●● ●●●	●●●● ●●●	●●● ●●●

| stands for 5 hundred thousands | stands for 5 ten thousands | stands for 7 thousands | stands for 6 hundreds | stands for 7 tens | stands for 6 ones |

	In Numerals	In Words
[5] hundred thousands	500 000	Five hundred thousand
[5] ten thousands	50 000	Fifty thousand
[7] thousands	7000	Seven thousand
[6] hundreds	(600)	Six hundred
[7] tens	(70)	Seventy
[6] ones	(6)	(Six)

In numerals, the number is ⬭. 557 676

In words, the number is ⬭. Five hundred and fifty-seven thousand, six hundred and seventy-six

b What is the number in numerals and in words?

Hundred Thousands	Ten Thousands	Thousands	Hundreds	Tens	Ones
●●● ●●●	○○○○ ○○○○	●●● ●●●		●● ●●	●● ●●

In numerals, the number is ⬭. 686 044

In words, the number is ⬭. Six hundred and eighty-six thousand and forty-four

4

Additional activity

Ask pupils to work in pairs. Pupil A writes three 6-digit numbers in numerals and Pupil B writes three 6-digit numbers in words. Pupils swap the numbers they have written and ask their partners to write the corresponding words or numerals. Ask pupils to swap roles.

Independent work

Practice I in Practice Book 5A, pp I to 4.

Teaching sequence

- Highlight the space between the last three digits and the first three digits of the number to pupils.
- Explain to pupils that the number 467 832 is read in two parts. '467' is read as 'four hundred and sixty-seven thousand' and '832' is read as 'eight hundred and thirty-two'.
- Demonstrate with another example: 360 450 is read as 'three hundred and sixty thousand, four hundred and fifty'.
- Guide pupils to realise that to read a large number, they only need to know how to read 3-digit numbers. With a 6-digit number, they can cover the last three digits with their hand and read the first three digits as a 3-digit number plus the word 'thousand'. They can then remove their hand to read the last 3 digits.

- Ask pupils to work on this question for further practice in reading 6-digit numbers.

---

5 Read these numbers.

a

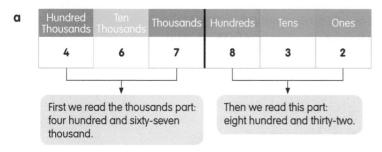

Hundred Thousands	Ten Thousands	Thousands	Hundreds	Tens	Ones
4	6	7	8	3	2

First we read the thousands part: four hundred and sixty-seven thousand.

Then we read this part: eight hundred and thirty-two.

467 832 is **four hundred and sixty-seven thousand, eight hundred and thirty-two**.

b

767 767

767 767 is **seven hundred and sixty-seven thousand, seven hundred and sixty-seven**.

6 Read these numbers.

a 325 176   b 438 834

c 906 096   d 555 555

e 680 806   f 700 007

a Three hundred and twenty-five thousand, one hundred and seventy-six
b Four hundred and thirty-eight thousand, eight hundred and thirty-four
c Nine hundred and six thousand and ninety-six
d Five hundred and fifty-five thousand, five hundred and fifty-five
e Six hundred and eighty thousand, eight hundred and six
f Seven hundred thousand and seven

Practice Book 5A, p. I

5

- Place value chart (see Photocopy master 2 on p 319)
- Counters

Teaching sequence

- Show a copy of the place value chart provided on Photocopy master 2. Place counters one at a time into the hundred thousands place of the place value chart and ask pupils to count in hundred thousands:
  1 hundred thousand,
  2 hundred thousands, …
  up to 9 hundred thousands.

- Pupils should note that 1 hundred thousand = 100 000, 2 hundred thousands = 200 000, … and 9 hundred thousands = 900 000.

- Add one more counter and ask pupils: *"What do you get when you add another 1 hundred thousand (100 000) to 9 hundred thousands (900 000)?"* (10 hundred thousands)

- Guide pupils to see that 100 000 + 900 000 = 1 000 000. Tell pupils that 1 000 000 is read as 1 million and so 10 hundred thousands = 1 million.

- On the place value chart, show that ten counters in the hundred thousands place can be replaced with one counter in the millions place. Emphasise to pupils that 10 hundred thousands = 1 million.

Unit 1 Whole Numbers (1)

7 Count in hundred thousands.
1 hundred thousand (100 000), 2 hundred thousands (200 000),
3 hundred thousands (300 000), 4 hundred thousands (400 000),
5 hundred thousands (500 000), 6 hundred thousands (600 000),
7 hundred thousands (700 000), 8 hundred thousands (800 000),
9 hundred thousands (900 000), _____ . 10 hundred thousands (1 000 000)

Add 1 hundred thousand to 9 hundred thousands to get 10 hundred thousands.

10 hundred thousands = 1 million
We write 1 million as 1 000 000.

1 thousand thousands = 1 million.

10 hundred thousands = 1 million

Millions	Hundred Thousands	Ten Thousands	Thousands	Hundreds	Tens	Ones

Millions	Hundred Thousands	Ten Thousands	Thousands	Hundreds	Tens	Ones
◯						
1	0	0	0	0	0	0
stands for 1 million or 1 000 000	stands for 0 hundred thousands or 0	stands for 0 ten thousands or 0	stands for 0 thousands or 0	stands for 0 hundreds or 0	stands for 0 tens or 0	stands for 0 ones or 0

6

Additional activity

Ask pupils to find some cities with a population of more than I million but less than 10 million and arrange them in order in a table.

8 Count in steps of 1 000 000.

1 000 000	one million
2 000 000	two million
3 000 000	three million
4 000 000	☐ four million
5 000 000	☐ five million
6 000 000	six million
7 000 000	seven million
8 000 000	☐ eight million
9 000 000	nine million
10 000 000	ten million

1 000 000

first second
space space

We leave two spaces. The first space helps us to read the millions. The second space helps us to read the thousands.

9 This house costs more than £1 000 000.

Can you think of other things that cost millions of pounds?

The population of Wales is more than 3 000 000.

According to the 2011 census, the population of Wales was about 3 060 000.

7

Teaching sequence

8

- Put counters one at a time into the millions place, and guide pupils to count in steps of 1 000 000 from I million to 10 million.

9

- Encourage pupils to talk about their understanding of a million pounds.

Teaching sequence

- Use the same procedure as in ③ to teach pupils to write 7-digit numbers in numerals and in words.

- This activity encourages mathematical communication. Use your judgement about whether to ask pupils to search for news websites themselves or to provide these examples for the pupils. Some news articles could include details some pupils may find distressing. Alternatively, a selection of articles could be printed out in advance of the lesson and provided for each group. Pupils work in groups to find news articles containing the word 'millions' and print these out, or they read through the articles provided. Ask each group to look at the use of 'millions' in the articles and to discuss this first in their groups and then as a class.

---

10 What is the number in numerals and in words?

Millions	Hundred Thousands	Ten Thousands	Thousands	Hundreds	Tens	Ones
●● ●	●●● ●●	●●● ●●●	●●●● ●●●		●● ●●	●●● ●●
stands for 3 millions	stands for 5 hundred thousands	stands for 6 ten thousands	stands for 7 thousands	stands for 0 hundreds	stands for 4 tens	stands for 5 ones

	In Numerals	In Words
3 millions	3 000 000	Three million
5 hundred thousands	500 000	Five hundred thousand
6 ten thousands	60 000	Sixty thousand
7 thousands	7 000	Seven thousand
0 hundreds	0	
4 tens	40	Forty
5 ones	5	Five

In numerals, the number is **3 567 045**.

In words, the number is **three million, five hundred and sixty-seven thousand and forty-five**.

Activity

11 Work in groups.

Go to a news website and do a search for news articles containing the word 'millions'.
Print out the search results your group gets.
Discuss the use of 'millions' in the news articles with your class.

8

a What is the number in numerals and in words?

Millions	Hundred Thousands	Ten Thousands	Thousands	Hundreds	Tens	Ones
● ● ● ●	● ● ● ● ● ●		● ● ● ● ●	● ● ●	● ● ● ● ● ● ●	● ● ● ● ● ● ● ● ●

| stands for 4 millions | stands for 6 hundred thousands | stands for 0 ten thousands | stands for 5 thousands | stands for 3 hundreds | stands for 7 tens | stands for 9 ones |

		In Numerals	**In Words**
4	millions	4 000 000	Four million
6	hundred thousands	600 000	Six hundred thousand
0	ten thousands	0	
5	thousands	5000	Five thousand
3	hundreds	300	Three hundred
7	tens	70	Seventy
9	ones	9	Nine

In numerals, the number is ◯. 4 605 379

In words, the number is ◯. Four million, six hundred and five thousand, three hundred and seventy-nine

b What is the number in numerals and in words?

Millions	Hundred Thousands	Ten Thousands	Thousands	Hundreds	Tens	Ones
● ● ● ● ● ●	● ● ●	● ● ● ●		● ● ● ● ●	● ● ● ● ● ● ●	●

In numerals, the number is ◯. 6 340 581

In words, the number is ◯. Six million, three hundred and forty thousand, five hundred and eighty-one

9

Additional activity

Ask pupils to work in pairs. Call out seven digits: 4, 7, 2, 5, 0, 8 and I. Pupil A arranges the digits to make a number. Pupil B reads it aloud and writes it in words. Pupil A then checks the answer. Ask pupils to swap roles.

Teaching sequence

- Ask pupils to work on these questions as an informal assessment.

Ask pupils to work in pairs.
Pupil A reads out a number
in words without showing the
numeral. Pupil B represents the
number on a place value chart.
Pupil A then checks the answer.
Pupils A and B swap roles.

Teaching sequence

a

- Use the same strategy as in 5 to teach pupils how to read a 7-digit number. The number 5 824 428 is read in three parts. '5' is read as 'five million', '824' is read as 'eight hundred and twenty-four thousand' and '428' is read as 'four hundred and twenty-eight'.

b

- Show another example: The number 6 035 350 is read as 'six million, thirty-five thousand, three hundred and fifty'.

- To read a 7-digit number, ask pupils to cover the last six digits with their hand. Read the first digit plus the word 'million', then reveal the next three digits and read them as a 3-digit number plus the word 'thousand'. Finally they can remove their hand and read the last three digits.

- Ask pupils to work on this question for further practice in reading 7-digit numbers.

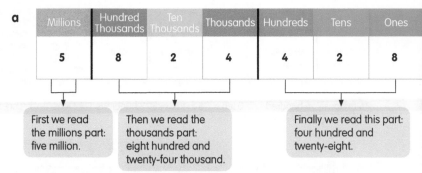

13 Read these numbers.

a

Millions	Hundred Thousands	Ten Thousands	Thousands	Hundreds	Tens	Ones
5	8	2	4	4	2	8

First we read the millions part: five million.

Then we read the thousands part: eight hundred and twenty-four thousand.

Finally we read this part: four hundred and twenty-eight.

5 824 428 is **five million, eight hundred and twenty-four thousand, four hundred and twenty-eight**.

b 6 035 350

6 035 350 is **six million, thirty-five thousand, three hundred and fifty**.

14 Read these numbers.

a	1 234 567	**b**	2 653 356
c	4 404 044	**d**	8 888 888
e	5 090 909	**f**	7 006 060

a One million, two hundred and thirty-four thousand, five hundred and sixty-seven.
b Two million, six hundred and fifty-three thousand, three hundred and fifty-six.
c Four million, four hundred and four thousand and forty-four.
d Eight million, eight hundred and eighty-eight thousand, eight hundred and eighty-eight.
e Five million, ninety thousand, nine hundred and nine.
f Seven million, six thousand and sixty.

Home Maths Explain that to read large numbers, your child only needs to know how to read up to three digits. For example, to read 9 375 608, they have to be able to read only 9 and 375 and 608. We say **million** after 9 and **thousand** after 375. This means 9 375 608 is read as nine **million**, three hundred and seventy-five **thousand**, six hundred and eight.

10

What you will need

Scientific calculator

Additional activity

Ask pupils the following questions:

(a) What is the greatest possible 7-digit number?

(b) What is the smallest possible 7-digit number?

(c) What are the whole numbers that come immediately before and after these two numbers?

You could extend this activity by asking additional questions, for example, by asking which numbers are two more, two less, ten more, ten less, one hundred more, one hundred less, one thousand more or one thousand less.

Independent work

- *Let's Practice!*
- Practice 2 in Practice Book 5A, pp 5 to 6.

Teaching sequence

15

- These activities provide reinforcement and consolidation in reading and writing large numbers.

Activity

15 Work in pairs.

a Take turns to make a 6-digit number using the digits 5, 2, 0, 0, 0 and 0. Start with the digit 2 or 5, for example, 500 200. Then tell your partner the first digit of your number. Your partner will try to guess your number. Each time they guess, they should write the number in numerals and in words. They score I point if they guess the number correctly within three tries.

b ▦ Turn your calculator on.

To display the number 3 210 456 on your calculator, press
[3], [2], [1], [0], [4], [5], [6] in order.

To clear the display on your calculator, press [C].

Take turns to type in a 6-digit or 7-digit number on your calculator and ask your partner to read the number.

Remember to press [C] before you type in a new number.

Let's Practise!

16 Write in numerals.

a Two hundred thousand, one hundred and six. 200 106

b Six hundred and seventy-three thousand, nine hundred and eleven. 673 911

c Five hundred and eighteen thousand and four. 518 004

d Seven million, three hundred and thirteen thousand. 7 313 000

e Nine million, five hundred and twenty. 9 000 520

f Five million, two thousand and twelve. 5 002 012

17 Write in words.

17
a Two hundred and fifteen thousand, nine hundred and five.
b Eight hundred and nineteen thousand and two.
c One hundred and twenty thousand and forty.

a 215 905 **b** 819 002 **c** 120 040

d 6 430 000 **e** 5 009 300 **f** 9 722 830

d Six million, four hundred and thirty thousand.
e Five million, nine thousand and three hundred.
f Nine million, seven hundred and twenty-two thousand, eight hundred and thirty.

Practice Book 5A, p. 5

II

Learning objectives: Place and value

Pupils will be able to:

- identify the value and place of each digit in a 6- and 7-digit number
- represent a number as the sum of the values of each digit in the number

Key concepts

- The actual value of a digit in a number is equal to the digit multiplied by the place value. For example, the value of the digit 5 in the number 4657809 is 5 ten thousands, i.e. $5 \times 10000 = 50000$.
- The value of a number is the sum of the values of each digit in the number.

Thinking skills

- Comparing
- Identifying relationships

Teaching sequence

- Use the place value chart up to the hundred thousands place to review the place and value of a digit in a number.
- For example, in 861257, ask pupils for the place and value of each of these digits, 7, 5, 2, 1 and 6. Encourage pupils to notice that since the digit 6 is in the ten thousands place, its value is 6 ten thousands or 6×10000, i.e. 60000. Similarly, the digit 1 is in the thousands place and its value is 1 thousand or 1×1000, i.e. 1000.

- Ask pupils which place the digit 8 is in. Guide pupils to conclude that since it is in the hundred thousands place, the digit 8 stands for 8 hundred thousands or 8×100000, i.e. its value is 800000.

- Ask pupils to work on these questions as an informal assessment.

Unit 1 Whole Numbers (1)

Let's Learn!

Place and value

Hundred Thousands	Ten Thousands	Thousands	Hundreds	Tens	Ones
8	6	1	2	5	7

In **861257**:

the digit 8 stands for **800000**
the **value** of the digit 8 is **800000**

the digit 6 stands for **60000**
the **value** of the digit 6 is **60000**

the digit 1 stands for **1000**
the **value** of the digit 1 is **1000**.

 In **861257**:

the digit 8 is in the **hundred thousands** place
the digit 6 is in the **ten thousands** place
the digit 1 is in the **thousands** place.

3 Answer these questions.

a In 670932, the value of the digit **6** is ⬚. 600000
b What is the value of the digit **2** in each of the following 6-digit numbers?
  i 81**2**679 2000   ii **2**60153 200000   iii 8**2**7917 20000

12

What you will need

Place value chart (see Photocopy master 2 on p 319)

Additional activity

Write some 6-digit numbers. Show the place value chart and ask pupils to write each digit in the correct place.

---

4 Answer these questions.

a In 937 016, the digit [0] is in the hundreds place.

b In 124 573, the digit in the hundred thousands place is [I].

c In 971 465, the digit 6 is in the [ ] place. tens

d In 289 219, the digit 8 is in the [ ] place. ten thousands

e In what place is the digit **2** in each of the following numbers?

   i   18**2** 679   ii   **2**60 153   iii   8**2**7 917
       thousands   hundred thousands   ten thousands

5

Look at the values of the digits in 381 492.
For example, the value of the digit 3 is 300 000.
We can add the values of the digits to get the number.

381 492 = 300 000 + 80 000 + 1000 + 400 + 90 + 2
         = 381 000 + 492

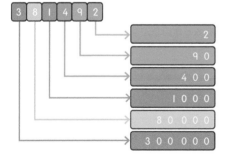

6 Answer these questions.

a 761 902 = 700 000 + [ ] + 1000 + 900 + 2 60 000

b 124 003 = [ ] + 3 124 000

c 900 356 = 900 000 + 300 + [50] + 6

d 368 215 = [ ] + 8000 + 200 + 15 360 000

13

Teaching sequence

4

- Ask pupils to work on these questions as an informal assessment.

5

- Explain to pupils that as each digit in a number has a particular value, the value of the number itself is the sum of these values, i.e. 381 492 = 300 000 + 80 000 + 1000 + 400 + 90 + 2.

6

- Ask pupils to work on these questions as an informal assessment.

Ask pupils to work in pairs. Pupil A calls out three place values, e.g. 70 thousands, 8 hundreds and 10. Pupil B writes the number in different ways, e.g. 70 810 or 70 000, 800 and 10. Pupil A checks the answer. Pupils A and B swap roles.

Teaching sequence

7

- Highlight to pupils that the millions place is to the left of the hundred thousands place and work through the question for reinforcement.

8

- Reinforce the steps on how to write the value of a number as the sum of the values of each digit. Guide pupils to see that any two or more of the values can be combined.

9

- Ask pupils to work on these questions as an informal assessment.

Unit 1 Whole Numbers (I)

7

Millions	Hundred Thousands	Ten Thousands	Thousands	Hundreds	Tens	Ones
1	6	4	9	0	0	0

In **1 649 000**:

the digit 1 stands for **1 000 000**
the value of the digit 1 is ⬭ 1 000 000

the digit 6 stands for **600 000**
the value of the digit 6 is ⬭ 600 000

the digit 4 is in the **ten thousands** place

the digit 9 is in the ⬭ place. thousands

8

| 5 0 0 0 0 0 0 |
| 6 0 0 0 0 0 |
| 4 0 0 0 0 |
| 9 0 0 0 |

5 649 000 = 5 000 000
         + 600 000 + 40 000 + 9000

or

5 649 000 = 5 000 000 + 649 000

9 Answer these questions.

  a In 7 296 000:

    i the digit ⬭ 7 is in the millions place

    ii the value of the digit 6 is ⬭ 6000

    iii the digit 2 stands for ⬭ 200 000

    iv the digit 9 is in the ⬭ place. ten thousands

  b 7 200 000 = 7 000 000 + ⬭ 200 000

  c 6 235 000 = ⬭ + 235 000 6 000 000

  d 2 459 000 = 2 000 000 + 400 000 + ⬭ + 9000 50 000

14

- *Let's Practise!*
- Practice 3 in Practice Book 5A, pp 7 to 10.

Whole Numbers (1) **Unit 1**

Teaching sequence

⑩

- Ask pupils to work in pairs to carry out this activity. Invite volunteers to share their questions and answers with the class.

Activity

⑩ Work in pairs. Write down a 6-digit or a 7-digit number. Give clues for your partner to guess your number. For example, if you wrote down 359100, you can say:

> My number has six digits.
> The digit 5 is next to the digit 3, which has a value of 300000.
> The digit 9 is in the thousands place.
> The value of the digit in the hundreds place is 100.
> There are two zeros in my number.
> What is my number?

Take turns to guess each other's numbers.

Let's Practise!

⑪ What is the value of the digit **5** in each of the following numbers?

a   64051   b   783562   c   157300   d   591368
   50   500   50000   500000

⑫ In the number 357921, the value of the digit 3 is ⬡ 300000 and the digit 7 is in the ⬡ place. thousands

⑬ 829359 = 800000 + ⬡ + 300 + 50 + 9   29000

⑭ What is the value of the digit **6** in each of the following numbers?

a   6390000   b   8100600   c   7620548
   6000000   600   600000

⑮ Answer these questions.

a   In 7005000, the digit ⬡7 is in the millions place.

b   In 2321654, the digit in the hundred thousands place is ⬡3.

⑯ a   2403800 = ⬡ + 400000 + 3000 + 800   2000000

   b   9197328 = 9000000 + 197000 + ⬡328   Practice Book 5A, p. 7

15

Learning objectives: Comparing numbers within 10 million

Pupils will be able to:

- state which number is greater or smaller using the strategy of comparing the values of their digits from the left
- arrange a set of numbers in order
- identify the pattern in a number sequence

Key concept

In a number, e.g. 1999, the value of the first digit (1000) is always greater than the sum of the values of the remaining digits (999).

Thinking skills

- Comparing
- Sequencing
- Identifying patterns and relationships

Teaching sequence

- Review with pupils how to compare numbers using the strategy of comparing the values of the digits starting from the left.
- Highlight to pupils that 1002 must be greater than 903 because 1000 is greater than 900 and not because 1002 has more digits than 903. While it is true that a whole number with more digits will always be greater, pupils who transfer this way of thinking to the comparison of decimals will not be correct.
- Explain to pupils that the same method is used for comparing the values of 6-digit numbers.

- Ask pupils to work on this question as an informal assessment.

Unit 1 Whole Numbers (1)

Let's Learn!

| Comparing numbers within 10 million |

> When we compare numbers, we look at the value of each digit starting from the left.

Which number is smaller: 237 981 or 500 600?

Hundred Thousands	Ten Thousands	Thousands	Hundreds	Tens	Ones
2	3	7	9	8	1
5	0	0	6	0	0

Compare the values of the digits starting from the left.
2 hundred thousands is smaller than 5 hundred thousands.
So 237 981 is smaller than 500 600.

 Which number is greater: 712 935 or 712 846?

Hundred Thousands	Ten Thousands	Thousands	Hundreds	Tens	Ones
7	1	2	9	3	5
7	1	2	8	4	6

Compare the values of the digits starting from the left.
If they are the same, continue to compare until the values of the digits are not the same.
Here the values of the digits in the hundreds place are not the same.

◯ is greater than ◯.
 9 hundreds   8 hundreds
So 712 935 is ◯ than 712 846.
            greater

16

3 Which number is smaller: 3 506 017 or 5 306 007?

Millions	Hundred Thousands	Ten Thousands	Thousands	Hundreds	Tens	Ones
3	5	0	6	0	1	7
5	3	0	6	0	0	7

Compare the values of the digits starting from the left.
3 millions is smaller than 5 millions.
So 3 506 017 is smaller than 5 306 007.

4 Which number is greater: 4 730 589 or 4 703 985?
4 **73**0 589
4 **70**3 985

Compare the values of the digits starting from the left.
Here the values of the digits in the ten thousands place are different.

Compare the values of the digits in the ten thousands place.

☐ is greater than ☐.
3 ten thousands   0 ten thousands
So ☐ is greater than ☐.
4 730 589   4 703 985

5 Which number is greater? Which is smaller?
Use greater than or smaller than.

a   345 932 is ☐ 435 990.   smaller than
b   100 400 is ☐ 99 900.   greater than
c   220 000 is ☐ 219 099.   greater than
d   5 245 721 is ☐ 524 572.   greater than
e   3 143 820 is ☐ 4 134 820.   smaller than
f   6 680 910 is ☐ 668 091.   greater than

17

Additional activity
Ask pupils to work in pairs.
Guide each of them to write a
6-digit number, then ask them to
compare their numbers to find
out which is greater.

Teaching sequence

3

- Show pupils that the same
  method that we used in **1**
  is used for comparing 7-digit
  numbers.

4 and **5**

- Ask pupils to work on these
  questions as an informal
  assessment.

Ask pupils to write sentences given the following information:
(a) 123 400, 133 400, more than
(b) 549 670, 589 670, less than

Teaching sequence

- Ask pupils to revise how to arrange numbers in ascending/increasing and descending/decreasing order. Encourage pupils to use a place value chart if they are not able to compare the numbers directly.
- Give pupils a few more sets of numbers as an informal assessment.

- Demonstrate how to identify the pattern in a number sequence. Ask pupils to note whether the number sequence is increasing or decreasing. Then they should look for the increase or decrease in the sequence. The increase or decrease can be found by subtraction.

- Ask pupils to work on these questions as an informal assessment.

Unit I Whole Numbers (I)

6 Arrange the numbers in order, beginning with the smallest.
   a   324 688, 32 468, 3 246 880   32 468, 324 688, 3 246 880
   b   1 600 456, 1 604 654, 1 064 645   1 064 645, 1 600 456, 1 604 654

7 What is the next number in each pattern?
   a   231 590, 331 590, 431 590, 531 590, …

   331 590 is 100 000 more than **2**31 590.
   431 590 is 100 000 more than **3**31 590.
   531 590 is 100 000 more than **4**31 590.

   100 000 more than **5**31 590 is **6**31 590.
   The next number is 631 590.

   b   755 482, 705 482, 655 482, 605 482, …

   705 482 is 50 000 less than **75**5 482.
   655 482 is 50 000 less than **70**5 482.
   605 482 is 50 000 less than **65**5 482.

   50 000 less than **60**5 482 is **55**5 482.
   The next number is 555 482.

8 What is the next number in each pattern?
   a   1 345 024, 3 345 024, 5 345 024, …

   3 345 024 is ⬭ more than **1** 345 024. 2 000 000

   5 345 024 is ⬭ more than **3** 345 024. 2 000 000

   ⬭ more than 5 345 024 is ⬭. 2 000 000, 7 345 024
   The next number is ⬭. 7 345 024

   b   820 346, 810 346, 800 346, …

   810 346 is ⬭ less than **82**0 346. 10 000

   800 346 is ⬭ less than **81**0 346. 10 000

   ⬭ less than 800 346 is ⬭. 10 000, 790 346
   The next number is ⬭. 790 346

18

- *Let's Practise!*
- Practice 4 in Practice Book 5A, pp 11 to 14.

Let's Practise!

9   **a**   Which is greater: 568 912 or 568 921?   568 921

     b   Which is smaller: 71 690 or 100 345?   71 690

10   **a**   Which is the greatest: 81 630, 81 603 or 816 300?   816 300

     b   Which is the smallest: 125 000, 12 500 or 25 000?   12 500

11   Arrange the following numbers in order, beginning with the smallest.
901 736, 714 800, 199 981   199 981, 714 800, 901 736

12   Arrange the following numbers in order, beginning with the greatest.
36 925, 925 360, 360 925   925 360, 360 925, 36 925

13   Complete this number pattern. Give the rule for the pattern.
325 410, ⬚, 305 410, 295 410, ⬚, 275 410   315 410, 285 410

    – 10 000 – 10 000 – 10 000 – 10 000 – 10 000   Rule: Count back by 10 000

14   Complete this number pattern. Give the rule for the pattern.
2 390 000, 3 400 000, 4 410 000, ⬚, 6 430 000   5 420 000

    + 1 010 000 + 1 010 000 + 1 010 000 + 1 010 000   Rule: Count on by 1 010 000

15   What is the next number in each pattern?

     a   580 356, 600 356, 620 356, 640 356, …

        600 356 is ⬚ more than 580 356.   20 000

        620 356 is ⬚ more than 600 356.   20 000

        640 356 is ⬚ more than 620 356.   20 000

        ⬚ more than 640 356 is ⬚.   20 000, 660 356

     b   4 030 875, 3 830 875, 3 630 875, 3 430 875, …

        ⬚ less than 3 430 875 is ⬚.   200 000, 3 230 875   **Practice Book 5A, p. 11**

19

Learning objectives:
Rounding to the nearest thousand and estimating

Pupils will be able to:

- round numbers to the nearest thousand
- recognise and use the symbol '≈'
- mark the approximate position of a number on a given number line
- use rounding to estimate answers in addition, subtraction, multiplication and division

Teaching sequence

- Revise how to round numbers to the nearest hundred. Work through this procedure with pupils:

  (a) Look at the digit in the hundreds place. In 6541, the digit 5 is in the hundreds place. 6541 must be between 6500 and 6600.

  (b) Then decide whether 6541 is nearer to 6500 or 6600. To do this, pupils will need to know that from 6500 to 6600, there are 10 tens. Use the number line to show this:

  ```
  6510 6520 6530 6540   6560 6570 6580 6590
  |----|----|----|----|----|----|----|----|----|----|
  6500              6550              6600
  ```

- Help pupils to notice that 6550 is midway between 6500 and 6600. So if the number is less than 6550, it will be nearer to 6500 and if it is greater than or equal to 6550, it will be nearer to 6600. Therefore when rounding to the nearest hundred, 6541 is rounded to 6500 and 6572 is rounded to 6600.

- Discuss the difference between the equal sign (=) and the approximately equal sign (≈) and show pupils how to write the rounding using the '≈' sign.

Key concept

There are 10 hundreds between two consecutive thousands.

Thinking skills

- Comparing
- Identifying patterns and relationships
- Analysing
- Evaluating

Let's Learn!

Rounding to the nearest thousand and estimating

We round numbers so that we are able to estimate.

I have £432. Noogol has £920. We need £2000 to buy a computer. How much more money do we need?

Zoogol has about £400. I have about £900. We have about £1300 altogether. We need about £700 more to buy the computer.

  Let's recall rounding to the nearest hundred.

```
                    6541        6572
                     ↓           ↓
  |----|----|----|----|----|----|----|----|----|
  6500              6550              6600
```

6541 is between 6500 and 6600.
6541 is nearer to 6500 than to 6600.
6541 is **6500** when rounded to the nearest hundred.

6572 is between 6500 and 6600.
6572 is nearer to 6600 than to 6500.
6572 is **6600** when rounded to the nearest hundred.

We say 6541 is approximately equal to **6500** and
6572 is approximately equal to **6600**.

We write 6541 ≈ **6500**
6572 ≈ **6600**

 We use the approximation sign (≈) to stand for **approximately equal to**. It shows what the numbers are rounded to.

2 **a**

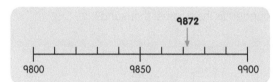

9872 is between 9800 and ⬭. 9900

9872 is nearer to ⬭ than ⬭. 9900, 9800

9872 is ⬭ when rounded to the nearest hundred. 9900

9872 ≈ ⬭ 9900

b What is 8137 rounded to the nearest hundred? ⬭ 8100

3 Let's round to the nearest thousand.
What is 6541 rounded to the nearest thousand?

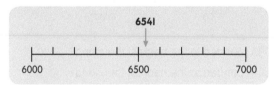

6541 is between 6000 and 7000.
6541 is nearer to 7000 than to 6000.
6541 is **7000** when rounded to the nearest thousand.
6541 ≈ 7000

4 What is 8276 rounded to the nearest thousand?

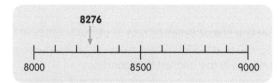

8276 is between 8000 and 9000.
8276 is nearer to 8000 than 9000.
8276 is **8000** when rounded to the nearest thousand.
8276 ≈ ⬭ 8000

21

Teaching sequence

a
- Ask pupils to name the two multiples of one hundred that are immediately before and after 9872. Then ask pupils to decide which multiple of one hundred 9872 is nearer to. Guide pupils to record the answer using the '≈' sign.

b
- Ask pupils to work on this question as an informal assessment.

- Use the same procedure as in ① to teach pupils how to round a number to the nearest thousand. Ask pupils to identify the multiples of one thousand immediately before and after 6541 by looking at the digit in the thousands place. The digit is 6, so 6541 is between 6000 and 7000.

- Ask pupils what number is midway between 6000 and 7000 (6500). Then ask whether they think 6541 is greater or less than 6500. Since 6541 is greater than 6500, it will be nearer to 7000.

- Ask pupils to use '≈' when rounding 6541 to the nearest thousand. (6541≈7000).

- Work through this question with pupils in the same way for reinforcement.

When rounding to the nearest thousand, pupils can just look at the digits in the thousands and hundreds places. For example, when rounding 65417 to the nearest thousand, we can see that the digit 5 is in the thousands place, so the answer is either 65000 or 66000.

Then look at the digit in the hundreds place. The digit 4 is less than 5, so we round to the smaller number, 65000. If the digit in the hundreds place is 5 or more, round to the greater number. This method should be taught only after pupils have understood the meaning of rounding.

Teaching sequence

- Use this question to demonstrate what to do when the number to be rounded is exactly midway in between. After pupils have identified that 9500 is midway between 9000 and 10000, explain to pupils that in this case, the number will be rounded to 10000 (the larger number).

6

- Ask pupils to work on these questions as an informal assessment.

7

- Ask pupils: *"What number is midway between 85000 and 86000?"* (85500).
- Next ask pupils: *"Is 85210 nearer to 85000 or 86000?"* (85000). So when rounded to the nearest thousand 85210 is 85000.

8

- Ask pupils to copy the number line and mark the positions where they think 125231 and 125780 are.
- Then ask pupils to round these numbers to the nearest thousand.

5 What is 9500 rounded to the nearest thousand?

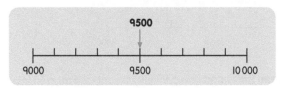

9500 is exactly halfway between 9000 and 10000.
In this case, we round 9500 to 10000.
So 9500 is **10000** when rounded to the nearest thousand.
9500 ≈ 10000

6

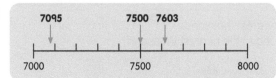

a   What is 7095 rounded to the nearest thousand? 7000
b   What is 7500 rounded to the nearest thousand? 8000
c   What is 7603 rounded to the nearest thousand? 8000

7 Round 85210 to the nearest thousand.

The number is between 85000 and 86000.
85210 is nearer to 85000 than to 86000.
85210 is 85000 when rounded to the nearest thousand.
85210 ≈ 85000

8 Copy the number line below. Estimate and mark the position of each of the numbers, 125780 and 125231 with a cross (✕) on the number line. Round these numbers to the nearest thousand.

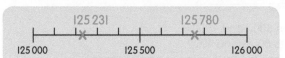

125780 ≈ 126000
125231 ≈ 125000

22

Additional activity

Ask pupils to work in pairs.
Pupil A thinks of a number
and then tells Pupil B what it is
rounded to (e.g. 7500). Pupil B
is asked to guess the possible
number that pupil A had.
Pupil A can give hints using the
words 'more than' and 'less than'.
Ask Pupils A and B to swap roles.

9 Round these numbers to the nearest thousand.

a   6321 6000   b   6509 7000

c   1098 1000   d   9873 10 000

e   6995 7000   f   12 051 12 000

g   65 500 66 000   h   89 773 90 000

i   325 699 326 000   j   600 039 600 000

10 Round these numbers to the nearest thousand.

6521 ≈ 7000
5079 ≈ 5000

Then estimate the value of: **a** 6521 + 5079   **b** 6521 − 5079

a   6521 + 5079 ≈ 7000 + 5000
         = 12 000

There is a change in sign because we
are not approximating the sum of 7000
and 5000. This is the actual sum of the
two rounded numbers.

b   6521 − 5079 ≈ 7000 − ⬚
              5000
        = ⬚
      2000

11 Round the numbers to the nearest thousand. Then estimate the
value of:

a   7192 + 1642 ≈ 7000 + 2000 = 9000

b   5701 − 3214 ≈ 6000 − 3000 = 3000

c   6290 + 5500 + 3719 ≈ 6000 + 6000 + 4000 = 16 000

d   9810 − 1600 − 7391 ≈ 10 000 − 2000 − 7000 = 1000

23

Teaching sequence

9

- Ask pupils to work on these
  questions as an informal
  assessment.

10

- Demonstrate how to estimate
  the sum and difference of
  two 4-digit numbers by
  rounding the numbers to the
  nearest thousand. Highlight
  to pupils that estimation is
  important as it enables them
  to check whether an answer
  is reasonable and to make
  quick calculations in practical
  situations.

11

- Ask pupils to work on these
  questions as practice.

Ask pupils to work in groups
of three. Pupil A calls out a
number, e.g. 42 000. Pupil A
then tells Pupils B and C that it
is an estimated number made
by multiplying a 4-digit number
by a I-digit number. Pupils B
and C think of any two possible
answers. Ask pupils to swap roles.

Teaching sequence

12

- Demonstrate how to estimate
the product of a 4-digit
number and a I-digit number
by rounding the 4-digit
number to the nearest
thousand. It is possible to
estimate the product when the
multiplier is 8 or 9 by rounding
8 or 9 to 10, but the estimation
here is based on rounding to
the nearest thousand.

13 and **14**

- Ask pupils to work on these
questions as practice.

15

- Show how to estimate the
quotient of a 4-digit number
divided by a I-digit number.
The procedure for estimation
in division is different from
estimation in addition,
subtraction or multiplication.
To estimate the quotient, the
dividend is approximated to
a number that is exactly
divisible and easily divided
by the divisor.

- To estimate 3465 ÷ 6, we look
for the closest useful multiple
of 6 that we can round 3465
to. 3465 can be approximated
to 3000 or 3600, which are
both easily divided and exactly
divisible by 6. 3600 is chosen
since it is nearer to 3465.

Unit I Whole Numbers (I)

12 Estimate the value of 7120 × 5.

First round 7120 to the nearest thousand.

7120 ≈ 7000

7120 × 5 ≈ 7000 × 5
        = 35 000

13 Estimate the value of 6327 × 7.

6327 × 7 ≈ ◯ × 7 6000

      = ◯ 42 000

> Round the 4-digit number to the nearest thousand first.

14 Round the 4-digit number to the nearest thousand. Then estimate the value of:

a 2145 × 7 14 000	**b** 8756 × 6 54 000	**c** 2632 × 8 24 000
d 4979 × 5 25 000	**e** 9218 × 4 36 000	**f** 6380 × 9 54 000

15 Estimate the value of 3465 ÷ 6.

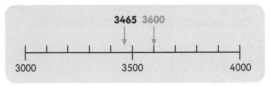

3465 3600

3000   3500   4000

To estimate 3465 ÷ 6, we choose a number
close to 3465 that can be divided by 6 exactly.

3465 is closer to 3600 than 3000.

So 3465 ÷ 6 ≈ 3600 ÷ 6 = 600.

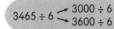

> 3465 ÷ 6   3000 ÷ 6
>   3600 ÷ 6

24

16 Estimate the value of 6742 ÷ 8.

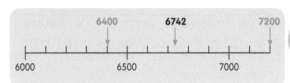

| 6400 | **6742** | 7200 |

6000   6500   7000

6742 ÷ 8 ⟶ 6400 ÷ 8
⟶ 7200 ÷ 8

6742 is nearer to
6400 than to 7200.

So 6742 ÷ 8 ≈ ⬚ ÷ 8 = ⬚ .
       6400   800

Activity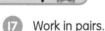

17 Work in pairs.
A house has 3 bedrooms, a living room,
a dining room, a bathroom and a kitchen.
The new owners want to renovate the
house. Estimate how much they would
need to spend on the renovation by first
rounding each cost to the nearest
thousand pounds.

Description	Cost	
Oak flooring for the living room, dining room and 3 bedrooms	£7650 per room	≈ £8000 × 5 = £40 000
Bookshelves in 2 rooms	£3840 per room	≈ £4000 × 2 = £8000
Cupboards in master bedroom	£4621	≈ £5000
New kitchen	£7705	≈ £8000
Other furniture	£16 500	≈ £17 000

£40 000 + £8000 + £5000 + £8000 + £17 000 ≈ £78 000.
The cost is approximately £78 000.

25

Teaching sequence

16

- To estimate 6742 ÷ 8, 6742 can be approximated to 6400 or 7200, which are both easily divided and exactly divisible by 8. Ask pupils which number they should choose.

17

- Ask pupils to work in pairs. This activity enables pupils to use estimation in a practical situation and consolidates their understanding of rounding to the nearest thousand.

Independent work

- *Let's Practise!*
- Practice 5 and *Maths Journal* in Practice Book 5A, pp 15 to 20.

Objectives of activity

These questions require pupils to:

- explain why a 6-digit number is greater than a 5-digit number
- explain the errors made in rounding numbers to the nearest hundred and thousand

Thinking skills

- Analysing
- Evaluating

Teaching sequence

㉑ *Maths Journal*

- Ask pupils to explain why a 6-digit number beginning with 1 is greater than a 5-digit number beginning with 9. Pupils should be able to compare the numbers using the strategy of comparing the value of the numbers.

㉒

- Here pupils are asked to explain some errors that are made in the rounding of numbers. These questions allow pupils to consolidate their understanding of the methods used to round numbers to the nearest hundred and the nearest thousand.

Let's Practise!

18 Round each number to the nearest: **i** hundred **ii** thousand.

a 7005 7000, 7000 **b** 8321 8300, 8000 **c** 7603 7600, 8000 **d** 8997 9000, 9000

19 Round the 4-digit numbers to the nearest thousand. Then estimate the value of:

a 3471 + 4207 7000

b 3670 − 2189 2000

c 9246 − 2355 − 1478 6000

d 3322 × 8 24 000

20 Estimate the value of:

a 1745 ÷ 3 600

b 2343 ÷ 4 600

c 4467 ÷ 6 700

d 4219 ÷ 5 800

e 6581 ÷ 7 900

f 8502 ÷ 9 900

Practice Book 5A, p. 15

Maths Journal

21 Compare 100 001 and 99 002.
Which number is greater? Explain why.
Comparing from the left, 100 001 is greater than 99 002 because 100 000 is greater than 90 000.

22 Round **a** 763 to the nearest hundred

b 3730 to the nearest thousand.

Ella rounded 763 to 700 and 3730 to 3000.
Explain the mistakes she made.
Ella thinks that to round a number to the nearest hundred, she should give the value of the hundreds digit; and to round a number to the nearest thousand, she should give the value of the thousands digit.

26

Let's Wrap It Up!

You have learnt to:

- count in ten thousands and hundred thousands
- read and write numbers up to 10 million in words and numerals
- identify the place and value of each digit of a number up to 10 million
- compare numbers within 10 million
- complete number patterns by adding or subtracting
- round numbers to the nearest thousand
- estimate sums, differences, products and quotients.

Let's Revise!

The land area of some countries are shown below.

Country	Land Area in km²
Canada	9 976 140
France	547 030
Hong Kong	1092
Indonesia	1 919 440
Maldives	300
Singapore	693
Belgium	30 280
Thailand	514 000

a Write the value of the land area of Canada in words.

Nine million, nine hundred and seventy-six thousand, one hundred and forty.

b Which country has the smallest land area? What is its land area in numerals?

Maldives has a land area of 300 km².

27

Teaching sequence

Let's Wrap It Up!

- Emphasise the key concepts, skills and processes that have been taught in the unit. Discuss the worked example with pupils to assess whether they have mastered these concepts, skills and processes. Provide further help on any difficulties they still have.

Objective of activity

These questions require pupils to list the possible whole numbers that round to 30.

Thinking skills

- Comparing
- Identifying patterns and relationships

Heuristics for problem solving

- Guess and check
- Look for a pattern

Independent work

Challenging Practice and *Problem Solving* in Practice Book 5A, pp 21 to 22.

Teaching sequence

23 *Put On Your Thinking Caps!*

- This question requires pupils to do the inverse of rounding. Given the rounded value, they have to find the whole numbers that round to that value.

24

- Ask pupils to use the strategy of compensation to find the sum of 99 + 99 and 99 + 99 + 99 + 99 + 99 + 99.

Let's Wrap It Up!

c Arrange the countries in order, beginning with the country with the greatest land area.
Canada, Indonesia, France, Thailand, Belgium, Hong Kong, Singapore and Maldives.

d Which countries have a land area of more than 1 000 000 km²?
Canada and Indonesia.

e Which country has a larger land area, France or Thailand?
France has a larger land area than Thailand.

f Which countries have a land area of 1000 km² when rounded to the nearest thousand?
Singapore and Hong Kong.

Put On Your Thinking Caps!

23 Three cards have different whole numbers on them.
Each number equals 30 when rounded to the nearest ten.

> ? ? ?

a What are the smallest and greatest possible numbers? 25 and 34

b What can the three numbers be? 25 to 34

24 Without adding the 99s together, use a quicker way to find the value of:

a 99 + 99 $2 \times 100 - 2 = 198$

b 99 + 99 + 99 + 99 + 99 + 99 $6 \times 100 - 6 = 594$
What is the value of the digit in the ones place in each case?
8 and 4

c What is the least number of 99s which must be added to get a I in the ones place? 9

> Practice Book 5A, p. 21   Practice Book 5A, p. 22

28

Unit 1 — Whole Numbers (I)

Date: _____

Practice 1   Numbers to 10 million

1 Count in ten thousands or hundred thousands. Then fill in the spaces.

a 80 000, 70 000, 60 000, 50 000, _____, 40 000

b 100 000, 200 000, 300 000, 400 000, _____, 500 000

c 900 000, 800 000, 700 000, 600 000, _____, 500 000

2 Complete the table. Then write the number in numerals and in words.

Hundred Thousands	Ten Thousands	Thousands	Hundreds	Tens	Ones
●●●●●●● (dots)	●● (dots)	●●●●● (dots)	●●● (dots)	● (dot)	●●●●●● (dots)

	In Numerals	In Words
7 hundred thousands	700 000	seven hundred thousand
2 ten thousands	20 000	twenty thousand
5 thousands	5000	five thousand
3 hundreds	300	three hundred
1 ten	10	ten
6 ones	6	six

In numerals, the number is 725 316.

In words, the number is seven hundred and twenty-five thousand, three hundred and sixteen.

PRACTICE BOOK 5A

INSPIRE MATHS

Koogol

Googol

Zoogol

Toogol

Noogol

Ooogol

Consultant and author
Dr Fong Ho Kheong

Authors
Gan Kee Soon and Chelvi Ramakrishnan

UK consultants
Carole Skinner, Simon d'Angelo and Elizabeth Gibbs

3 Write the numbers in numerals.

a

Hundred Thousands	Ten Thousands	Thousands	Hundreds	Tens	Ones
● ● ● ●	● ●	● ● ●	● ● ● ● ● ● ●	● ●	

The number is ___835 720___ .

b

Hundred Thousands	Ten Thousands	Thousands	Hundreds	Tens	Ones
● ●	● ● ●	● ● ● ● ● ● ● ● ●	● ● ● ● ● ●	● ● ● ● ●	● ● ●

The number is ___239 653___ .

c Eight hundred and sixteen thousand, nine hundred and forty-three
___816 943___ .

First read the thousands parts: Eight hundred and sixteen thousand, 816 000.   Then read this part: Nine hundred and forty-three, 943.

d Six hundred and five thousand and five hundred ___605 500___ .

e One hundred and three thousand and thirty-one ___103 031___ .

f Eight hundred and seventy thousand and three ___870 003___ .

g Three hundred thousand and twelve ___300 012___ .

h Twenty-two thousand, six hundred and ninety-seven ___22 697___ .

4 Fill in the table headings with 'Tens', 'Hundreds', 'Ten Thousands' or 'Hundred Thousands'. Then write the numbers in words.

a

Hundred Thousands	Ten Thousands	Thousands	Hundreds	Tens	Ones
●		● ● ● ● ●	● ● ●	● ● ● ● ● ●	● ●

The number is ___one hundred and five thousand, three hundred___
___and sixty-two___ .

b

Hundred Thousands	Ten Thousands	Thousands	Hundreds	Tens	Ones
● ● ● ● ●	● ● ● ● ● ●			● ●	●

The number is ___five hundred and sixty thousand and twenty-one___ .

5 Write the numbers in words.

65 000: sixty-five thousand
142: one hundred and forty-two

a 65 142   ___sixty-five thousand, one hundred and forty-two___

b 368 400   ___three hundred and sixty-eight thousand and four hundred___

c 700 070   ___seven hundred thousand and seventy___

Practice 2 Numbers to 10 million

1 Write the number in numerals and in words.

Millions	Hundred Thousands	Ten Thousands	Thousands	Hundreds	Tens	Ones

In Numerals	In Words
9 ___ millions → 9 000 000	nine million
___ hundred thousands → 100 000	one hundred thousand
5 ___ ten thousands → 50 000	fifty thousand
6 ___ thousands → 6000	six thousand
3 ___ hundreds → 300	three hundred
4 ___ tens → 40	forty
2 ___ ones → 2	two

In numerals, the number is ___9 156 342___ .

In words, the number is ___nine million, one hundred and fifty-six thousand, three hundred and forty-two___ .

---

6 Fill in the spaces with the missing words.

a Eight hundred and two thousand, one hundred and ___one___ . → 802 101

b Three hundred and twenty-four ___thousand___ , three hundred and six. → 324 306

c One hundred and fifty thousand, ___two___ hundred and sixty. → 150 260

d Nine hundred and ___ninety-nine___ thousand, one hundred and ___ninety-eight___ . → 999 198

7 The populations of some countries are shown below.

Country	Population
Bahamas	46 000
Mauritius	2030
Greenland	56 361
Iceland	299 388
Luxembourg	502 207
Pitcairn Islands	45

a Write the population of Iceland in words.

Two hundred and ninety-nine thousand, three hundred and eighty-eight.

b Which country has the smallest population? What is its population?

Pitcairn Islands has a population of forty-five /45.

c Which country has a population of about 500 000?

Luxembourg

Date: _____

Practice 3 Place and value

1 Fill in the spaces.

Hundred Thousands	Ten Thousands	Thousands	Hundreds	Tens	Ones
⦿⦿⦿	⦿⦿ ⦿⦿	⦿⦿⦿ ⦿⦿⦿	⦿⦿		⦿
3	4	5	2	0	1

In 345201:

a i the digit 3 stands for __300000__

   ii the value of the digit 3 is __300000__

b i the digit 4 stands for __40000__

   ii the value of the digit 4 is __40000__

c i the digit 5 stands for __5000__

   ii the value of the digit 5 is __5000__ .

2 Fill in the boxes with the values of the digits.

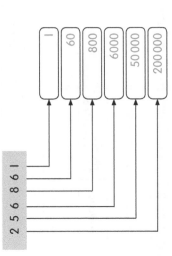

2 5 6 8 6 1 → 1, 60, 800, 6000, 50000, 200000

---

2 Write the numbers in numerals.

a Nine million __9000000__

b Two million, one hundred and fifty-six thousand and four __2156004__

c Five million, two hundred and thirty-eight thousand __5238000__

d Seven million, one hundred and fifty thousand __7150000__

e Six million, sixty thousand and fifty __6060050__

f Three million and three __3000003__

3 Write the numbers in words.

a 2543000 __two million, five hundred and forty-three thousand__

b 5050000 __five million and fifty thousand__

c 8147600 __eight million, one hundred and forty-seven thousand and six hundred__

d 2150000 __two million, one hundred and fifty thousand__

e 7230014 __seven million, two hundred and thirty thousand and fourteen__

f 5192622 __five million, one hundred and ninety-two thousand, six hundred and twenty-two__

g 9009009 __nine million, nine thousand and nine__

8 Fill in the spaces.

Millions	Hundred Thousands	Ten Thousands	Thousands	Hundreds	Tens	Ones
1	5	0	8	3	6	9

In 1 508 369:

a **i** the digit 1 stands for 1 000 000

ii the value of the digit 1 is 1 000 000

b **i** the digit 8 stands for 8000

ii the value of the digit 8 is 8000

c the digit 0 is in the ten thousands place.

9 Fill in the boxes with the values of the digits.

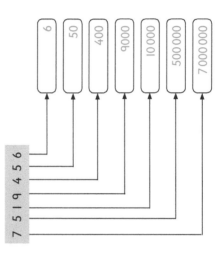

7 5 1 9 4 5 6

6
50
400
9000
10 000
500 000
7 000 000

---

3 In the number 346 812:

a the digit 3 stands for 300 000

b the digit 6 stands for 6000

4 What is the value of the digit **2** in each of the numbers below?

a 3**2**9 051   20 000

b 903 5**2**1   20

c 71**2** 635   2000

d **2**58 169   200 000

5 Fill in the spaces.

a In 320 187, the digit 0 is in the thousands place.

b In 835 129, the digit 8 is in the hundred thousands place.

c In 348 792, the digit 4 is in the ten thousands place.

6 Read the clues to find the number.

It is a 6-digit number.
The digit 1 is in the ones place.
The greatest digit is in the hundred thousands place.
The value of the digit 5 is 500.
The digit in the ten thousands place is 3 less than the digit in the hundred thousands place.
The digit in the thousands place stands for 4000.
The digit in the tens place is more than 7 but less than 9.

The number is 964 581.

7 Fill in the spaces.

a 153 420 = 100 000 + 50 000 + 3000 + 420

b 760 300 = 760 000 + 300

c 700 000 + 8000 + 500 + 4 = 708 504

d 200 000 + 2000 + 10 = 202 010

Left page

10 Fill in the spaces.

a In 5 420 000, the digit 5 is in the _millions_ place.

b In 1 077 215, the digit in the hundred thousands place is _0_.

c In 9 400 210, the digit 9 stands for _9 000 000_.

d 4 130 000 = _4 000 000_ + 100 000 + 30 000

e 6 123 750 = 6 000 000 + 123 000 + _750_

f 7 550 100 = 7 000 000 + _550 000_ + 100

g 5 000 000 + 200 000 + 7000 + 70 = _5 207 070_

11 Read the clues to find the number.

It is a 7-digit number.
The value of the digit 7 is 700.
The greatest digit is in the millions place.
The digit 1 is next to the digit in the millions place.
The value of the digit 8 is 8 tens.
The value of the digit 3 is 3 ones.
The digit 5 is in the thousands place.
The digit 6 stands for 60 000.

The number is _9 165 783_.

Right page

Date: _____

Practice 4 Comparing numbers within 10 million

Compare the place values of the digits starting from the left.

1. Which is greater, 97 210 or 125 302? Write the values in the place value chart to compare.

Hundred Thousands	Ten Thousands	Thousands	Hundreds	Tens	Ones
	9	7	2	1	0
1	2	5	3	0	2

_1_ hundred thousand is greater than _9_ ten thousands.

So _125 302_ is greater than _97 210_.

2. Circle the smaller number.

a 128 758 or (74 906)

b 523 719 or (523 689)

3. Circle the greater number.

a (712 400) or 89 000

b 635 002 or (635 100)

4. Circle the smallest number and cross (✗) out the greatest number.

~~375 061~~ 172 503 (127 503) 157 203 371 560 371 605

5. Arrange the numbers in order, beginning with the smallest.

a 739 615, 795 316, 315 679, 615 379

315 679, 615 379, 739 615, 795 316

b 245 385, 805 342, 97 632, 300 596

97 632, 245 385, 300 596, 805 342

6 Look at the two numbers in the place value charts and fill in the spaces.

a

Millions	Hundred Thousands	Ten Thousands	Thousands	Hundreds	Tens	Ones
1	0	7	9	7	2	0
	9	9	0	3	9	5

9 hundred thousands is smaller than 1 million.

So 990 395 is smaller than 1 079 720 .

b

Millions	Hundred Thousands	Ten Thousands	Thousands	Hundreds	Tens	Ones
1	0	8	3	9	5	2
5	0	9	6	3	5	7

5 096 357 is greater than 1 083 952 .

c

Millions	Hundred Thousands	Ten Thousands	Thousands	Hundreds	Tens	Ones
6	4	1	2	5	8	6
6	4	3	8	6	7	1

6 438 671 is greater than 6 412 586 .

7 Circle the greater number.

a (4 015 280) or 2 845 000

b 999 098 or (1 000 000)

8 Circle the smaller number.

a (2 007 625) or 2 107 625

b 7 405 319 or (905 407)

9 Arrange the numbers in order, beginning with the greatest.

a 2 432 000, 480 000, 2 720 000, 3 190 000

3 190 000, 2 720 000, 2 432 000, 480 000

b 513 900, 3 150 000, 913 000, 2 020 000

3 150 000, 2 020 000, 913 000, 513 900

10 What is the next number in each pattern? Fill in the spaces.

a 738 561, 938 561, 1 138 561, …

i 938 561 is 200 000 more than 738 561.

ii 1 138 561 is 200 000 more than 938 561.

iii 1 338 561 is 200 000 more than 1 138 561.

The next number in the pattern is 1 338 561 .

b 4 655 230, 4 555 230, 4 455 230, …

i 4 555 230 is 100 000 less than 4 655 230.

ii 4 455 230 is 100 000 less than 4 555 230.

iii 4 355 230 is 100 000 less than 4 455 230.

The next number in the pattern is 4 355 230 .

Practice 5 | Rounding to the nearest thousand and estimating

1 Look at the number lines. Fill in the numbers in the boxes.

a
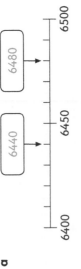
6400   6450   6500
boxes: 6440, 6480

b

7000   7500   8000
boxes: 7100, 7700

c
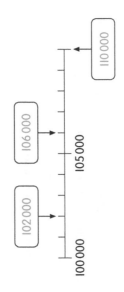
100000   105000   110000
boxes: 102000, 106000, 110000

---

11 Complete the number patterns. Give the rule for each pattern.

a   230180, 231180, 232180, 233180, 234180

   i   231180 is __1000__ more than 230180.

   ii   232180 is __1000__ more than 231180.

   Rule: Count on by 1000.

b   850400, 845400, 840400, __835400__, __830400__

   Rule: Count back by 5000.

c   2650719, 3650719, 4650719, __5650719__, __6650719__

   Rule: Count on by 1000000.

d   6298436, 5198436, 4098436, __2998436__, __1898436__

   Rule: Count back by 1100000.

12 Fill in the spaces. Then solve the riddle below.

a   5083000 = 5000000 + __83000__   M

b   5000000 + 600000 + 2000 = __5602000__   T

c   Which is greater, 509900 or 562000? __562000__   S

d   Which is smaller, 1020000 or 1002000? __1002000__   A

e   The value of the digit 1 in 7120000 is __100000__.   P

f   Complete the number pattern. 508900, 509000, 509100, ... The next number is __509200__.   K

What goes around the world but remains in the corner?

S	T	A	M	P
562000	5602000	1002000	83000	100000

2 Mark the given number with a cross (X) on the number line. Then round the number as specified.

Example

656

650 ⎯⎯ X ⎯⎯ 660

656 rounded to the nearest ten is **660**.

656 ≈ **660**

a 9709

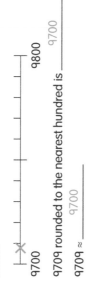

9700 ⎯⎯ 9800

9709 rounded to the nearest hundred is ⎯⎯9700⎯⎯.

9709 ≈ ⎯⎯9700⎯⎯

b 31600

31000 ⎯⎯ 32000

31600 rounded to the nearest thousand is ⎯⎯32000⎯⎯.

31600 ≈ ⎯⎯32000⎯⎯

3 Round to the nearest thousand.

a 5637 ≈ ⎯⎯6000⎯⎯

b 9541 ≈ ⎯⎯10 000⎯⎯

c 1399 ≈ ⎯⎯1000⎯⎯

d 72245 ≈ ⎯⎯72 000⎯⎯

e 473075 ≈ ⎯⎯473 000⎯⎯

f 69547 ≈ ⎯⎯70 000⎯⎯

g 20100 ≈ ⎯⎯20 000⎯⎯

h 756715 ≈ ⎯⎯757 000⎯⎯

4 Estimate the sum by first rounding each number to the nearest thousand.

a 9286 + 5703
≈ 9000 + 6000
= 15000

b 6789 + 4200
≈ 7000 + 4000
= 11000

c 7264 + 7153
≈ 7000 + 7000
= 14 000

d 4885 + 6075
≈ 5000 + 6000
= 11000

e 3105 + 9940
≈ 3000 + 10 000
= 13000

f 7083 + 2607
≈ 7000 + 3000
= 10000

5 Estimate the difference by first rounding each number to the nearest thousand.

a 8156 − 6109
≈ 8000 − 6000
= 2000

b 4924 − 4127
≈ 5000 − 4000
= 1000

c 7105 − 3940
≈ 7000 − 4000
= 3000

d 4885 − 1075
≈ 5000 − 1000
= 4000

Date: _____

Maths Journal

1 Jack and Ella used a calculator to find 8642 + 9328.

Jack's answer is 17 970.   Ella's answer is 1897.

One of them had typed in the numbers incorrectly. How would you use estimation to check whose answer is more reasonable?

Answers vary.

Estimate by rounding the numbers to the nearest thousand.

Example: 8642 ≈ 9000 (rounded to the nearest thousand)
9328 ≈ 9000 (rounded to the nearest thousand)

8642 + 9328 ≈ 9000 + 9000
= 18 000

So Jack's answer is more reasonable. Ella's answer is too far off the estimate of 18 000.

6 Estimate the product by first rounding the 4-digit number to the nearest thousand.

a 4512 × 2 ≈ 5000 × 2
= 10 000

b 3765 × 7 ≈ 4000 × 7
= 28 000

c 2521 × 5 ≈ 3000 × 5
= 15 000

d 5108 × 6 ≈ 5000 × 6
= 30 000

e 8497 × 9 ≈ 8000 × 9
= 72 000

f 6060 × 3 ≈ 6000 × 3
= 18 000

7 Estimate the quotient.

2786 ÷ 5   2500 ÷ 5 / 3000 ÷ 5

Which number is nearer to 2786?

a 2786 ÷ 5 ≈
3000 ÷ 5 = 600

b 6509 ÷ 7 ≈
6300 ÷ 7 = 900

c 5512 ÷ 6 ≈
5400 ÷ 6 = 900

d 2785 ÷ 3 ≈
2700 ÷ 3 = 900

e 6287 ÷ 8 ≈
6400 ÷ 8 = 800

f 2963 ÷ 9 ≈
2700 ÷ 9 = 300

Challenging Practice

1 Arrange the digits below to make three possible 6-digit numbers which are 756 000 when rounded to the nearest thousand.

2	5	5	6	7	8

Answers vary.
Accept any of the possible answers: 755 628, 755 682, 755 826, 755 862, 756 258, 756 285

---

2 Millie did the following for her homework.

a 7986 ÷ 8 = 998 r2   b 2659 ÷ 3 = 264 r3

She was asked to check her answers. Show what she would do to check how reasonable her answers are in **a** and **b**.

a

7986 ÷ 8 ≈ 8000 ÷ 8 = 1000

Her answer is reasonable.

b

2659 ÷ 3 ≈ 2700 ÷ 3 = 900
or
3000 ÷ 3 = 1000

Her answer is not reasonable.

Date: _____

Problem Solving

1 The number 3200 has the digit 3 in the thousands place and the digit 2 in the hundreds place. What number must you subtract from 3200 so that the answer is a 4-digit number with the digit 2 in the thousands place, the digit 3 in the hundreds place and zeros in the tens and ones places?

<u>2 3 0 0</u>

3200 – 2300 = 900
The number to be subtracted is 900.

2 A 3-digit number when divided by 5 gives an even number. When it is divided by 3, it also gives an even number.

a What is the digit in the ones place? 0
b What can the number be?
120, 150, 180, 210, 240, etc. (multiples of 3 with 0 in the ones place or multiples of 30)

Unit 1: Whole Numbers (1)

22

Answers Unit 1: Whole Numbers (1)

Unit 2: Whole Numbers (2)

Week	Learning Objectives	Thinking Skills	Resources
3	**(1) Using a calculator** Pupils will be able to use a calculator to: • type in whole numbers • add whole numbers • subtract whole numbers • multiply whole numbers • divide whole numbers	• Sequencing	• Pupil Textbook 5A, pp 29 to 32 • Practice Book 5A, pp 23 to 24 • Teacher's Guide 5A, pp 49 to 52
3	**(2) Multiplying by tens, hundreds or thousands** Pupils will be able to: • multiply a number by 10, 100 or 1000 by: (i) moving each digit 1, 2 or 3 places to the left respectively in the place value chart (ii) adding 1, 2 or 3 zeros respectively at the end of the number • multiply numbers up to 4 digits by tens, hundreds or thousands • use rounding and approximation to estimate answers in multiplication	• Comparing • Identifying patterns and relationships	• Pupil Textbook 5A, pp 33 to 41 • Practice Book 5A, pp 25 to 30 • Teacher's Guide 5A, pp 53 to 61

Unit 2: Whole Numbers (2)

Week	Learning Objectives	Thinking Skills	Resources

3 – 4	**(3) Dividing by tens, hundreds or thousands**
	
	Pupils will be able to:
	• divide a number by 10, 100 or 1000 by:
	  (i) moving each digit 1, 2 or 3 places to the right respectively in the place value chart
	  (ii) dropping 1, 2 or 3 zeros respectively from the end of the number
	• divide numbers up to 6 digits by tens, hundreds or thousands
	• use rounding and approximation to estimate answers in division
	
	Let's Explore!
	
	This activity allows pupils to explore division of any whole number by 10, 100 or 1000 without using a calculator.
		• Comparing
		• Identifying patterns and relationships
			• Pupil Textbook 5A, pp 42 to 49
			• Practice Book 5A, pp 31 to 34
			• Teacher's Guide 5A, pp 62 to 69

Unit 2: Whole Numbers (2)

Week	Learning Objectives	Thinking Skills	Resources
4	**(4) Order of operations** Pupils will be able to: • state the order of operations in a number sentence with two or three operations and use a calculator to compute it • state the order of operations in a number sentence which has brackets and two or three operations, and use a calculator to compute it *Let's Explore!* • Pupils should compare the order of computation and answers of a scientific calculator with a non-scientific calculator. • This task enables pupils to verify that in a number sentence with multiplication followed by division, the order of operations is not relevant.	• Classifying	• Pupil Textbook 5A, pp 50 to 56 • Practice Book 5A, pp 35 to 40 • Teacher's Guide 5A, pp 70 to 76
4	**(5) Word problems (I)** Pupils will be able to solve multi-step word problems.	• Applying concepts and processes	• Pupil Textbook 5A, pp 57 to 61 • Practice Book 5A, pp 41 to 44 • Teacher's Guide 5A, pp 77 to 81

Unit 2: Whole Numbers (2)

Week	Learning Objectives	Thinking Skills	Resources
4	**(6) Word problems (2)** Pupils will be able to use a number of heuristics such as 'model drawing', 'make a systematic list', 'guess and check', 'unitary method', and 'before and after strategy' to solve multi-step word problems. *Let's Wrap It Up!* Emphasise the key concepts, skills and processes that have been taught in the unit. Discuss the worked example with pupils to assess whether they have mastered these concepts, skills and processes. *Put On Your Thinking Caps!* Pupils will be able to apply their understanding of multiplication as repeated addition to solve this problem.	• Applying concepts and processes • Identifying relationships Heuristics for problem solving: • Look for a pattern • Restate the problem	• Pupil Textbook 5A, pp 62 to 69 • Practice Book 5A, pp 45 to 52 • Teacher's Guide 5A, pp 82 to 89
	Review 1		• Practice Book 5A, pp 53 to 64

Summative assessment opportunity

Assessment Book 5, Test 1, pp 1 to 6

Whole Numbers (2)

Learning objectives:
Using a calculator
Pupils will be able to use a calculator to:
- type in whole numbers
- add whole numbers
- subtract whole numbers
- multiply whole numbers
- divide whole numbers

Key concept
Understanding the concepts of place value and the four operations.

Thinking skill
Sequencing

What you will need
Scientific calculator

Calculator tip
- The 'clear display' button is sometimes marked 'AC' (standing for 'All Clear') rather than 'C'.
- The display boxes in the textbook help to show pupils what they will see when they press the relevant buttons. These have been kept simple for clarity, so pupils may find that the display on their calculators looks slightly different. One useful feature of a scientific calculator is that it will also show the whole calculation being entered at the top of the screen.

Unit 2 Whole Numbers (2)

Let's Learn!

Using a calculator

Get to know your calculator

1. Follow the steps to type in numbers on your calculator.

   Turn your calculator on.
   To type in 12345, press: [1] [2] [3] [4] [5]
   To clear the display on your calculator, press: [C]

   Display
0
12345
0

Activity

2. Work in pairs.

   Type in these numbers on your calculator. Clear the display on your calculator before typing in the next number.

   a 735   **b** 9038   **c** 23104   **d** 505602

   Check the numbers displayed on your calculator with those on your partner's calculator.
   Do you both get the same numbers on the display screen?

Addition

3. **a** Add 417 and 9086.

Press	Display
[C]	0
[4] [1] [7]	417
[+] [9] [0] [8] [6]	9086
[=]	9503

   The sum is 9503.

Teaching sequence

1
- Using a visualiser, highlight to the pupils the 'On', 'Clear', number and operation buttons on a calculator.
- Show pupils the steps to type in a number, e.g. 12345, on the calculator. Ask pupils to read the number as twelve thousand, three hundred and forty-five.
- Illustrate with a few more examples. Remind pupils to clear the calculator before typing in a new number.

2
- Allow pupils to practise typing in the given numbers on their calculators. Encourage pupils to read the numbers to each other.

3
a
- Demonstrate how addition of two whole numbers is done with a calculator.
- Ask pupils to join in by pressing the relevant buttons on their calculators. Pupils can check the answer by carrying out the addition without using a calculator.

Unit 2: Whole Numbers (2)   49

Write a number on the board, e.g. 3467. Ask pupils to work in pairs to find:

(a) two numbers which have this sum,

e.g. 1234 + 2233 = 3467

(b) two numbers which have this difference,

e.g. 4701 – 1234 = 3467.

 Calculator tip

Ask pupils to type in '12 + 345', then type in '+ 98 ='. Explain to pupils that the calculator will continue using the previous answer as long as the calculator is still switched on and another operation is entered.

What you will need

Scientific calculator

Teaching sequence

b

- Explain to pupils that the calculator does not display the units of the answer. Emphasise that they must write the units in their answers.

- Demonstrate how subtraction of two whole numbers is done with a calculator. Ask pupils to press the relevant buttons on their calculators. Ask pupils to read out the answer in words. Pupils can check the answer by carrying out the subtraction without using a calculator.
- Remind pupils to write the units in their answers.

Unit 2 Whole Numbers (2)

b Find the sum of £1275 and £876.

Remember to write the correct unit in your answer.

Press	Display
C	0
1 2 7 5	1275
+ 8 7 6	876
=	2151

The sum of £1275 and £876 is £2151.

Subtraction

4 a Subtract 6959 from 17358.

Press	Display
C	0
1 7 3 5 8	17358
– 6 9 5 9	6959
=	10399

The answer is 10399.

b Find the difference between 1005 kg and 248 kg.

Remember to write **kg** in your answer.

Press	Display
C	0
1 0 0 5	1005
– 2 4 8	248
=	757

The difference between 1005 kg and 248 kg is 757 kg.

30

Additional activity

Ask pupils to estimate the number of times their hearts beat in a year. Help pupils to find their pulse and count the number of times their hearts beat in a minute. Then ask them to multiply that number by 60 (hour), then by 24 (day) and finally by 365 (year).

Whole Numbers (2) **Unit 2**

Activity

(5)

Remember to press [C] before you start working on each question.

 Work in pairs to answer these questions:

a 7064 + 2378 9442   b 10 213 + 897 11 110

c 3675 – 1976 1699   d 12 310 – 9342 2968

e 734 km + 9868 km   f £3250 – £1865 £1385

   10 602 km

Think of one addition and one subtraction sentence.
Ask your partner to work them out using a calculator. Use your calculator to check whether your partner's answers are correct.

Multiplication

(6) a   Multiply 253 by 127.

Press	Display
[C]	0
[2][5][3]	253
[×][1][2][7]	127
[=]	32 131

The answer is 32 131.

b   Find the area of a rectangle with a length of 36 cm and a width of 24 cm.

Area = Length × Width
Remember that the unit for area is cm², m², etc.

Press	Display
[C]	0
[3][6]	36
[×][2][4]	24
[=]	864

The area of the rectangle is 864 cm².

31

Teaching sequence

(5)

• Ask pupils to work in pairs to practise using a calculator to add and subtract.

• Remind pupils to clear the display before working on a new calculation.

• Encourage pupils to read out the answers in words to each other.

(6)

a

• Show how multiplication is done with the use of a calculator.

b

• Revise the method to find the area of a rectangle with pupils:

  Area of a rectangle
  = Length × Width

Additional activity
Write 4056 on the board.
Ask pupils to work in pairs to find two numbers which have this quotient when the larger number is divided by the smaller number. This can be done by multiplying 4056 by any number, e.g. 4056 × 123 = 498 888.
So 498 888 ÷ 123 = 4056.

Calculator tip
If the scientific calculator you have has a 'back' button, you can demonstrate this to pupils. The 'back' button is usually called 'replay' and it allows pupils to change any of the numbers they have typed in, without typing in all the numbers again.

What you will need
Scientific calculator

Independent work
Practice I in Practice Book 5A, pp 23 to 24.

Teaching sequence

7
- Demonstrate how division is done with the use of a calculator.

8
- Ask pupils to work in pairs to practise using a calculator for multiplication and division.
- Remind pupils to clear the display before working on a new calculation.
- Encourage pupils to read out the answers in words to each other. Remind pupils how to read out decimal numbers, for example that I·5 is read as "*one point five*".

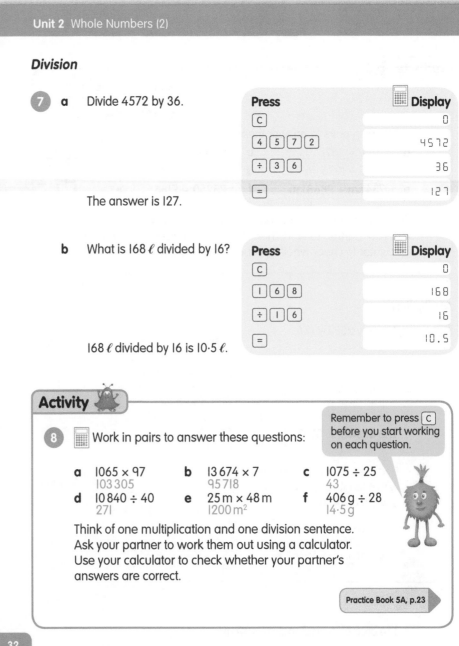

Learning objectives: Multiplying by tens, hundreds or thousands

Pupils will be able to:

- multiply a number by 10, 100 or 1000 by:
  - (i) moving each digit 1, 2 or 3 places to the left respectively in the place value chart
  - (ii) adding 1, 2 or 3 zeros respectively at the end of the number
- multiply numbers up to 4 digits by tens, hundreds or thousands

- use rounding and approximation to estimate answers in multiplication

Key concept

In the base ten number system:

- Ones × 10 = tens,
  Tens × 10 = hundreds,
  Hundreds × 10 = thousands
- Ones × 100 = hundreds,
  Tens × 100 = thousands,
  Hundreds × 100 = ten thousands
- Ones × 1000 = thousands,
  Tens × 1000 = ten thousands,
  Hundreds × 1000 = hundred thousands

Thinking skills

- Comparing
- Identifying patterns and relationships

Teaching sequence

- Review the 10 times table with pupils up to 12 × 10.
- Draw pupils' attention to the chart showing that the digits of a number move one place to the left when it is multiplied by 10.
- Ask pupils whether there will be any 'ones' after a number is multiplied by 10. Guide pupils to notice that since there are no 'ones', we write a '0' in the ones place.

Let's Learn!

Multiplying by tens, hundreds or thousands

Multiplying by 10

1 | 10 | 10 | 10 | 10 | 10 | 10 | 10 |

7 × 10 = 70

| 10 | 10 | 10 | 10 | 10 | 10 | 10 | 10 | 10 |

9 × 10 = 90

| 10 | 10 | 10 | 10 | 10 | 10 | 10 | 10 | 10 | 10 |

10 × 10 = 100

| 10 | 10 | 10 | 10 | 10 | 10 | 10 | 10 | 10 | 10 | 10 | 10 |

12 × 10 = 120

7 × 10 = 7 tens
= 70

9 × 10 = 9 tens
= 90

10 × 10 = 10 tens
= 100

12 × 10 = 12 tens
= 120

Look at the chart below.

	Hundreds	Tens	Ones
7			7
7 × 10		7	0
9			9
9 × 10		9	0
10		1	0
10 × 10	1	0	0
12		1	2
12 × 10	1	2	0

What do you notice about the digits of a number when it is multiplied by **10**?

You can see in the chart that each digit moves **one** place to the **left**.

33

Teaching sequence

- Ask pupils to complete the chart by moving each digit one place to the left when the given numbers are multiplied by 10. Remind pupils that we write a '0' in the ones place when there are no 'ones'.

- Ask pupils to work on these questions as an informal assessment. Guide pupils to see that when a whole number is multiplied by 10, a quick way to get the answer is to write a '0' after the number. This can be done because each digit has moved one place to the left and so the ones place is empty. Explain that this technique only works with whole numbers.

- Guide pupils to apply their understanding of multiplying by 10 to find the missing numbers in the multiplication statements.

Activity

2 Copy the chart below.

	Hundred Thousands	Ten Thousands	Thousands	Hundreds	Tens	Ones
231				2	3	1
231 × 10			2	3	1	0
2345			2	3	4	5
2345 × 10		2	3	4	5	0
4108			4	1	0	8
4108 × 10		4	1	0	8	0

Complete the chart and write down the value of:

a 231 × 10 2310 **b** 2345 × 10 23 450 **c** 4108 × 10 41 080

3 Find the value of:

a 60 × 10 600   **b** 135 × 10 1350   **c** 503 × 10 5030
d 2876 × 10 28 760   **e** 6082 × 10 60 820   **f** 6210 × 10 62 100

When a **whole number** is multiplied by **10**, what is a quick way to get the answer?

4 Find the missing numbers.

a 8 × ☐10☐ = 80   **b** 22 × ☐10☐ = 220
c ☐   ☐ × 10 = 5280   **d** ☐   ☐ × 10 = 74 600
        528   7460

34

Whole Numbers (2) **Unit 2**

Multiplying by tens

5 6 × 20

20	20	20	20	20	20

10	10	10	10	10	10	10	10	10	10	10	10

6 × 20 = 6 × 2 tens
= 6 × 2 × 10
= 12 × 10
= 120

27 × 30 = 27 × 3 tens
= 27 × 3 × 10
= 81 × 10
= 810

Multiplying a number by 20 is the same as multiplying it by 2 and then by 10.

Activity

6 Copy this table and complete it by multiplying each number by 6 and by 60. An example is shown.

	× 6	**× 60**
42	252	2520
65		
861		

390 … 3900
5166 … 51 660

Look at the answers in the table. What are the missing numbers?

a 42 × 60 = 42 × 6 × ⎡10⎤

b 65 × 60 = 65 × ⎡6⎤ × ⎡10⎤

c 861 × 60 = 861 × ⎡6⎤ × ⎡10⎤

---

7 Find the missing numbers.

a 62 × 40 = 62 × 4 × 10

248 = ⎡ ⎤ × 10

2480 = ⎡ ⎤

b 307 × 80 = 307 × ⎡8⎤ × 10

2456 = ⎡ ⎤ × 10

24 560 = ⎡ ⎤

 Home Maths — Show your child how they can use their calculator to check that:
723 × 30 = 723 × 10 × 3 = 723 × 3 × 10.

35

5

- Show pupils that multiplying a number by 20 is equivalent to multiplying the number by 2 and then by 10.

6

- Pupils are allowed to use a calculator in this activity which reinforces the concept that multiplying a number by 60 is equivalent to multiplying the number by 6 and then by 10.

7

- Ask pupils to work on these questions as practice.

Note

Highlight to pupils that:

- when a number is multiplied by 100, the tens and ones places will be empty and so we write '0' in each of these places
- when a number is multiplied by 1000, the hundreds, tens and ones places will be empty, and so we write '0' in each of these places.

Teaching sequence

- Ask pupils to work on these questions as an informal assessment.

- Explain that 5 × 100 means 5 groups of 1 hundred, so:
  5 × 100 = 5 hundreds
  = 500
- 5 × 1000 means 5 groups of 1 thousand, so:
  5 × 1000 = 5 thousands
  = 5000
- 12 × 100 = 12 × 1 hundred
  = 12 hundreds
  = 1200
  12 × 1000 = 12 × 1 thousand
  = 12 thousands
  = 12 000
- Draw pupils' attention to the chart showing how the digits of a number move when it is multiplied by 100 and 1000.
- Guide pupils to see that when a number is multiplied by 100, the digits move two places to the left and when it is multiplied by 1000, the digits move three places to the left.

Unit 2 Whole Numbers (2)

8 Find the value of:

a	31 × 60 1860	**b**	274 × 50 13 700
c	1970 × 90 177 300	**d**	8145 × 40 325 800

Multiplying by 100 or 1000

5 × 100 = 500

100 100 100 100 100 100 100 100 100 100 100 100
12 × 100 = 1200

5 × 1000 = 5000

12 × 1000 = 12 000

5 × 100 = 5 hundreds
= 500

12 × 100 = 12 hundreds
= 1200

5 × 1000 = 5 thousands
= 5000

12 × 1000 = 12 thousands
= 12 000

Look at the chart below.

	Ten Thousands	Thousands	Hundreds	Tens	Ones
5					5
5 × 100			5	0	0
12				1	2
12 × 100		1	2	0	0
5					5
5 × 1000		5	0	0	0
12				1	2
12 × 1000	1	2	0	0	0

What do you notice about the digits of a number when it is multiplied by **100** and by **1000**?

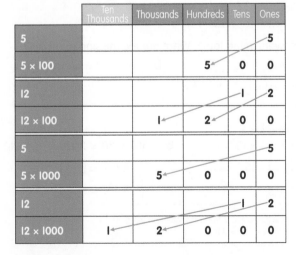

36

Activity

10 Copy the chart below.

	Millions	Hundred Thousands	Ten Thousands	Thousands	Hundreds	Tens	Ones
174					1	7	4
174 × 100			1	7	4	0	0
174 × 1000		1	7	4	0	0	0
3298				3	2	9	8
3298 × 100		3	2	9	8	0	0
3298 × 1000	3	2	9	8	0	0	0

Complete the chart and write down the value of:

a   174 × 100 17 400
b   174 × 1000 174 000
c   3298 × 100 329 800
d   3298 × 1000 3 298 000

When a **whole number** is multiplied by **100**, what is a quick way to get the answer?

When a **whole number** is multiplied by **1000**, what is a quick way to get the answer?

11 Find the value of:

a   27 × 100 2700
b   615 × 100 61 500
c   9670 × 100 967 000
d   18 × 1000 18 000
e   487 × 1000 487 000
f   5346 × 1000 5 346 000

12 Find the missing numbers.

a   26 × 100 = 2600
b   195 × 1000 = 195 000
c   490 × 100 = 49 000
d   168 × 1000 = 168 000

37

10

- Ask pupils to complete the chart by moving each digit two places or three places to the left when the given numbers are multiplied by 100 and 1000 respectively.

- Guide pupils to see that a quick way to get the answer when a number is multiplied by 100 or 1000 is to write '00' or '000' after the number respectively. Ask pupils to explain why this works to check their understanding of the method. Explain that this technique only works with whole numbers.

11

- Ask pupils to work on these questions as an informal assessment.

12

- Pupils should apply their understanding of multiplying by 100 and 1000 to find the missing numbers in the multiplication statements.

Teaching sequence

- Show pupils that multiplying a number by 200 is equivalent to multiplying the number by 2 and then by 100.

- Pupils are allowed to use a calculator in this activity which reinforces the concept that multiplying a number by 700 is equivalent to multiplying the number by 7 and then by 100.

- Ask pupils to work on these questions as practice.

Multiplying by hundreds or thousands

13 7 × 200

200	200	200	200	200	200	200

100	100	100	100	100	100	100	100	100	100	100	100	100	100

$$7 \times 200 = 7 \times 2 \text{ hundreds}$$
$$= 7 \times 2 \times 100$$
$$= 14 \times 100$$
$$= 1400$$

> Multiplying a number by 200 is the same as multiplying it by 2 and then by 100.

$$93 \times 300 = 93 \times 3 \text{ hundreds}$$
$$= 93 \times 3 \times 100$$
$$= 279 \times 100$$
$$= 27\,900$$

Activity

14 Copy this table and complete it by multiplying each number by 7 and by 700. An example is shown.

	× 7	× 700	
78	546	54 600	
113	791		79 100
251	1757		175 700

Look at the answers in the table. What are the missing numbers?

a   78 × 700 = 78 × 7 × 100   b   113 × 700 = 113 × 7 × 100

c   251 × 700 = 251 × 7 × 100

15 Find the missing numbers.

a   72 × 400 = 72 × 4 × 100   b   123 × 700 = 123 × 7 × 100

$$= 288 \times 100 \qquad\qquad\qquad = 861 \times 100$$

$$= \boxed{}\,28\,800 \qquad\qquad\qquad = \boxed{}\,86\,100$$

38

16 Find the value of:

    a   81 × 500 40 500

    b   932 × 800 745 600

    c   6455 × 900 5 809 500

    d   6007 × 800 4 805 600

17 5 × 3000

3000	3000	3000	3000	3000
1000 1000 1000	1000 1000 1000	1000 1000 1000	1000 1000 1000	1000 1000 1000

$$5 × 3000 = 5 × 3 \text{ thousands}$$
$$= 5 × 3 × 1000$$
$$= 15 × 1000$$
$$= 15\,000$$

Multiplying a number by 3000 is the same as multiplying it by 3 and then by 1000.

$$67 × 5000 = 67 × 5 \text{ thousands}$$
$$= 67 × 5 × 1000$$
$$= 335 × 1000$$
$$= 335\,000$$

Activity

18   Copy this table and complete it by multiplying each number by 7 and by 7000. An example is shown.

		× 7	× 7000	
	56	392	392 000	
1421	203			1 421 000
2884	412			2 884 000

Look at the answers in the table. What are the missing numbers?

    a   56 × 7000 = 56 × 7 × (1000)

    b   203 × 7000 = 203 × (7) × (1000)

    c   412 × 7000 = 412 × (7) × (1000)

39

Teaching sequence

16

- Ask pupils to work on these questions as an informal assessment.

17

- Show pupils that multiplying a number by 3000 is equivalent to multiplying it by 3 and then by 1000.

18

- Pupils are allowed to use a calculator in this activity which reinforces the concept that multiplying a number by 7000 is equivalent to multiplying it by 7 and then by 1000.

Additional activity

Ask pupils to work in pairs.
Pupil A writes down a 5-digit number ending with 3 zeros.
Pupil B finds two numbers which when rounded and multiplied will give the 5-digit number written by Pupil A. The two numbers cannot end with a zero.
Pupils A and B swap roles.

Teaching sequence

19 and **20**

- Ask pupils to work on these questions as an informal assessment.

21

- Show pupils how to estimate the product of a 3-digit number and a 2-digit number. Guide pupils to see that to find an estimate, they can round the numbers to the nearest 10 and 100 and then multiply.

- Highlight to pupils that it is also possible to find an estimate by just rounding 632 to 600 and then multiplying by 26.

22 and **23**

- Ask pupils to work on these questions as an informal assessment.

Unit 2 Whole Numbers (2)

19 Find the missing numbers.

    a $6 \times 5000 = 6 \times 5 \times 1000$
                 $= \boxed{30} \times 1000$
                 $= \boxed{}\ 30\,000$

    b $18 \times 6000 = 18 \times \boxed{6} \times \boxed{1000}$
                    $= \boxed{108} \times 1000$
                    $= \boxed{}\ 108\,000$

20 Find the value of:

    a 73×4000 292 000
    b 905×8000 7 240 000
    c 654×3000 1 962 000
    d 807×9000 7 263 000

21 Estimate the value of 632×26.

$$632 \times 26 \approx 600 \times 30$$
$$= 600 \times 3 \times 10$$
$$= 1800 \times 10$$
$$= 18\,000$$

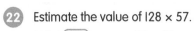

> Round 632 to the nearest hundred.
> $632 \approx 600$
> Round 26 to the nearest ten.
> $26 \approx 30$
> $632 \times 26 = 16\,432$
> 18 000 is a reasonable estimate.

22 Estimate the value of 128×57.

$$128 \approx \boxed{100} \qquad 57 \approx 60$$

$$\text{So } 128 \times 57 \approx \boxed{100} \times 60$$
$$= \boxed{100} \times 6 \times 10$$
$$= \boxed{600} \times 10$$
$$= \boxed{}\ 6000$$

> Even if you have a calculator, it is important to use estimation to check that your answers are reasonable.

23 Estimate.

    a 702×15 14 000
    b 38×246 8000
    c 511×62 30 000

40

What you will need

Scientific calculator

Independent work

- *Let's Practise!*
- Practice 2 and *Maths Journal* in Practice Book 5A, pp 25 to 30.

24 Kerry sold 1215 packets of plastic spoons at her shop. There were 26 spoons in each packet. Estimate the number of spoons she sold.

$1215 \times 26 \approx 1000 \times 30$
$\qquad = 1000 \times 3 \times 10$
$\qquad = 3000 \times 10$
$\qquad = 30\,000$

Round 1215 to the nearest thousand.
$1215 \approx 1000$
Round 26 to the nearest ten.
$26 \approx 30$
$1215 \times 26 = 31\,590$
$30\,000$ is a reasonable estimate.

She sold about 30 000 spoons.

25 Estimate the value of 1238×56.

$1238 \times 56 \approx 1000 \times \boxed{60}$
$\qquad = 1000 \times \boxed{6} \times \boxed{10}$
$6000 = \boxed{} \times \boxed{10}$
$\qquad = \boxed{} \; 60\,000$

26 Estimate.

a $99 \times 38 \approx 4000$
b $67 \times 439 \approx 28\,000$
c $9281 \times 32 \approx 270\,000$
d $2065 \times 41 \approx 80\,000$

Let's Practise!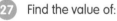

27 Find the value of:

a 412×10
　 4120
b 792×100
　 $79\,200$
c 740×1000
　 $740\,000$

28 Find the value of:

a 703×60
　 $42\,180$
b 815×700
　 $570\,500$
c 169×3000
　 $507\,000$

29 A machine in a factory produced 452 beads in a minute. Estimate the number of beads it would produce in 56 minutes. About 30 000 beads

30 Use your calculator to work out the following:

a 3711×9
　 $33\,399$
b 2087×37
　 $77\,219$
c 1985×302
　 $599\,470$

Use estimation to check if your answers are reasonable.

Practice Book 5A, p.25

41

Teaching sequence

24

- Demonstrate how to estimate the product of a 4-digit number and a 2-digit number.
- Ask pupils to round 2-digit numbers to the nearest 10, 3-digit numbers to the nearest 100 and 4-digit numbers to the nearest 1000 when doing estimation.

Example:
Estimate 385×89.
$385 \approx 400$ and $89 \approx 90$
$385 \times 89 \approx 400 \times 90$
$\qquad\qquad = 36\,000$

25 and **26**

- Ask pupils to work on these questions as an informal assessment.

Learning objectives: Dividing by tens, hundreds or thousands

Pupils will be able to:

- divide a number by 10, 100 or 1000 by:
  - (i) moving each digit 1, 2 or 3 places to the right respectively in the place value chart
  - (ii) dropping 1, 2 or 3 zeros respectively from the end of the number
- divide numbers up to 6 digits by tens, hundreds or thousands

Teaching sequence

- Revise what $70 \div 10$ means with pupils. Ask pupils to interpret it as partitioning 70 into 10 equal groups or finding how many 'tens' there are in 70. The models show the partitioning or sharing concept of division.
- Guide pupils to see that in the sharing concept, there are ten sevens in 70 and so $70 \div 10 = 7$. In the grouping concept, there are seven tens in 70 and so $70 \div 10 = 7$.
- Draw pupils' attention to the chart, which shows how the digits of a number move when it is divided by 10. Note the appearance of the tenths column in the chart and the black column that splits numbers before and after the decimal point. Guide pupils to conclude that when a number is divided by 10, the digits move one place to the right. Review with pupils that $7 \cdot 0 = 7$, $16 \cdot 0 = 16$ and $180 \cdot 0 = 180$.

- use rounding and approximation to estimate answers in division

Key concept

In the base ten number system:

- Thousands $\div 10$ = hundreds,
  Hundreds $\div 10$ = tens,
  Tens $\div 10$ = ones,
  Ones $\div 10$ = tenths
- Ten thousands $\div 100$ = hundreds,
  Thousands $\div 100$ = tens,
  Hundreds $\div 100$ = ones,
  Tens $\div 100$ = tenths,
  Ones $\div 100$ = hundredths

- Hundred thousands $\div 1000$ = hundreds,
  Ten thousands $\div 1000$ = tens,
  Thousands $\div 1000$ = ones,
  Hundreds $\div 1000$ = tenths,
  Tens $\div 1000$ = hundredths,
  Ones $\div 1000$ = thousandths

Thinking skills

- Comparing
- Identifying patterns and relationships

Let's Learn!

Dividing by tens, hundreds or thousands

Dividing by 10

70

| 7 | 7 | 7 | 7 | 7 | 7 | 7 | 7 | 7 | 7 |

$70 \div 10 = 7$

$7 \times 10 = 70$
So $70 \div 10 = 7$.

160

| 16 | 16 | 16 | 16 | 16 | 16 | 16 | 16 | 16 | 16 |

$160 \div 10 = 16$

$16 \times 10 = 160$
So $160 \div 10 = 16$.

1800

| 180 | 180 | 180 | 180 | 180 | 180 | 180 | 180 | 180 | 180 |

$1800 \div 10 = 180$

$180 \times 10 = 1800$
So $1800 \div 10 = 180$.

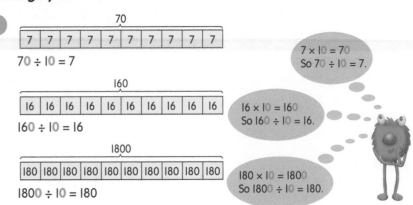

Look at the chart below.

	Thousands	Hundreds	Tens	Ones	•	Tenths
70			7	0		
70 ÷ 10				7		0
160		1	6	0		
160 ÷ 10			1	6		0
1800	1	8	0	0		
1800 ÷ 10			1	8	0	0

7·0 is 7.
16·0 is 16.
180·0 is 180.

What do you notice about the digits of a number when it is divided by **10**?

42

Additional activity

Ask pupils to work in pairs. Pupil A writes down a 3-digit number. Pupil B then writes a division sentence that gives this result. Pupils should try to find all the possible ways that they can do it. Pupils A and B swap roles.

Teaching sequence

- Ask pupils to complete the chart by moving each digit one place to the right when the given numbers are divided by 10.

- Guide pupils to see that a quick way to get the answer when a whole number with 0 in the ones place is divided by 10, is to discard the '0'. This can be done because the '0' has moved to the tenths place and 0 tenths has no value.

- Ask pupils to work on these questions as an informal assessment.

- Encourage pupils to apply their understanding of dividing by 10 to find the missing numbers in division statements.

- Show pupils that since 30 = 10 × 3, dividing by 30 is equivalent to dividing by 10 and then by 3.

- Demonstrate with a simple example:

$24 \div 6 = 24 \div 3 \div 2$
$= 8 \div 2$
$= 4$

Activity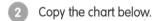

2 Copy the chart below.

	Thousands	Hundreds	Tens	Ones	•	Tenths
360		3	6	0		
360 ÷ 10			3	6		0
1580	1	5	8	0		
1580 ÷ 10		1	5	8		0

Complete the chart and write down the value of:

When a **whole number** with **0** in the **ones place** is divided by **10**, what is a quick way to get the answer?

a 360 ÷ 10 36   **b** 1580 ÷ 10 158

3 Find the value of:

a 90 ÷ 10 9   **b** 380 ÷ 10 38   **c** 1900 ÷ 10 190

d 43 650 ÷ 10 4365   **e** 23 040 ÷ 10 2304   **f** 53 600 ÷ 10 5360

4 Find the missing numbers.

a 2600 ÷ ⬚10⬚ = 260   **b** 19 500 ÷ ⬚10⬚ = 1950

c ⬚ ÷ 10 = 4900 49 000   **d** ⬚ ÷ 10 = 1680 16 800

Dividing by tens

5
$60 \div 30 = 60 \div 10 \div 3$
$= 6 \div 3$
$= 2$

$420 \div 70 = 420 \div 10 \div 7$
$= 42 \div 7$
$= 6$

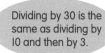

Dividing by 30 is the same as dividing by 10 and then by 3.

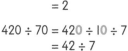

Show your child how they can use their calculator to check that: 420 ÷ 70 = 420 ÷ 10 ÷ 7 = 420 ÷ 7 ÷ 10.

43

Unit 2: Whole Numbers (2)   63

What you will need
Scientific calculator

Teaching sequence

- Pupils are allowed to use a calculator in this activity, which reinforces the concept that dividing a number by 90 is equivalent to dividing it by 10 and then by 9.

7 and **8**

- Ask pupils to work on these questions as an informal assessment.

9

- Review with pupils.

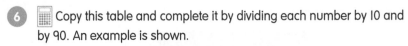

Activity

6 Copy this table and complete it by dividing each number by 10 and by 90. An example is shown.

	÷ 10	÷ 90
540	54	6
720	72	8
810	81	9

Look at the answers in the table. What are the missing numbers?

a 540 ÷ 90 = 540 ÷ 10 ÷ 9 **b** 720 ÷ 90 = 720 ÷ 10 ÷ 9

c 810 ÷ 90 = 810 ÷ 10 ÷ 9

7 Find the missing numbers.

a 850 ÷ 50 = 850 ÷ 10 ÷ 5 **b** 7200 ÷ 80 = 7200 ÷ 10 ÷ 8
  = 85 ÷ 5   = 720 ÷ 8
  = 17   = 90

8 Find the value of:

a 160 ÷ 40 4   **b** 700 ÷ 50 14
c 6320 ÷ 20 316 **d** 8400 ÷ 60 140

Dividing by 100 or 1000

9 9 × 100 = 900
So 900 ÷ 100 = 9.

14 × 100 = 1400
So 1400 ÷ 100 = 14.

9 × 1000 = 9000
So 9000 ÷ 1000 = 9.

14 × 1000 = 14 000
So 14 000 ÷ 1000 = 14.

44

⑩ Look at the chart below.

	Ten Thousands	Thousands	Hundreds	Tens	Ones	•	Tenths	Hundredths	Thousandths
900			9	0	0				
900 ÷ 100					9		0	0	
1400		1	4	0	0				
1400 ÷ 100				1	4		0	0	
9000		9	0	0	0				
9000 ÷ 1000					9		0	0	0
14 000	1	4	0	0	0				
14 000 ÷ 1000				1	4		0	0	0

What do you notice about the digits of a number when it is divided by **100** and by **1000**?

9·00 is 9.
14·00 is 14.

9·000 is also 9.
14·000 is also 14.

45

Teaching sequence

- Draw pupils' attention to the chart showing how the digits of a number move when it is divided by 100 and by 1000.
- Guide pupils to see that the digits of a number move two places to the right when it is divided by 100 and three places to the right when it is divided by 1000.
- Encourage pupils to notice that 9·00 = 9, 14·00 = 14 and 14·000 = 14. Ask pupils to explain this to check their understanding.

Teaching sequence

- Ask pupils to complete the chart by moving each digit two or three places to the right when the given numbers are divided by 100 and 1000.
- Guide pupils to see that when a whole number with 0 in the tens and ones places is divided by 100, and when a whole number with 0 in the hundreds, tens and ones places is divided by 1000, a quick way to get the answer is to discard the zeros. This can be done because 0 tenths, 0 hundredths and 0 thousandths have no value.

- Ask pupils to work on these questions as an informal assessment.

- Show pupils that dividing by 300 is equivalent to dividing by 100 and then by 3, and that dividing by 2000 is equivalent to dividing by 1000 and then by 2.

Activity

11 Copy the chart below.

	Ten Thousands	Thousands	Hundreds	Tens	Ones	•	Tenths	Hundredths	Thousandths
700			7	0	0				
700 ÷ 100					7		0	0	
3600		3	6	0	0				
3600 ÷ 100				3	6		0	0	
8000		8	0	0	0				
8000 ÷ 1000					8		0	0	0
54 000	5	4	0	0	0				
54 000 ÷ 1000				5	4		0	0	0

Complete the chart and write down the value of:

a 700 ÷ 100   7   **b** 3600 ÷ 100   36

c 8000 ÷ 1000   8   **d** 54 000 ÷ 1000   54

When a **whole number with two zeros** as the last two digits is divided by **100**, what is a quick way to get the answer?

When a **whole number with three zeros** as the last three digits is divided by **1000**, what is a quick way to get the answer?

12 Find the value of:

a 400 ÷ 100   4   **b** 1500 ÷ 100   15   **c** 20 500 ÷ 100   205

d 10 000 ÷ 1000   10   **e** 124 000 ÷ 1000   124   **f** 3 230 000 ÷ 1000   32

Dividing by hundreds or thousands

13
$$600 ÷ 300 = 600 ÷ 100 ÷ 3$$
$$= 6 ÷ 3$$
$$= 2$$

$$6000 ÷ 2000 = 6000 ÷ 1000 ÷ 2$$
$$= 6 ÷ 2$$
$$= 3$$

Dividing a number by 300 is the same as dividing it by 100 and then by 3.

Dividing a number by 2000 is the same as dividing it by 1000 and then by 2.

46

What you will need
Scientific calculator

 Activity

14 Copy this table and complete it by dividing each number by 100 and by 600. An example is shown.

	÷ 100	÷ 600
1200	12	2
4200	42	7
5400	54	9

Look at the answers in the table. What are the missing numbers?

a 1200 ÷ 600 = 1200 ÷ 100 ÷ 6

b 4200 ÷ 600 = 4200 ÷ 100 ÷ 6

c 5400 ÷ 600 = 5400 ÷ 100 ÷ 6

15 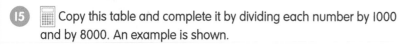 Copy this table and complete it by dividing each number by 1000 and by 8000. An example is shown.

	÷ 1000	÷ 8000
32 000	32	4
48 000	48	6
64 000	64	8

Look at the answers in the table. What are the missing numbers?

a 32 000 ÷ 8000 = 32 000 ÷ 1000 ÷ 8

b 48 000 ÷ 8000 = 48 000 ÷ 1000 ÷ 8

c 64 000 ÷ 8000 = 64 000 ÷ 1000 ÷ 8

16 Find the missing numbers.

a 2400 ÷ 400 = 2400 ÷ 100 ÷ 4   **b** 35 000 ÷ 7000 = 35 000 ÷ 1000 ÷ 7

  = 24 ÷ 4   = 35 ÷ 7

  = 6   = 5

 Home Maths Encourage your child to use their calculator to check that:
2400 ÷ 400 = 2400 ÷ 100 ÷ 4 and 35 000 ÷ 7000 = 35 000 ÷ 1000 ÷ 7.

47

Teaching sequence

14 and **15**

- Pupils are allowed to use a calculator in these activities which reinforce the concept of division by hundreds and thousands.

16

- Ask pupils to work on these questions as practice.

Teaching sequence

• Ask pupils to work on these questions as practice.

• Show pupils how to estimate the quotient of 1728 ÷ 38. We round the divisor 38 to 40, and approximate the dividend 1728 to a number that can be easily divided by 40. In this case, 1728 can be approximated to 1600 or 2000, two numbers that are easily divided by 40. Guide pupils to see that they should choose 1600 because it is closer to 1728.

19 and **20**

• Ask pupils to work on these questions as an informal assessment.

21

• This activity reinforces the concept of division by tens, hundreds and thousands.

---

17 Find the value of:
- **a** 800 ÷ 200   4
- **b** 5400 ÷ 600   9
- **c** 7200 ÷ 900   8
- **d** 18 000 ÷ 3000   6
- **e** 45 000 ÷ 5000   9
- **f** 102 000 ÷ 2000   51

18 Estimate the value of 1728 ÷ 38.

> To estimate 1728 ÷ 38, we round 38 to 40 and choose a number close to 1728 that can be divided by 40 exactly.

1728 is closer to 1600 than 2000.

$$1728 ÷ 38 ≈ 1600 ÷ 40$$
$$= 1600 ÷ 10 ÷ 4$$
$$= 160 ÷ 4$$
$$= 40$$

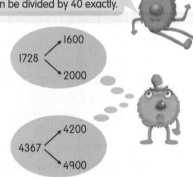

1728 → 1600 / 2000

19 Estimate the value of 4367 ÷ 670.

$$4367 ÷ 670 ≈ \boxed{} ÷ 700 \quad 4200$$
$$4200 = \boxed{} ÷ \boxed{100} ÷ 7$$
$$= \boxed{6}$$

4367 → 4200 / 4900

20 Estimate the value of the following:
- **a** 987 ÷ 17   1000 ÷ 20 = 50
- **b** 6106 ÷ 28   6000 ÷ 30 = 200
- **c** 4932 ÷ 96   5000 ÷ 100 = 50
- **d** 3785 ÷ 379   3600 ÷ 400 = 9

Activity

21 Find three whole numbers that can divide each of the numbers shown below exactly. The whole numbers must be multiples of tens, hundreds or thousands.

4500   420   2000   40   88 000

Draw and complete a table as shown below for each number.

Example	Number	Can be Divided By	Answer
	4500	10	4500 ÷ 10 = 450
	4500	30	4500 ÷ 30 = 150
	4500	500	4500 ÷ 500 = 9

48

Objective of activity

This activity allows pupils to explore division of any whole number by 10, 100 or 1000 without using a calculator.

What you will need

Scientific calculator

Independent work

- *Let's Practise!*
- Practice 3 in Practice Book 5A, pp 31 to 34.

Let's Explore!

22 Work in pairs.

Discuss how you can work these out **without** using a calculator.

a   43 ÷ 10   b   735 ÷ 100   c   2046 ÷ 1000

Use the following chart to help you.

Thousands	Hundreds	Tens	Ones	•	Tenths	Hundredths	Thousandths

Let's Practise!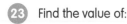

23 Find the value of:

a   870 ÷ 10 87   b   9000 ÷ 10 900   c   7100 ÷ 100 71

d   82 000 ÷ 100 820   e   3000 ÷ 1000 3   f   97 000 ÷ 1000 97

24 Find the value of:

a   500 ÷ 20 25   b   7070 ÷ 70 101   c   8100 ÷ 300 27

d   65 600 ÷ 800 82   e   6000 ÷ 3000 2   f   54 000 ÷ 9000 6

25 Use your calculator to work out the following:

a   6726 ÷ 19 354

b   4008 ÷ 12 334

Use estimation to check if your answers are reasonable.

> Practice Book 5A, p.31

49

Teaching sequence

22 *Let's Explore!*

- Encourage pupils to apply their understanding of division by 10, 100 or 1000 to divide whole numbers which are not exactly divisible by 10, 100 or 1000.

Learning objectives: Order of operations

Pupils will be able to:

- state the order of operations in a number sentence with two or three operations and use a calculator to compute it
- state the order of operations in a number sentence which has brackets and two or three operations, and use a calculator to compute it

Teaching sequence

- Ask pupils how they would solve the problem. They may give the following solution:

  Step 1: 96 – 26 = 70

  Step 2: 70 + 48 = 118

- Show pupils that the two steps can be combined into a single number sentence: 96 – 26 + 48.

- Explain to pupils that in a number sentence with more than one operation, there is an **order of operations** to be followed.

- Explain that when there are only addition and subtraction operations, to follow this approach they are advised to **work from left to right**.

  96 – 26 + 48 = <u>96 – 26</u> + 48

             = <u>70 + 48</u> = 118

- Write a few examples for pupils to work out. Ask: *"Which operation do you do first?"* (The operation that comes first from the left.)

- Show pupils what happens if they do not follow the order. E.g.:

  <u>15 – 4</u> + 2 = 11 + 2 = 13 **(correct)**

  15 – <u>4 + 2</u> = 15 – 6 = 9 **(incorrect)**

- Show pupils how to use their calculator to work out 96 – 26 + 48.

Key concepts

- In number sentences with only addition and subtraction or only multiplication and division, the order of operations is from left to right.
- In number sentences with multiplication and/or division together with addition and/or subtraction, the order of operations is from left to right with multiplication and/or division carried out first.
- In number sentences with brackets, the order of operations is from left to right with the operations in the brackets carried out first.

Thinking skill

Classifying

Note

- Explain that not following the order of operations will result in an incorrect answer.
- Ask pupils to underline the operation they are going to carry out each time. Highlight to pupils that they must write the entire number sentence whenever they carry out an operation.

Let's Learn!

Order of operations

1   **Work from left to right when there's only addition and subtraction.**

In a primary school, there were 96 children in Year 1. The following year, 26 children left and 48 new children started. How many children were there in Year 2?

Working from left to right:

First number sentence	96 – 26 + 48
Second number sentence	= 70 + 48
	= 118

96 – 26 + 48 is a number sentence.

There were 118 children in Year 2.

You can use your calculator to work out 96 – 26 + 48 like this:

Which operation was carried out first? Which operation was carried out next?

Press	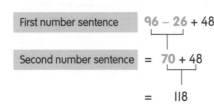 Display
C	0
9 6	96
– 2 6	26
+ 4 8	48
=	118

96 – 26 + 48 = 118

Home Maths   Explain to your child that addition, subtraction, multiplication and division are called the four operations.

50

What you will need

Scientific calculator

Additional activities

- Ask a few pupils to think of a problem calculation involving addition and subtraction. Then ask the other pupils to write the number sentence and work it out.

- Ask a few pupils to think of a problem calculation involving multiplication and division. Ask the other pupils to write the number sentence and work it out.

2 Work out the following. Then use your calculator to check your answers.

    a   37 + 8 − 25 20   **b**   67 − 21 + 20 66

    c   32 − 12 + 26 − 15 31   **d**   50 + 27 − 19 − 35 23

3 **Work from left to right when there's only multiplication and division.**

A shop owner ordered 40 boxes of fruit juice. Each box contained 24 cartons. He sells 60 cartons every day. How many days will he take to sell all the fruit juice?

Working from left to right:

First number sentence	$40 \times 24 \div 60$
Second number sentence	$= 960 \div 60$
	$= \quad 16$

He will take 16 days to sell all the fruit juice.

You can use your calculator to work out $40 \times 24 \div 60$ like this:

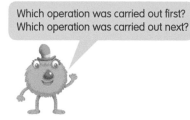

Which operation was carried out first? Which operation was carried out next?

Press	Display
C	0
4 0	40
× 2 4	24
÷ 6 0	60
=	16

$40 \times 24 \div 60 =$ 16

4 Work out the following. Then use your calculator to check your answers.

    a   12 × 20 ÷ 6 40   **b**   63 ÷ 9 × 12 84

    c   28 × 5 ÷ 10 ÷ 7 2   **d**   48 ÷ 8 × 60 ÷ 3 120

51

Teaching sequence

- Ask pupils to work on these questions as practice.

3

- Highlight to pupils that the two steps 40 × 24 and 960 ÷ 60 can be written as 40 × 24 ÷ 60.

- Ask pupils: *"What are the operations in this number sentence?"* (Multiplication and division only.)

- Explain that when there are only multiplication and division operations, they again need to **work from left to right** to follow the order of operations. $\underline{40 \times 24} \div 60 = \underline{960 \div 60} = 16$

- Show pupils how to use the calculator to work out this number sentence.

- Write a few more examples on the board and ask pupils to state the order of operations to be carried out.

- Ask pupils to work on these questions as practice.

What you will need

Scientific calculator

 **Calculator tip**

Explain to pupils that scientific calculators will automatically work out multiplication or division first, before addition or subtraction. Most basic calculators will not because they are not programmed to follow the rules of priority of operations.

Teaching sequence

- Read out the word problem to pupils. Ask pupils to think of a single number sentence that solves the problem in one step.
- Write the number sentence on the board: 26 + 56 ÷ 4
- Ask pupils: *"What are the operations in this number sentence?"* (Addition and division.)
- Explain to pupils that when there are addition or subtraction operations together with multiplication or division, they should **carry out multiplication and division first, before addition and subtraction,** then they are advised **to work out the whole calculation working from left to right.**
- Show pupils how to use the calculator to work out this number sentence.
- The model below could also be used to help pupils understand this word problem.

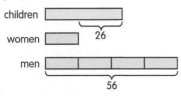

Unit 2 Whole Numbers (2)

 Carry out multiplication and division first, then work from left to right.

There were 26 more children than women at a park. There were 4 times as many men as there were women. There were 56 men at the park. How many children were there?

Dividing first:

| First number sentence | 26 + 56 ÷ 4 |

| Second number sentence | = 26 + 14 |

= 40

There were 40 children.

You can use your calculator to work out **26 + 56 ÷ 4** like this:

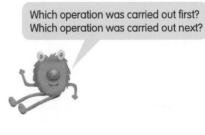

Which operation was carried out first? Which operation was carried out next?

26 + 56 ÷ 4 = 40

Press	Display
C	0
2 6	26
+ 5 6	56
÷ 4	4
=	40

The calculator worked out **56 ÷ 4** first.
Then it worked out **26 + 14**.
It considers the order of operations automatically during computation.

 Most everyday calculators, such as the ones on mobile phones, do not consider the order of operations automatically during calculations. A scientific calculator considers the order of operations automatically. Ask your child to type in 2 + 4 × 2 using the two types of calculators. They will get different answers: 12 and 10. The answer on a scientific calculator is correct because it follows the order of operations by calculating 4 × 2 before adding 2 to the result, while the other calculator adds 2 and 4 before multiplying the result by 2.

52

Whole Numbers (2) **Unit 2**

6 Peter had 900 stickers. He arranged 25 stickers on each page of an album. The album had 30 pages. How many stickers were left?

Multiplying first:

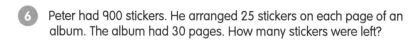

First number sentence	$900 - 25 \times 30$
Second number sentence	$= 900 - 750$
	$= 150$

There were 150 stickers left.

You can use your calculator to work out $900 - 25 \times 30$ like this:

Press	Display
C	0
9 0 0	900
− 2 5	25
× 3 0	30
=	150

$900 - 25 \times 30 = \boxed{150}$

Which operation did the calculator work out first?

Which operation did the calculator work out next?

7 Work out the following. Then use your calculator to check your answers.

a $13 + 20 \times 7$ 153
b $70 - 75 \div 5$ 55
c $15 + 18 \times 5 \div 9$ 25
d $80 - 54 \div 9 \times 11$ 14
e $48 - 6 \times 6 + 34$ 46
f $33 + 210 \div 30 - 25$ 15

53

Teaching sequence

6
- Show pupils an example of a number sentence with subtraction and multiplication.

7
- Ask pupils to work on these questions as practice.

Teaching sequence

8 *Let's Explore!*

- Pupils should write the order of operations carried out by each calculator and identify which gives the correct answer.
- Pupils should notice that a scientific calculator follows the order of operations whereas a non-scientific calculator does not.

- Read the word problem together. Ask pupils to solve the problem in two steps and show pupils how 670 + 530 and 1200 ÷ 40 can be combined into one number sentence using brackets: (670 + 530) ÷ 40
  The brackets tell us to add 670 and 530 before dividing the sum by 40.
- Explain to pupils that in a number sentence with brackets, they should carry out the operation in the brackets first. When there is more than one operation in the brackets, ask pupils to follow the previous rule: **carry out multiplication and division first, before addition and subtraction, then work from left to right.**
- The model below could also be used to help pupils understand this word problem.

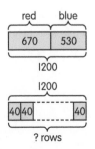

Objective of activity

- Pupils should compare the order of computation and answers of a scientific calculator with a non-scientific calculator.
- This task enables pupils to verify that in a number sentence with multiplication followed by division, the order of operations is not relevant.

What you will need

- Scientific calculator
- Non-scientific calculator (you can also find non-scientific calculators on some mobile phones and computers)

Note

Most calculators on mobile phones and in shops are not scientific. There are a few types of non-scientific calculators that do follow the order of operations automatically, but most do not. Pupils can use the *Let's Explore!* activity here to check how their calculator works out answers.

Unit 2 Whole Numbers (2)

Let's Explore!

8 Work in pairs.

Each pair will need a scientific calculator and a standard calculator.

1 Using the scientific calculator, work out the following questions. Start with the operation on the left.

   a 178 − 25 × 6   **b** 85 + 120 ÷ 8

2 Next use the standard calculator to work out **a** and **b**. Are the answers you get on both calculators the same?

3 Write the order of operations carried out in **a** and **b** using

   i the scientific calculator   **ii** the standard calculator.

   Which calculator gave the correct answers?

---

9 **When there are brackets, carry out the operations in the brackets first.**

There are 670 red seats and 530 blue seats in a theatre. Each row has 40 seats. How many rows are there in the theatre?

Work out the operation in the brackets first:

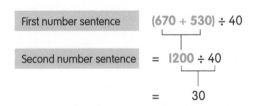

First number sentence	(670 + 530) ÷ 40
Second number sentence	= 1200 ÷ 40
	= 30

There are 30 rows in the theatre.

You can use your calculator to work out **(670 + 530) ÷ 40** like this:

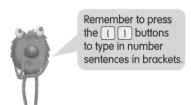

Remember to press the $($ $)$ buttons to type in number sentences in brackets.

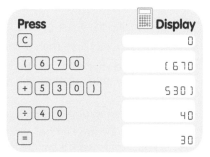

Press	Display
C	0
(6 7 0	(670
+ 5 3 0)	530)
÷ 4 0	40
=	30

(670 + 530) ÷ 40 = [30]

Which operation did the calculator work out first? (+)
Which operation did the calculator work out next? (÷)

10 Work out the following. Then use your calculator to check your answers.

a   17 – (38 – 29) 8   b   690 ÷ (15 × 2) 23
c   107 + (44 – 33) × 7 184   d   80 × (40 ÷ 5) ÷ 10 64

 Activity

11 Work in pairs.

Prepare three sets of number cards (0 to 9), operation cards (+, –, ×, ÷) and bracket cards.

Use the cards to make a number sentence with two or more operations.

Example

Use your calculator to work out the answer and compare your answer with your partner's answer.

55

Teaching sequence

9

- Show pupils how to use the calculator to work out this number sentence.

10

- Ask pupils to work on these questions as practice.

11

- Give each pair of pupils three sets of the number and operation cards provided on Photocopy master 3 and encourage them to make number sentences. Explain to pupils that they must not use more than three operations in each number sentence.

- When using a calculator, pupils often write down the answer without showing the calculation involved. To avoid this ensure that pupils write down each number sentence before they calculate its value. Pupils can then use their calculators to solve the number sentences that they have made.

What you will need

- Scientific calculator
- Number cards and operation cards (see Photocopy master 3 on p 320)

Independent work

- *Let's Practise!*
- Practice 4 in Practice Book 5A, pp 35 to 40.

What you will need

Scientific calculator

Teaching sequence

12 *Let's Explore!*

- This task enables pupils to verify that in a number sentence with multiplication followed by division, the order of operations is not relevant.

13

- This task requires each of the three pupils to compute number sentences using incorrect and correct procedures. Encourage pupils to compare their answers and discuss the results.

14 *Let's Practise!*

- Ask pupils to first work out the values without using a calculator. Then they can use the calculator to check their answers.

Let's Explore!

12 To find the value of 1350 × 27 ÷ 25, use your calculator to work out 1350 × 27 first. Then divide the result by 25.

Next use your calculator to work out 27 ÷ 25 first. Then multiply the result by 1350. What do you notice? Try with other numbers.

13 Work in groups of three.

Look at the five number sentences in the table below.
Pupil A is to work them out from left to right **without** using a calculator.
Pupil B is to work them out according to the rules of order of operations **without** using a calculator.
Pupil C is to work them out using a calculator by typing in the number sentences from left to right.

Copy the table and record your answers as shown. Discuss your results.

Number Sentence	Pupil A's Answers	Pupil B's Answers	Pupil C's Answers
9 + 6 − 5			
48 ÷ 4 × 2			
36 ÷ 6 − 3			
14 + 4 × 2			
50 − 8 ÷ 2			

Let's Practise!

14 Find the value of the following. Then use your calculator to check your answers.

a 96 − 50 + 64 110
b 175 + 25 − 95 105
c 6 × 40 ÷ 3 80
d 250 ÷ 5 × 53 2650
e 79 + 27 × 2 133
f 280 − 72 ÷ 8 271
g 35 × (560 ÷ 70) 280
h 540 ÷ (293 − 203) 6

Practice Book 5A, p.35

56

Learning objective:
Word problems (I)

Pupils will be able to solve multi-step word problems.

Key concept

Application of concepts and skills of the four operations to solving word problems.

Thinking skill

Applying concepts and processes

What you will need

Scientific calculator

Let's Learn!

Word problems (I)

  An artist wants to make a picture using tiles mounted on a rectangular board measuring 103 cm by 59 cm.

a What is the area of the board?
b Each tile costs £12. How much will it cost to cover the board completely with 1 cm² tiles?

a Area = Length × Width
= 103 × 59
= 6077 cm²

> Estimate the answer
> 103 × 59 ≈ 100 × 60
> = 6000
> 6077 is a reasonable answer.

The area of the board is 6077 cm².

b Cost of tiling = area × cost of 1 cm² tile
= 6077 × £12
= £72 924

> Estimate to check if the answer is reasonable.

It will cost £72 924 to cover the board completely with the tiles.

Teaching sequence

1

• Review the process of solving word problems:

Step 1: Ask pupils to read the problem carefully. Then ask pupils to state what is given and what they are required to find.

Step 2: Ask pupils whether any number sentences can be written.

Step 3: Ask pupils to write the first number sentence. In this case, the formula for area of a rectangle is used. Then ask pupils to write the second number sentence. Ask them to explain why they have to multiply.

Step 4: Ask pupils how they can check the reasonableness of their answers. Remind pupils that they should always check that their answers are reasonable.

Teaching sequence

- Ask pupils to work on this question as practice.

- Explain to pupils that this word problem involves the repeated addition concept of multiplication and the grouping concept of division.

Unit 2 Whole Numbers (2)

2 ▦ A container can hold 450 cm³ of orange juice. Mr Thomas has to fill 19 of these containers with orange juice at 15 p per cm³. How much does he have to pay altogether?

Total amount of orange juice = 450 cm³ × 19 = ⬜ 8550 cm³

Cost of orange juice = 8550 × 15 p = £⬜ 1282·50

He would have to pay £⬜. 1282·50

3 ▦ Mr James bought 32 boxes of stickers. There were 140 stickers in each box. He packed them into bags of 35 stickers each. He sold each bag for 98 p. How much money did he make after selling all the stickers?

First find the total number of stickers.

Total number of stickers = number of boxes × number of stickers in each box
= 32 × 140
= 4480

There were 4480 stickers.

Next find the number of bags.

Number of bags = total number of stickers ÷ number of stickers in each bag
= 4480 ÷ 35
= 128

There are 128 bags of stickers.

(32 × 140) ÷ 35
= 128

Then find how much money he collected.

Amount collected = number of bags × cost of each bag
= 128 × 98 p
= ⬜p 12 544
= £⬜ 125·44

58

He collected £⬜. 125·44

What you will need
Scientific calculator

4   Miya's uncle buys a boat and pays for it in instalments.
Each instalment is £1235. After paying 64 instalments, he still
has to pay another £2960. How much would each instalment be
if he pays for the boat in 100 instalments?

First find the total amount paid in instalments.

Amount paid = number of instalments × amount for each instalment
    = 64 × £1235
    = £⬚ 79 040

Then find the cost of the boat.

Cost of boat = total amount paid + amount he still has to pay
    = £⬚ + £2960 79 040
    = £⬚ 82 000

(64 × £1235) + £2960
= £⬚ 82 000

What operation do you need to carry out to find out how much he would
have to pay for each of the 100 instalments?

£⬚ (÷) (100) = £(820)
82 000
He would have to pay £(820) for each of the 100 instalments.

59

Teaching sequence
4
- Ask pupils to work on this
  question as practice.

Additional activity

Show pupils a picture of the parking charges in a car park. Ask pupils to calculate how much they would need to pay if a car was parked there for $4\frac{1}{2}$ hours. Would they have to pay more if they park for 4 h 50 mins?

Teaching sequence

- This problem involves the concept of multiplication as a rate.

- Ask pupils to work on this question as practice.

Unit 2 Whole Numbers (2)

5 The table on the right shows how much it costs to hire a stall in a market.

Weekdays	£32 per day
Saturdays and Sundays	£55 per day

Peter's dad had a stall from Tuesday to the following Monday. How much did it cost him?

First find the number of weekdays and the number of Saturdays and Sundays he hired the stall.

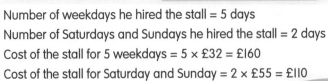

Number of weekdays he hired the stall = 5 days

Number of Saturdays and Sundays he hired the stall = 2 days

Cost of the stall for 5 weekdays = 5 × £32 = £160

Cost of the stall for Saturday and Sunday = 2 × £55 = £110

Total cost = £160 + £110 = £270

(5 × £32) + (2 × £55)
= £270

Hiring the stall cost him £270.

6 The table shows the charges at a car park.

First Hour	Second Hour	After the Second Hour
free	£1	£2 per hour

Mrs Lee parked her car at the car park from 9:00 a.m. to 2:00 p.m. on the same day. How much did she have to pay?

Total number of hours = 5 h

Parking fee for first hour = £ 0

Parking fee for second hour = £ 1

Parking fee from 11:00 a.m. to 2:00 p.m. = 3 × £ 2 = £ 6

Total parking fee = £ 0 + £ 1 + £ 6 = £ 7

Mrs Lee had to pay £ 7 .

60

What you will need
Scientific calculator

Independent work
- *Let's Practise!*
- Practice 5 in Practice Book 5A, pp 41 to 44.

Whole Numbers (2) **Unit 2**

Let's Practise!

Solve these word problems. Show your workings clearly.

7 Ruby's mum sold 78 boxes of raffle tickets. Each box contained 34 books of tickets. She sold each book for £17. How much did she collect altogether? £45 084

8 A supermarket had a total of 6707 tins of food. They sold 569 of the tins. Then they put the remaining tins equally into 18 crates. How many tins were there in each crate? 341 tins

9 A greengrocer had 49 boxes of strawberries. Each box contained 75 strawberries. The strawberries were repacked into packets of 15. How many packets of strawberries were there? 245 packets

10 Mr Marsh paid £2 for a packet of 12 buns. He sold each bun for 50 pence. In a week, he sold a total of 4385 buns. 366 packets
  a What was the smallest number of packets of buns he bought?
  b How much did he pay for this number of packets of buns? £732
  c How much money did he make after he sold 4385 buns? £1460·50

11 A restaurant owner bought 245 boxes of tinned tomatoes. Each box contained 28 tins of tomatoes. There were 2198 tins of whole tomatoes and the rest were chopped tomatoes. All the tins of chopped tomatoes were used over 42 months. If the restaurant owner used the same number of tins of chopped tomatoes each month, how many tins of chopped tomatoes did he use each month? 111 tins

12 The table on the right shows the cost of sending parcels.

Tai and Miya sent parcels.
  a Tai posted a parcel with a mass of 45 g. Find the postage for the parcel. 160 p or £1·60
  b Miya paid £6·10 for posting a parcel. Find the mass of the parcel. 200 g

Mass	Postage
First 20 g	70 p
Per additional 10 g	30 p

Practice Book 5A, p.41

61

Teaching sequence

10 *Let's Practise!*
- You could allow pupils who are confident in performing calculations without a calculator to do so for this question. They will need to perform long division with a divisor of 12 to answer part **a.** The other parts to this question involve doubling and halving strategies.

Unit 2: Whole Numbers (2)   81

Learning objective:
Word problems (2)

Pupils will be able to use a number of heuristics such as 'model drawing', 'make a systematic list', 'guess and check', 'unitary method', and 'before and after strategy' to solve multi-step word problems.

Key concept

Application of concepts and skills of the four operations and various strategies to solving word problems.

Thinking skill

- Applying concepts and processes
- Identifying relationships

Teaching sequence

- Revise the use of model drawing as a heuristic for solving word problems. Work through the process of solving word problems:

  Step 1: Read the problem carefully and state what is given and what needs to be found.

  Step 2: Can a number sentence be written? If not, think of a strategy or heuristic that can be used. In this case, ask pupils to close their books and draw a model from the given information.

  Step 3: From the model, write the required number sentences.

  Step 4: Check the reasonableness of the answers using estimation.

Let's Learn!

Word problems (2)

 Omar, Farha and Jack scored a total of 4670 points during a competition. Farha scored 316 fewer points than Omar. Farha scored 3 times as many points as Jack. How many points did Farha score?

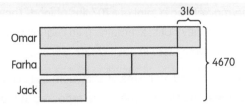

First subtract 316 points from Omar's score so that he will have the same number of points as Farha. This is the same as subtracting 316 points from the total number of points.

4670 – 316 = ⬜ 4354

Then Omar has 3 units, Farha has 3 units and Jack has 1 unit. In all, they have 7 units.

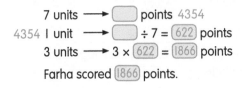

7 units ⟶ ⬜ points 4354
4354 1 unit ⟶ ⬜ ÷ 7 = (622) points
3 units ⟶ 3 × (622) = (1866) points
Farha scored (1866) points.

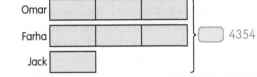

62

Teaching sequence

2

- Ask pupils to work on this question as practice.

2 The cost of 4 belts and 5 ties was £247. Each tie cost 3 times as much as a belt. What was the total cost of a tie and a belt?

Draw models. Represent I belt with I unit and I tie with 3 units.

4 belts

5 ties

£ 247

19 units ⟶ £247

I unit ⟶ £247 ÷ 19 = £ 13

Each belt cost £ 13.

3 units ⟶ 3 × £ 13 = £39

Each tie cost £ 39.

£ 13 + £ 39 = £ 52

The total cost of a belt and a tie was £ 52.

63

Additional activity

Ask pupils to study the models to the right. Then ask them to work in groups of four to write a question related to these models. Ask them to solve the question and swap questions with another group.

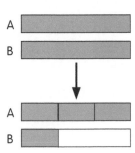

Teaching sequence

3

- Ask pupils to work on this question as practice.
- This question involves a 'before and after' situation. Explain to pupils that in a situation like this, they should draw different models to show the 'before' and the 'after' situation.

4

- This problem uses the grouping concept of division and the concept of multiplication as a rate.

---

3 Mr Austin had an equal number of red and yellow tulips. He sold 624 red tulips. Then there were 4 times as many yellow tulips as red tulips. How many tulips did he have at first?

Before

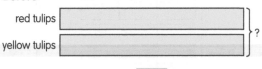

red tulips

yellow tulips

} ?

After

624

red tulips

yellow tulips

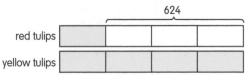

I unit represents the number of red tulips left and 4 units represent the number of yellow tulips.

3 units ⟶ 624 tulips
I unit ⟶ 624 ÷ 3 = 208 tulips
8 units ⟶ 8 × 208 = 1664 tulips

He had 1664 tulips at first.

4 A greengrocer bought 588 mangoes at 4 for £5. She then sold all of them at 7 for £10. How much money did she make?

588 ÷ 4 = 147
147 × £5 = £735

She bought the mangoes for £735.

How many groups of 4 are there in 588?

588 ÷ 7 = 84
84 × £10 = £840

She sold them for £840.

How many groups of 7 are there in 588?

£840 − £735 = £105

She made £105.

64

---

5 Miss Bell and Mr Michaels had £1250. Miss Bell and Mrs Campbell had £830. Mr Michaels had 4 times as much as Mrs Campbell. How much did Miss Bell have?

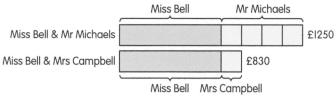

£1250 − £830 = £420

The difference between the amount Mr Michaels and Mrs Campbell had was £420.

3 units ⟶ £420
1 unit ⟶ £420 ÷ 3 = £ 140

Mrs Campbell had £ 140 .

£830 − £ 140 = £ 690

Miss Bell had £ 690 .

6 Mary is 12 years old and Abby is 15 years older than her. In how many years' time will Abby be twice as old as Mary?

Method 1

12 + 15 = 27

Abby is 27 years old now.

Mary's Age	Abby's Age	Is it Twice?
12 (now)	27 (now)	No
13	28	No
14	29	No
15	30	Yes

We can guess and check for this question. Start by making a systematic list.

Abby will be twice Mary's age in 3 years' time.

65

Teaching sequence

5

- Ask pupils to work on this question as an informal assessment.

6

- This problem can be solved by using the strategy of 'making a systematic list' or by 'drawing a model'.

- Ask pupils to work on this question as practice.

Unit 2 Whole Numbers (2)

Method 2

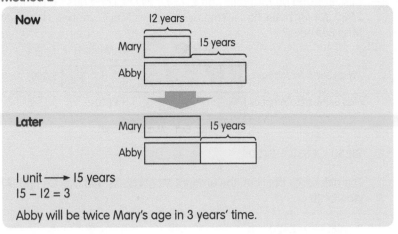

Now

Mary | 12 years
15 years

Abby

Later

Mary | 15 years

Abby

I unit ⟶ 15 years
15 – 12 = 3

Abby will be twice Mary's age in 3 years' time.

7 There are 20 cars and motorbikes altogether in a car park. The total number of wheels is 50. How many motorbikes are there?

Use the data — number of vehicles and number of wheels — to make guesses and a systematic list.

Remember, the number of cars and motorbikes must always add up to 20.

Number of Cars	Number of Motorbikes	Number of Wheels	Are there 50 Wheels?
10	10	40 + 20 = 60	No (too many)
9	11	36 + 22 = 58	No (too many)
8	12	32 + 24 = 56	No (too many)
5	15	20 + 30 = 50	Yes

There are 15 motorbikes.

What you will need
Scientific calculator

Independent work
- *Let's Practise!*
- Practice 6 in Practice Book 5A, pp 45 to 47.

Let's Practise!

Solve these word problems. Show your workings clearly.

8 Mr Williams gave a total sum of £3600 to his brother and 2 sisters. His brother received £500 more than the first sister. The second sister received half as much as the first sister. How much did the first sister receive? £1240

9 Apples are sold at 3 for £2 at Stall A. At Stall B, the same apples are sold at 5 for £2. Daniel buys 15 apples from Stall B instead of Stall A. How much does he save? £4

10 Mr Jacobs paid £87 altogether for a pair of boots and a pair of shoes. The boots cost twice as much as the shoes. What was the cost of the boots? £58

11 A shopkeeper sold 15 boxes of pencils altogether on Monday and Tuesday. He sold 3 more boxes on Monday than on Tuesday. There were 12 pencils in each box. How many pencils did he sell on Monday? 108 pencils

12 Ella had £7 and her sister had £2. After their parents gave each of them an equal amount of money, Ella had twice as much as her sister. How much did their parents give each of them? £3

13 A group of people paid £720 altogether for tickets to an amusement park. The price of a ticket for an adult was £15 and the price for a child was £8. There were 25 more adults than children. How many children were there in the group? 15

14 A tank and a bucket contained a total of 8346 ml of water. When 314 ml of water was poured from the bucket into the tank, the amount of water in the tank was 12 times that in the bucket. How much water was in the bucket at first? 956 ml

Practice Book 5A, p.45

67

What you will need

Scientific calculator

Teaching sequence

Let's Wrap It Up!

- Review each bullet point in *Let's Wrap It Up!* with pupils. This helps them to see if they have mastered the current topic.
- You could ask pupils to think of an example question for each bullet point in *Let's Wrap It Up!* Invite some pupils to present their questions and answers to the class.
- Work through the questions in *Let's Revise!* to check pupils have understood the concepts.

Let's Wrap It Up!

You have learnt to:

- use a calculator to add, subtract, multiply and divide
- multiply and divide a whole number by 10, 100 and 1000
- multiply and divide a whole number by tens, hundreds and thousands
- use rounding and approximation to estimate the products and quotients
- work out a number sentence using the correct order of operations.

Let's Revise!

 Miss Austin bought 48 packets of red balloons, 66 packets of blue balloons and 35 packets of yellow balloons. Each packet cost £3 and contained a dozen balloons. She mixed them up and gave away 213 balloons. Then she repacked the remainder into packets of 25 balloons each.

a How many balloons did Miss Austin buy altogether?

$$(48 + 66 + 35) \times 12 = 149 \times 12$$
$$= 1788$$

She bought 1788 balloons altogether.

b How many packets of balloons did she repack?

$$(1788 - 213) \div 25 = 1575 \div 25$$
$$= 63$$

She repacked 63 packets of balloons.

c If she sold each repacked packet of 25 balloons at £10 each, how much money did she make?

$$63 \times £10 - 149 \times £3 = £630 - £447$$
$$= £183$$

She made £183.

68

88

Objective of activity

Pupils will be able to apply their understanding of multiplication as repeated addition to solve this problem.

Thinking skill

Identifying relationships

Heuristics for problem solving

- Look for a pattern
- Restate the problem

Independent work

Maths Journal, Challenging Practice, Problem Solving and *Review I* in Practice Book 5A, pp 48 to 64.

Put On Your Thinking Caps!

15   🖩 The 9 button on a calculator is not working.

Explain how you can use this calculator to work out 1234×79 in at least two different ways.

Method I: $(1234 \times 80) - 1234 = 97\,486$

Method 2: $(1234 \times 78) + 1234 = 97\,486$

| Practice Book 5A, p.49 | Practice Book 5A, p.51 |

Teaching sequence

15 *Put On Your Thinking Caps!*

- Pupils have to look for a pattern and restate the problem so they can work out the mathematical sentence without using the number 9 button on the calculator.

69

Unit 2: Whole Numbers (2)   89

Unit 2 Whole Numbers (2)

Date: _____

Practice I Using a calculator

1 🖩 Add.

a 215 + 9843 = ___10 058___

b 6789 + 18 = ___6807___

c 97 + 8154 = ___8251___

d 1693 + 8157 = ___9850___

2 🖩 Subtract.

a 8215 – 79 = ___8136___

b 6286 – 129 = ___6157___

c 2159 – 1998 = ___161___

d 26 145 – 9354 = ___16 791___

3 🖩 Multiply.

a 359 × 12 = ___4308___

b 217 × 58 = ___12 586___

c 1975 × 5 = ___9875___

d 7050 × 8 = ___56 400___

4 🖩 Divide.

a 504 ÷ 9 = ___56___

b 4104 ÷ 6 = ___684___

c 8160 ÷ 85 = ___96___

d 17 604 ÷ 18 = ___978___

Practice 2

Multiplying by tens, hundreds or thousands

1 Find the values of the following:

a $47 \times 10 = \underline{470}$

b $109 \times 10 = \underline{1090}$

c $7140 \times 10 = \underline{71\,400}$

d $1503 \times 10 = \underline{15\,030}$

e $3702 \times 10 = \underline{37\,020}$

f $9342 \times 10 = \underline{93\,420}$

2 Fill in the spaces.

a $96 \times \underline{10} = 960$

b $\underline{70} \times 10 = 700$

c $514 \times \underline{10} = 5140$

d $\underline{9176} \times 10 = 91\,760$

e $308 \times \underline{10} = 3080$

f $\underline{500} \times 10 = 5000$

3 Fill in the spaces.

a $65 \times 40 = 65 \times \underline{4} \times 10$
  $= \underline{260} \times 10$
  $= \underline{2600}$

b $39 \times 30 = 39 \times \underline{3} \times 10$
  $= \underline{117} \times 10$
  $= \underline{1170}$

c $120 \times 50 = 120 \times \underline{5} \times 10$
  $= \underline{600} \times 10$
  $= \underline{6000}$

d $143 \times 90 = 143 \times \underline{9} \times 10$
  $= \underline{1287} \times 10$
  $= \underline{12\,870}$

e $360 \times 30 = 360 \times \underline{3} \times 10$
  $= \underline{1080} \times 10$
  $= \underline{10\,800}$

f $285 \times 80 = 285 \times \underline{8} \times 10$
  $= \underline{2280} \times 10$
  $= \underline{22\,800}$

---

5 [calculator] Trace Peter's path by finding the values of the following:

75 × 16   712 × 32   968 × 76   1625 + 127   125 ÷ 25   (1708 – 1372)

120   22784   1044   73568   16372   1752   1200   5   1498   3125   3080   336

playground   football stadium   train station   supermarket   cinema   library

Peter's path leads to the:

train station

4 Multiply.

M	25 × 100 = 2500	T	7 × 1000 = 7000
P	86 × 100 = 8600	E	70 × 1000 = 70000
A	95 × 100 = 9500	L	400 × 1000 = 400000
P	217 × 100 = 21700	H	726 × 1000 = 726000
C	803 × 100 = 80300	O	8032 × 1000 = 8032000
B	3810 × 100 = 381000	S	3936 × 1000 = 3936000

What is this cat's name? Match the letters above to the answers below to find out.

P	A	T	C	H	E	S
21700	9500	7000	80300	726000	70000	3936000

5 Fill in the spaces.

a 17 × 100 = 1700

b 25 × 1000 = 25000

c 478 × 1000 = 478000

d 320 × 1000 = 320000

e 1315 × 100 = 131500

f 2662 × 1000 = 2662000

6 Fill in the spaces.

a 4 × 300
= 4 × 3 × 100
= 12 × 100
= 1200

b 12 × 500
= 12 × 5 × 100
= 60 × 100
= 6000

c 35 × 600
= 35 × 6 × 100
= 210 × 100
= 21000

d 814 × 700
= 814 × 7 × 100
= 5698 × 100
= 569800

e 5400 × 800
= 5400 × 8 × 100
= 43200 × 100
= 4320000

f 8 × 5000
= 8 × 5 × 1000
= 40 × 1000
= 40000

g 12 × 3000
= 12 × 3 × 1000
= 36 × 1000
= 36000

h 15 × 2000
= 15 × 2 × 1000
= 30 × 1000
= 30000

i 300 × 4000
= 300 × 4 × 1000
= 1200 × 1000
= 1200000

j 663 × 6000
= 663 × 6 × 1000
= 3978 × 1000
= 3978000

9 Imagine you are the owner of an electronics shop. Estimate the amount of earnings you will get from the sales of each group of items below.

> 58 all-in-one printers at £219 each.
> 652 digital radios at £73 each.
> 99 games consoles at £217 each.
> 39 plasma television sets at £4156 each.
> 13 computers at £2415 each.
> 37 home entertainment systems at £6814 each.

Round the 2-digit numbers to the nearest ten, the 3-digit numbers to the nearest hundred and the 4-digit numbers to the nearest thousand. Then estimate the product.

a $58 \times 219 \approx 60 \times 200$
= 12000

b $652 \times 73 \approx 700 \times 70$
= 49000

c $99 \times 217 \approx 100 \times 200$
= 20000

d $39 \times 4156 \approx 40 \times 4000$
= 160000

e $13 \times 2415 \approx 10 \times 2000$
= 20000

f $37 \times 6814 \approx 40 \times 7000$
= 280000

---

7 Answer these questions.

	Multiplying by Tens	Multiplying by Hundreds	Multiplying by Thousands
a	$17 \times 70 = 1190$	$17 \times 700 = 11900$	$17 \times 7000 = 119000$
b	$65 \times 30 = 1950$	$65 \times 300 = 19500$	$65 \times 3000 = 195000$
c	$90 \times 40 = 3600$	$90 \times 400 = 36000$	$90 \times 4000 = 360000$
d	$812 \times 10 = 8120$	$812 \times 100 = 81200$	$812 \times 1000 = 812000$
e	$634 \times 20 = 12680$	$634 \times 200 = 126800$	$634 \times 2000 = 1268000$

8 Fill in the spaces.

a $31 \times 100 = 3100$

b $30 \times 3000 = 90000$

c $103 \times 30 = 3090$

d $25 \times 200 = 5000$

Maths Journal

Date: _____

🖩 Use your calculator to work out:

> 1164 × 97

Explain how you can check if your answer is reasonable.

1164 × 97 = 112 908

Round 1164 to the nearest thousand,
1164 ≈ 1000

Round 97 to the nearest ten,
97 ≈ 100

1000 × 100 = 100 000
My answer is reasonable. It is close to the estimate of 100 000.

Date: _____

Practice 3 | Dividing by tens, hundreds or thousands

1 Find the values of the following:

a 100 ÷ 10 = _10_

b 670 ÷ 10 = _67_

c 1050 ÷ _10_ = 105

d _19740_ ÷ 10 = 1974

e 52260 ÷ 10 = _5226_

f 30500 ÷ _10_ = 3050

2 Fill in the spaces.

a 5610 ÷ 30 = 5610 ÷ 10 ÷ 3
   = 561 ÷ 3
   = 187   (J)

b 3000 ÷ 60 = 3000 ÷ 10 ÷ 6
   = 300 ÷ 6
   = 50   (M)

c 1040 ÷ 40 = 1040 ÷ 10 ÷ 4
   = 104 ÷ 4
   = 26   (A)

d 8700 ÷ 60 = 8700 ÷ 10 ÷ 6
   = 870 ÷ 6
   = 145   (T)

e 3450 ÷ 50 = 3450 ÷ 10 ÷ 5
   = 345 ÷ 5
   = 69   (R)

f 34230 ÷ 70 = 34230 ÷ 10 ÷ 7
   = 3423 ÷ 7
   = 489   (N)

What is Ruby's favourite treat? Write the letters which match the answers to find out.

J	A	M	T	A	M	T	A	R	T
187	26	50	145	26	50	145	26	69	145

3 Divide.

3400 ÷ 100 = 34	**P**	560000 ÷ 1000 = 560	**H**
5000 ÷ 100 = 50	**S**	38000 ÷ 1000 = 38	**I**
7700 ÷ 100 = 77	**N**	360000 ÷ 1000 = 360	**M**
2000 ÷ 100 = 20	**B**	415000 ÷ 1000 = 415	**A**

Which group of animals does the frog belong to? Write the letters which match the answers to find out.

$$\frac{A}{415}\ \frac{M}{360}\ \frac{P}{34}\ \frac{H}{560}\ \frac{I}{38}\ \frac{B}{20}\ \frac{I}{38}\ \frac{A}{415}\ \frac{N}{77}\ \frac{S}{50}$$

4 Divide.

a 300 ÷ 300 = 300 ÷ 100 ÷ 3
$= 3 ÷ 3$
$= 1$

b 1600 ÷ 400 = 1600 ÷ 100 ÷ 4
$= 16 ÷ 4$
$= 4$

c 81000 ÷ 900 = 90

d 45000 ÷ 500 = 90

e 9000 ÷ 3000 = 3

f 56000 ÷ 7000 = 8

g 60000 ÷ 400 = 150

h 31500 ÷ 500 = 63

i 36000 ÷ 4000 = 9

j 150000 ÷ 2000 = 75

k 133000 ÷ 7000 = 19

l 120000 ÷ 8000 = 15

5 Answer these questions.

	Dividing by Tens	Dividing by Hundreds	Dividing by Thousands
a	1190 ÷ 70 = 17	11900 ÷ 700 = 17	119000 ÷ 7000 = 17
b	1950 ÷ 30 = 65	19500 ÷ 300 = 65	195000 ÷ 3000 = 65
c	3600 ÷ 40 = 90	36000 ÷ 400 = 90	360000 ÷ 4000 = 90
d	12680 ÷ 20 = 634	126800 ÷ 200 = 634	1268000 ÷ 2000 = 634

Practice 4 Order of operations

1. Find the value of each of the following. Write down each step. Then use your calculator to check your answers.

a $18 - 11 - 4 =$ ___3___
Step 1: ___$18 - 11 = 7$___
Step 2: ___$7 - 4 = 3$___

b $26 + 8 - 19 =$ ___15___
Step 1: ___$26 + 8 = 34$___
Step 2: ___$34 - 19 = 15$___

c $12 + 16 - 9 + 3 =$ ___22___
Step 1: ___$12 + 16 = 28$___
Step 2: ___$28 - 9 = 19$___
Step 3: ___$19 + 3 = 22$___

d $58 - 23 + 11 - 6 =$ ___40___
Step 1: ___$58 - 23 = 35$___
Step 2: ___$35 + 11 = 46$___
Step 3: ___$46 - 6 = 40$___

2. Find the value of each of the following. State the order of operations.

	Order
a $12 + 14 + 9 = 35$	+ +
b $60 + 18 - 7 = 71$	+ −
c $26 - 12 + 7 = 21$	− +
d $70 - 15 - 49 = 6$	− −
e $23 + 16 - 7 + 12 = 44$	+ − +
f $15 - 12 + 17 - 6 = 14$	− + −

---

6. Fill in the spaces.

a $430 \div$ ___10___ $= 43$

b $9000 \div$ ___300___ $= 30$

c $49000 \div$ ___7000___ $= 7$

d $2400 \div$ ___20___ $= 120$

e $64000 \div$ ___400___ $= 160$

f $85000 \div$ ___5000___ $= 17$

A national cycle route runs from the Trent and Mersey Canal to Wisbech. Colour the numbers below that match the answers above to find out the cycle route number.

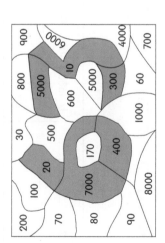

200	100	30	800	900
70		20	500	5000	6000
80	7000		170	600	10	5000
90	400		1000	300	4000
	8000		60	700

7. Estimate the quotient.

a $6452 \div 27 \approx \dfrac{6000}{200} \div \dfrac{30}{}$
$= 200$

b $7865 \div 41 \approx \dfrac{8000}{200} \div \dfrac{40}{}$
$= 200$

c $9125 \div 345 \approx \dfrac{9000}{30} \div \dfrac{300}{}$
$= 30$

d $9825 \div 206 \approx \dfrac{10\,000}{50} \div \dfrac{200}{}$
$= 50$

e $7226 \div 871 \approx \dfrac{7200}{8} \div \dfrac{900}{}$
$= 8$

f $5299 \div 49 \approx \dfrac{5000}{100} \div \dfrac{50}{}$
$= 50$

3 Find the value of each of the following. Write down each step. Then use your calculator to check your answers.

a $9 \times 6 \div 2 = \underline{27}$

Step 1: $\underline{9 \times 6 = 54}$

Step 2: $\underline{54 \div 2 = 27}$

b $25 \times 3 \div 5 = \underline{15}$

Step 1: $\underline{25 \times 3 = 75}$

Step 2: $\underline{75 \div 5 = 15}$

c $200 \div 10 \times 3 \div 5 = \underline{12}$

Step 1: $\underline{200 \div 10 = 20}$

Step 2: $\underline{20 \times 3 = 60}$

Step 3: $\underline{60 \div 5 = 12}$

d $250 \div 5 \div 10 \times 2 = \underline{10}$

Step 1: $\underline{250 \div 5 = 50}$

Step 2: $\underline{50 \div 10 = 5}$

Step 3: $\underline{5 \times 2 = 10}$

4 Find the value of each of the following. State the order of operations.

		Order
a	$30 \times 2 \times 5 = 300$	$\times \ \times$
b	$6 \times 10 \div 5 = 12$	$\times \div$
c	$28 \div 7 \times 4 = 16$	$\div \times$
d	$40 \div 8 \div 5 = 1$	$\div \div$
e	$20 \div 10 \times 8 \div 2 = 8$	$\div \times \div$
f	$120 \div 12 \div 2 \times 16 = 80$	$\div \div \times$

5 Find the value of each of the following. Write down each step. Then use your calculator to check your answers.

a $7 \times 8 - 6 = \underline{50}$

Step 1: $\underline{7 \times 8 = 56}$

Step 2: $\underline{56 - 6 = 50}$

b $14 + 9 \times 7 = \underline{77}$

Step 1: $\underline{9 \times 7 = 63}$

Step 2: $\underline{14 + 63 = 77}$

c $200 \div 20 + 5 = \underline{15}$

Step 1: $\underline{200 \div 20 = 10}$

Step 2: $\underline{10 + 5 = 15}$

d $80 - 16 \div 4 = \underline{76}$

Step 1: $\underline{16 \div 4 = 4}$

Step 2: $\underline{80 - 4 = 76}$

6 Find the value of each of the following. State the order of operations.

		Order
a	$25 - 5 \times 3 = 10$	$\times \ -$
b	$90 + 16 \div 8 = 92$	$\div +$
c	$83 - 72 \div 6 = 71$	$\div -$
d	$5 + 90 \times 7 = 635$	$\times +$
e	$240 \div 20 + 15 = 27$	$\div +$
f	$7 \times 80 - 160 = 400$	$\times -$

7 Find the value of each of the following. Write down each step. Then use your calculator to check your answers.

a $54 ÷ 6 + 20 × 4 =$ ___89___

Step 1: ___$54 ÷ 6 = 9$___

Step 2: ___$20 × 4 = 80$___

Step 3: ___$9 + 80 = 89$___

b $40 − 6 + 10 × 3 =$ ___64___

Step 1: ___$10 × 3 = 30$___

Step 2: ___$40 − 6 = 34$___

Step 3: ___$34 + 30 = 64$___

c $36 ÷ 6 − 25 ÷ 5 =$ ___1___

Step 1: ___$36 ÷ 6 = 6$___

Step 2: ___$25 ÷ 5 = 5$___

Step 3: ___$6 − 5 = 1$___

d $25 × 4 − 36 ÷ 9 =$ ___96___

Step 1: ___$25 × 4 = 100$___

Step 2: ___$36 ÷ 9 = 4$___

Step 3: ___$100 − 4 = 96$___

8 Find the value of each of the following. State the order of operations.

		Order
a	$60 ÷ 3 + 14 × 2 = 48$	÷ × +
b	$20 − 5 × 2 + 6 = 16$	× − +
c	$13 − 6 × 2 + 12 ÷ 4 = 4$	× ÷ − +
d	$27 ÷ 3 + 40 × 6 = 249$	÷ × +
e	$64 − 60 + 12 × 3 = 40$	× − +
f	$42 ÷ 7 − 2 + 7 = 11$	÷ − +

9 Find the value of each of the following. Write down each step. Then use your calculator to check your answers.

a $(15 − 11) × 9 =$ ___36___

Step 1: ___$15 − 11 = 4$___

Step 2: ___$4 × 9 = 36$___

b $(11 + 5) ÷ 16 =$ ___1___

Step 1: ___$11 + 5 = 16$___

Step 2: ___$16 ÷ 16 = 1$___

c $63 − (9 × 7) =$ ___0___

Step 1: ___$9 × 7 = 63$___

Step 2: ___$63 − 63 = 0$___

d $32 ÷ (14 + 2) =$ ___2___

Step 1: ___$14 + 2 = 16$___

Step 2: ___$32 ÷ 16 = 2$___

10 Find the value of each of the following. State the order of operations.

		Order
a	$3 × 72 ÷ 8 = 27$	÷ ×
b	$40 ÷ 5 × 11 = 88$	÷ ×
c	$(36 − 15) × 2 = 42$	(−) ×
d	$36 − 15 × 2 = 6$	× −
e	$(62 + 10) ÷ 6 = 12$	(+) ÷
f	$70 ÷ (16 − 9) = 10$	(−) ÷

Practice 5 | Word problems (I)

Solve these word problems. Show your workings clearly.

1. [calculator] A cricket club had 146 members. Each member paid £30 a month for training fees. How much did the club collect in fees in a year?

   $146 \times £30 = £4380$
   The club collected £4380 a month.
   $12 \times £4380 = £52\ 560$
   The club collected £52 560 in a year.

2. [calculator] Mrs Lake has £4500 to buy each person in a group a present.

   a If she can spend £25 on each person, how many people are there in the group?

   b If the presents cost £32 each, how much more money does she need?

   a $4500 \div 25 = 180$
   There are 180 people in the group.

   b $180 \times £32 = £5760$
   $£5760 - £4500 = £1260$
   or
   $£32 - £25 = £7$
   $180 \times £7 = £1260$
   She needs £1260 more.

---

11. Find the value of each of the following. Write down each step. Then use your calculator to check your answers.

a $21 + (12 + 6) \div 3 = \underline{27}$

Step 1: $\underline{12 + 6 = 18}$

Step 2: $\underline{18 \div 3 = 6}$

Step 3: $\underline{21 + 6 = 27}$

b $7 + (8 - 4) \times 10 = \underline{47}$

Step 1: $\underline{8 - 4 = 4}$

Step 2: $\underline{4 \times 10 = 40}$

Step 3: $\underline{7 + 40 = 47}$

c $32 \div (7 + 1) \times 9 - 5 = \underline{31}$

Step 1: $\underline{7 + 1 = 8}$

Step 2: $\underline{32 \div 8 = 4}$

Step 3: $\underline{4 \times 9 = 36}$

Step 4: $\underline{36 - 5 = 31}$

d $(47 + 12) - 10 \div 5 \times 3 = \underline{53}$

Step 1: $\underline{47 + 12 = 59}$

Step 2: $\underline{10 \div 5 = 2}$

Step 3: $\underline{2 \times 3 = 6}$

Step 4: $\underline{59 - 6 = 53}$

12. Find the value of each of the following. State the order of operations.

	Order
a $100 + (720 + 200) \div 2 = 560$	$(+) \div +$
b $24 \times 5 - (125 - 80) = 75$	$(-) \times -$
c $60 \div (5 + 7) \times 20 - 30 = 70$	$(+) \div \times -$
d $11 + (34 + 16) \div 5 = 21$	$(+) \div +$
e $7 \times 6 - (18 - 6) = 30$	$(-) \times -$
f $21 \div (2 + 5) \times 12 - 8 = 28$	$(+) \div \times -$

3 A group of tourists visited Underwater World. The entrance fees were £13 for each adult and £7 for each child. There were 10 adults and 18 children in the group. How much did they pay altogether?

Total cost for adults = 10 × £13

= £130

Total cost for children = 18 × £7

= £126

Total cost for adults and children = £130 + £126

= £256

4 The length of a rectangular wooden plank is 10 cm longer than its width. It is 26 cm wide. The wooden plank is cut into 9 identical pieces. What is the area of each piece of wooden plank?

Length: 26 + 10 = 36 cm

Area: 36 × 26 = 936 cm^2

936 ÷ 9 = 104 cm^2

The area of each piece is 104 cm^2.

5 There are 918 yellow chairs and blue chairs altogether in the hall. The blue chairs are arranged in 36 rows with 12 chairs in each row. The yellow chairs are arranged in rows of 18. How many rows of yellow chairs are there?

36 × 12 = 432
There are 432 blue chairs.

918 − 432 = 486
There are 486 yellow chairs.

486 ÷ 18 = 27
There are 27 rows of yellow chairs.

6 The table below shows how much it costs to hire a van. Gemma hires one from Tuesday to Sunday one week. How much does it cost her?

Weekdays	£56 per day
Saturday and Sunday	£78 per day

Number of weekdays hired = Tuesday, Wednesday, Thursday, Friday
= 4 days

Number of Saturdays and Sundays hired = 2 days

1 weekday → £56
4 weekdays → 4 × £56 = £224

1 day on the weekend → £78
1 weekend → 2 × £78 = £156

£224 + £156 = £380
It costs her £380.

Practice 6 Word problems (2)

Solve these word problems. Show your workings clearly.

1. Mr Elm and Mr Castro have £120. Mr Elm and Miss Wilson have £230. Miss Wilson has 6 times as much money as Mr Castro. How much money does Mr Elm have?

Mr Elm Mr Castro

£120

£230

Mr Elm   Miss Wilson

5 units → £230 − £120 = £110
1 unit → £22

£120 − £22 = £98
Mr Elm has £98.

2. Lewis is 10 years old and his sister is 7 years old. In how many years' time will their total age be 41 years?

Method 1

Lewis' Age	Sister's Age	Total Age
10	7	17
10 + 5 = 15	7 + 5 = 12	27 (too little)
10 + 10 = 20	7 + 10 = 17	37 (too little)
10 + 15 = 25	7 + 15 = 22	47 (too much)
10 + 12 = 22	7 + 12 = 19	41

Method 2

10 + 7 = 17
Their total age now is 17 years.

41 − 17 = 24
24 ÷ 2 = 12
In 12 years' time, their total age will be 41 years.

---

7. The table shows the charges at a car park.

First hour	£2
Every additional $\frac{1}{2}$ hour	£1

a. Ava parked her car at the car park from 9:30 a.m. to 11:00 a.m. on the same day. How much did she have to pay?

b. Serge parked his car there from 9:00 a.m. to 12:30 p.m. on the same day. How much did he have to pay?

a. Total number of hours = 1·5 h
Parking fee for the first hour = £2
Parking fee from 10:30 a.m. to 11:00 a.m. = £1
Total parking fee = £2 + £1 = £3
Ava had to pay £3.

b. Total number of hours = 3·5 h
Parking fee for the first hour = £2
Parking fee from 10:00 a.m. to 12:30 p.m. = £1 × 5 = £5
Total parking fee = £2 + £5 = £7
Serge had to pay £7.

5 A basket with 65 plums has a mass of 3200 g. The same basket with 40 plums has a mass of 2125 g. Each plum has the same mass. What is the mass of the basket?

| basket | 65 plums | 3200 g |

| basket | 40 plums | 2125 g |

Difference in number of plums = 65 − 40 = 25

Mass of each plum = (3200 − 2125) ÷ 25
$\qquad\qquad\qquad\quad$ = 43 g

Mass of basket = 2125 − 40 × 43
$\qquad\qquad\quad$ = 405 g

The mass of the basket is 405 g.

6 A carton can hold 850 cm³ of apple juice. Miss Roberts wants to buy 15 cartons of apple juice. Every 250 cm³ of apple juice costs £1. How much does she have to pay altogether?

Total amount of apple juice = 850 cm³ × 15
$\qquad\qquad\qquad\qquad\qquad$ = 12 750 cm³

Cost of apple juice = 12 750 ÷ 250 × £1
$\qquad\qquad\qquad\quad$ = £51

She has to pay £51 altogether.

3 A box of envelopes and 2 staplers cost £10.
3 boxes of envelopes and 2 staplers cost £18.
Find the total cost of 1 box of envelopes and 1 stapler.

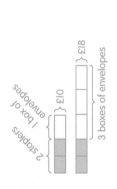

£18 − £10 = £8
£8 ÷ 2 = £4
A box of envelopes costs £4.

£10 − £4 = £6
£6 ÷ 2 = £3
A stapler costs £3.

£4 + £3 = £7
The total cost is £7.

4 Ella and Hardeep had the same number of cards at first. After Ella gave 18 of her cards away, Hardeep had 4 times as many cards as Ella. How many cards did each child have at first?

Before
Ella
Hardeep

After
Ella
Hardeep
18 cards were given away

3 units → 18 cards
1 unit → 18 ÷ 3 = 6 cards
4 units → 4 × 6 = 24 cards
Each child had 24 cards at first.

Maths Journal

1 Write down how you feel about using a calculator for your maths lessons.

Answers vary

_____
_____
_____
_____
_____

2 Omar was asked to work out 6 + 4 × 2. He worked out the steps like this:

$$6 + 4 \times 2 = 10 \times 2 = 20$$

Is he correct? Explain why.

In a sentence with + and × operations, × comes before +.
Working from left to right, he should carry out multiplication before addition.
So the correct solution would be:
6 + 4 × 2 = 6 + 8 = 14

Challenging Practice

1 A box of raisins cost 15 pence and a packet of 8 similar boxes of raisins cost £1. Carl bought exactly 37 boxes of raisins. What was the least amount of money that Carl spent on the raisins?

37 ÷ 8 = 4 r 5
4 × £1 = £4
5 × 15p = 75p
£4 + 75p = £4·75
The least amount that Carl spent was £4·75.

2 40 children made some triangles for bunting. One child became unwell so the rest of the children made 3 more triangles each. How many triangles did they make altogether?

39 × 3 = 117
117 × 40 = 4680
They made 4680 triangles altogether.

Problem Solving

1 Miss Robinson, Mr Brown and Miss Clarke share £268. Mr Brown has £20 more than Miss Robinson and Miss Clarke has twice as much money as Mr Brown. How much money do Miss Robinson and Mr Brown have altogether?

$£268 + £20 = £288$
$4 \text{ units} \rightarrow £288$
$1 \text{ unit } \rightarrow £72$
$(£72 \times 2) - £20 = £124$
Miss Robinson and Mr Brown have £124 altogether.

2 Joshua and Rachel had the same number of marbles. After Rachel gave away 10 marbles and Joshua gave away 22 marbles, Rachel had 3 times as many marbles as Joshua. How many marbles did each of them have at first?

$22 - 10 = 12$
$2 \text{ units} \rightarrow 12 \text{ marbles}$
$1 \text{ unit } \rightarrow 6 \text{ marbles}$

$6 \times 3 + 10 = 28$ or $22 + 6 = 28$ marbles
Each of them had 28 marbles at first.

3 Mr Tate puts up poles from one end of a road to the other at equal distances apart. There are 27 wooden poles. The width of each pole is 10 cm. The distance between 2 poles is 3000 cm. Find the length of the road.

$(26 \times 3000) + (10 \times 27) = 78\,270 \text{ cm}$
The length of the road is 78 270 cm.

4 Tai has 64 coins in his money box. There are 20 pence coins and 50 pence coins. The total value of all the coins is £18·50. How many 20 pence coins and how many 50 pence coins are there?

Number of 50p Coins	Value	Number of 20p Coins	Value	Total Value	Is the Total Value £18·50?
20	1000p	44	880p	1880p	No
19	950p	45	900p	1850p	Yes

There are nineteen 50 pence coins and forty-five 20 pence coins.

or

$64 \times 20p = 1280p$
$1850p - 1280p = 570p$
$\dfrac{570}{30} =$ nineteen 50 pence coins
$64 - 19 =$ forty-five 20 pence coins

Review 1

3 George had a total of 30 pens and pencils at first. He then decided to exchange all his pens for pencils. If he exchanged every pen for 2 pencils, he would have 48 pencils. How many pens and pencils did he have at first?

Number of Pens	Number of Pencils	Total	If One Pen is Exchanged for 2 Pencils, is 48 the Total Number of Pencils?
10	20	30	10 × 2 + 20 = 40 ✗
15	15	30	15 × 2 + 15 = 45 ✗
18	12	30	18 × 2 + 12 = 48 ✓

George had 18 pens and 12 pencils at first.

Date: _____

1 Write the numbers in numerals.

a one hundred thousand and seventy   100070

b five hundred and sixty thousand   560000

c five million, eighty thousand and five   5080005

d two million, four hundred thousand, seven hundred and twenty   2400720

2 Write the numbers in words.

a 120450   one hundred and twenty thousand, four hundred and fifty

b 500312   five hundred thousand, three hundred and twelve

c 1050400   one million, fifty thousand and four hundred

d 5732800   five million, seven hundred and thirty-two thousand and eight hundred

3 a Write a 6-digit number with the digit 1 in the ten thousands place.

2	1	0	5	4	0	Answers vary

b Write this number in words.

Two hundred and ten thousand, five hundred and forty.

4 In 1 238 906:

a the digit 8 stands for _8000_

b the digit 6 stands for _6_

c the digit 9 stands for _900_

d the digit 1 stands for _1 000 000_ .

5 What is the value of the digit 3 in the numbers below?

a 538 426: _30 000_   b 1 325 407: _300 000_

6 Fill in the spaces.

a In 807 456, the digit _7_ is in the thousands place.

b In 5 486 302, the digit _5_ is in the millions place.

c In 305 128, the digit 0 is in the _ten thousands_ place.

d In 7 614 892, the digit 6 is in the _hundred thousands_ place.

7 Fill in the spaces.

a 918 230 = _900 000_ + 10 000 + 8000 + 200 + 30

b 538 417 = 500 000 + _30 000_ + 8000 + 400 + 10 + 7

c 6 000 000 + 30 000 + 90 = _6 030 090_

d 128 531 = 100 000 + 20 000 + 8000 + 500 + 30 + 1

= _128 000_ + 500 + 31

= 128 000 + _531_

8 Fill in the spaces with **greater than** or **smaller than**.

a 185 263 is _greater than_ 183 256.

b 5 060 345 is _greater than_ 995 863.

c 899 506 is _smaller than_ 900 650.

d 231 623 is _greater than_ 231 621.

9 Arrange these numbers in order, beginning with the greatest.

528 010   1 280 500   62 815   258 100   528 100

_1 280 500, 528 100, 528 010, 258 100, 62 815_

10 What is the next number in the pattern? Fill in the spaces.

276 300, 286 300, 296 300, …

286 300 is _10 000_ more than 276 300.

286 300 is _10 000_ less than 296 300.

_10 000_ more than 296 300 is _306 300_ .

The next number is _306 300_ .

11 Estimate the values of the following: Answers vary. Examples:

a $7512 + 3281 \approx$ _8000 + 3000 = 11 000_

b $6528 - 5938 \approx$ _7000 - 6000 = 1000_

c $1592 \times 5 \approx$ _2000 \times 5 = 10 000_

d $2576 \div 3 \approx$ _2700 \div 3 = 900_

12 A 4-digit number when rounded to the nearest thousand is 5000.

a What is the smallest possible number? _4500_

b What is the greatest possible number? _5499_

13 Make a 6-digit number using all the cards shown for each of the following. Do **not** start with the digit 0.

5	0	1	4	9	6

a   An odd number: _Answers vary. Example: 501 469_.

b   An even number: _Answers vary. Example: 501 496_.

c   A number with the digit 0 in the thousands place: _Answers vary. Example: 510 496_.

d   A number beginning with the greatest digit. _Answers vary. Example: 964 501_.

e   A number with the digit 6 in the tens place and the digit 5 in the ones place: _Answers vary. Example: 490 165_.

f   A number ending with the smallest digit: _Answers vary. Example: 496 510_.

g   A number where the digit 1 stands for 100 000 and the digit 9 is in the ones place: _Answers vary e.g. 150 649_.

h   A number greater than 496 501: _Answers vary e.g. 501 496_.

i   A number where the digit 4 is in the ten thousands place and the digit 6 stands for 600 000: _Answers vary e.g. 641 509_.

j   The greatest possible number: _965 410_.

k   The smallest possible number: _104 569_.

l   The difference between the greatest possible number and the smallest possible number: _860 841_.

14 Answer these questions. Remember to write the correct units in your answers. You may use your calculator where necessary.

a   Find the area of a square of which each side is 96 cm.

$96 \times 96 = 9216 \text{ cm}^2$

9216 cm²

b   Mr Jenkins has £5651. Mrs Kim has £853 more than Mr Jenkins. How much does Mrs Kim have?

£5651 + £853 = £6504

_£6504_

c   There is 176 ℓ of petrol in Container A. There is 19 ℓ less petrol in Container B. How many litres of petrol is there in Container B?

176 − 19 = 157 ℓ

_157 ℓ_

d   The mass of a cake is 2 kg. It is cut into 25 equal pieces. What is the mass of each piece of cake? Give your answer in grams.

2000 ÷ 25 = 80 g

_80 g_

e   What number can be subtracted from 5400, so that the answer has the digit 2 in the thousands place and the digit 3 in the hundreds place?

Answers vary. Accept any number from 3001 to 3100. Example: 3050

Answers Unit 2: Whole Numbers (2)

---

15 Fill in the spaces.

a $315 \times 10 = \underline{3150}$

b $\underline{1000} \times 10 = 10\,000$

c $147 \times 50 = \underline{7350}$

d $3050 \times 70 = \underline{213\,500}$

e $25 \times 100 = \underline{2500}$

f $25 \times 1000 = \underline{25\,000}$

g $\underline{5062} \times 100 = 506\,200$

h $9236 \times \underline{1000} = 9\,236\,000$

i $63 \times 200 = \underline{12\,600}$

j $63 \times 2000 = \underline{126\,000}$

k $906 \times 7000 = \underline{6\,342\,000}$

l $1145 \times 600 = \underline{687\,000}$

16 Fill in the spaces.

a $3560 \div 10 = \underline{356}$

b $81\,000 \div 10 = \underline{8100}$

c $9150 \div \underline{10} = 915$

d $20\,500 \div 10 = 2050$

e $900 \div 60 = \underline{15}$

f $3150 \div 70 = \underline{45}$

g $1900 \div 100 = \underline{19}$

h $17\,000 \div 1000 = \underline{17}$

i $3600 \div \underline{100} = 36$

j $40\,000 \div 1000 = 40$

k $96\,000 \div 400 = \underline{240}$

l $504\,000 \div 9000 = \underline{56}$

17 Estimate the values of the following:
Answers vary

a $4593 \div 53 \approx 4500 \div 50 = 90$

b $6298 \div 164 \approx 6000 \div 200 = 30$

c $7623 \div 4451 \approx 8000 \div 4000 = 2$

d $4593 \div 73 \approx 4200 \div 70 = 60$

18 Find the value of each of the following.

a $15 + 90 + 42 = 147$

b $60 + 12 - 36 = 36$

c $50 - 30 - 12 = 8$

d $3 \times 8 \times 5 = 120$

e $10 \times 9 \div 3 = 30$

f $29 + 42 \div 6 = 36$

g $(23 + 40) \div (34 - 25) = 7$

h $(90 - 85) \times 7 = 35$

i $50 \times 8 + 12 \div 4 = 403$

j $69 \div 3 - 3 + 10 = 30$

Solve these word problems. Show your workings clearly.

19 Tony had an equal number of cheese sandwiches and tuna sandwiches. He sold 66 cheese sandwiches. He had 4 times as many tuna sandwiches as cheese sandwiches left. How many sandwiches did he have at first?

Before

cheese sandwiches

tuna sandwiches

After

66

cheese sandwiches

tuna sandwiches

3 units → 66 sandwiches
1 unit → 66 ÷ 3 = 22 sandwiches
8 units → 8 × 22 = 176 sandwiches
He had 176 sandwiches at first.

20 Mr Bell had 20 m of material. He made 5 curtains. He used 3 m of material for making each curtain. Then he used 2 m of material to make a cushion cover. How much material did he have left?

5 × 3 = 15 m (5 curtains)
15 + 2 = 17 m (5 curtains + 1 cushion)
20 − 17 = 3 m (left)
He had 3 m of material left.

21 At a school fair, Mrs Smith's class sold 25 ℓ of orange juice. The orange juice was sold in cups containing 200 ml and 300 ml. An equal number of cups containing 200 ml and 300 ml were sold. How many cups of orange juice did her class sell?

25 ℓ = 25 000 ml
200 + 300 = 500 ml
25 000 ÷ 500 = 50
50 × 2 = 100 cups
Her class sold 100 cups of orange juice.

22 Michael used 220 cm of wire to make the shape below.

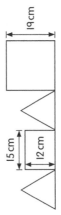

15 cm

12 cm

19 cm

The shape is made up of two identical triangles, a rectangle measuring 15 cm by 12 cm and a square of which each side is 19 cm. What is the length of one side of the triangle if all the sides of the triangle are the same?

Perimeter of rectangle: 12 + 15 + 12 + 15 = 54 cm
Perimeter of square: 4 × 19 = 76 cm
220 − 54 − 76 = 90 cm (6 sides of two triangles)
90 ÷ 6 = 15 cm
The length of one side of the triangle is 15 cm.

23 William bought 260 bags at 5 for £25. He then sold all of them at 2 for £18. How much money did he make?

260 ÷ 5 = 52
52 × £25 = £1300
He bought the bags for £1300.

260 ÷ 2 = 130
130 × £18 = £2340
He sold them for £2340.

£2340 − £1300 = £1040
He made £1040.

24 Farha scores a total of 14 points for attempting 15 questions in a maths quiz. For every correctly answered question, Farha gets 2 points. For every wrong answer, she loses 2 points. How many questions has she answered correctly?

Correct	Wrong	Total Score
8	7	16 − 14 = 2
9	6	18 − 12 = 6
10	5	20 − 10 = 10
11	4	22 − 8 = 14

She has answered 11 questions correctly.

Answers Unit 2: Whole Numbers (2)

25 If Beth feeds her goldfish 14 fish pellets a day, a tin of pellets will last 20 days. If she feeds her goldfish 8 fish pellets a day instead, how many more days will the same tin of pellets last?

Total number of pellets = 20 × 14
= 280

8 pellets → 1 day
280 pellets → 280 ÷ 8 = 35 days
35 − 20 = 15
The tin of pellets will last 15 more days.

26 Miss Barton could pick 8 kg of strawberries per hour at a farm. In the first week, she picked a total of 144 kg of strawberries after some time. Miss Barton was paid £12 per hour for picking strawberries.

a How long did she take to pick 144 kg of strawberries?

b If she picked the same mass of strawberries in the second week, how much did she earn for both weeks altogether?

a   8 kg → 1h
144 kg → 144 ÷ 8 = 18h
She took 18h to pick 144 kg of strawberries.

b   2 × 144 kg = 288 kg
8 kg → 1h
288 kg → 288 ÷ 8 = 36h   or   18 × 2 = 36h
1h → £12   36 × £12 = £432
36h → 36 × £12 = £432
She earned £432 for both weeks altogether.

27 There are 11 488 residents in the town of Ashton. There are 160 more residents in the town of Greenford. The number of residents in the town of Upside is half the total number of residents in Ashton and Greenford. How many residents are there in Upside?

Number of residents in Greenford = 11 488 + 160 = 11 648
Total number of residents in Ashton
and Greenford = 11 648 + 11 488
= 23 136

23 136 ÷ 2 = 11 568
There are 11 568 residents in Upside.

28 Jasmine mixed 1250 ml of juice with twice as much water to make some lemon squash. She poured the squash equally into 15 glasses. How much lemon squash was there in each glass? Give your answer in millilitres.

Amount of water = 1250 × 2 = 2500 ml
Total amount of lemon squash = 1250 + 2500 = 3750 ml
3750 ÷ 15 = 250 ml
Each glass had 250 ml of lemon squash.

Unit 3: Fractions (I)

Week	Learning Objectives	Thinking Skills	Resources
5	**(I) Like and unlike fractions** Pupils will be able to: • identify two or more like fractions and two or more unlike fractions • differentiate a like fraction from an unlike fraction	• Comparing	• Pupil Textbook 5A, p 70 • Teacher's Guide 5A, p 116
5	**(2) Adding unlike fractions** Pupils will be able to: • list the multiples of the denominators of two unlike fractions and find the lowest common multiple from the lists • add two unlike fractions using the above strategy • draw a model to show equivalent fractions in the addition of unlike fractions	Heuristics for problem solving: • Make a systematic list • Guess and check	• Pupil Textbook 5A, pp 71 to 73 • Practice Book 5A, pp 65 to 68 • Teacher's Guide 5A, pp 117 to 118
5	*Maths Journal* This *Maths Journal* enables pupils to reflect on the model method of adding fractions and recognise the common mistakes made in drawing models.	• Analysing parts and whole	• Pupil Textbook 5A, p 73 • Teacher's Guide 5A, p 119

Unit 3: Fractions (I)

Week	Learning Objectives	Thinking Skills	Resources
5	**(3) Subtracting unlike fractions** Pupils will be able to: • list the multiples of the denominators of two unlike fractions and find the lowest common multiple from the lists • subtract two unlike fractions without regrouping • draw a model to show equivalent fractions in the subtraction of unlike fractions	Heuristics for problem solving: • Make a systematic list • Guess and check	• Pupil Textbook 5A, pp 74 to 76 • Practice Book 5A, pp 69 to 72 • Teacher's Guide 5A, pp 120 to 122
6	**(4) Fractions and division** Pupils will be able to: • associate fractions with division • use 'conversion of improper fraction to mixed number' to express division as a mixed number • use the long division method to express an improper fraction as a mixed number	• Relating part-whole concept to fractions • Identifying patterns and relationships	• Pupil Textbook 5A, pp 77 to 81 • Practice Book 5A, pp 73 to 76 • Teacher's Guide 5A, pp 123 to 127

Unit 3: Fractions (I)   113

Unit 3: Fractions (I)

Week	Learning Objectives	Thinking Skills	Resources
6	**(5) Converting fractions to decimals** Pupils will be able to: • convert proper fractions, improper fractions and mixed numbers by changing the denominators to 10, 100 or 1000 • convert proper fractions, improper fractions and mixed numbers using long division • convert proper fractions, improper fractions and mixed numbers using a calculator	• Comparing	• Pupil Textbook 5A, pp 82 to 86 • Practice Book 5A, pp 77 to 80 • Teacher's Guide 5A, pp 128 to 132
7	**(6) Adding mixed numbers** Pupils will be able to: • add two mixed numbers with or without regrouping • add two mixed numbers using a calculator	• Relating part-whole, adding on and comparing concepts to fractions	• Pupil Textbook 5A, pp 87 to 90 • Practice Book 5A, pp 81 to 82 • Teacher's Guide 5A, pp 133 to 136
7	**(7) Subtracting mixed numbers** Pupils will be able to: • subtract a mixed number from another mixed number with or without regrouping • subtract a mixed number from another mixed number using a calculator	• Relating part-whole, taking away and comparing concepts to fractions	• Pupil Textbook 5A, pp 91 to 95 • Practice Book 5A, pp 83 to 84 • Teacher's Guide 5A, pp 137 to 141

Unit 3: Fractions (I)

Week	Learning Objectives	Thinking Skills	Resources
7	**(8) Word problems** Pupils will be able to: • solve word problems by relating to concepts in addition and subtraction • solve word problems using models	• Relating concepts in addition and subtraction • Comparing	• Pupil Textbook 5A, pp 96 to 99 • Practice Book 5A, pp 85 to 92 • Teacher's Guide 5A, pp 142 to 145
7	*Maths Journal* This journal enables pupils to reflect on the concept of adding fractions and recognise the common mistakes that they might make. *Let's Wrap It Up!* Emphasise the key concepts, skills and processes that have been taught in the unit. Discuss the worked example with pupils to assess whether they have mastered these concepts, skills and processes. *Put On Your Thinking Caps!* Pupils will be able to draw a comparison model and use the before-after concept to find the solution to the problem posed.	• Analysing parts and whole Heuristics for problem solving: • Draw a model • Use before-after concept	• Pupil Textbook 5A, pp 100 to 101 • Practice Book 5A, pp 93 to 94 • Teacher's Guide 5A, pp 146 to 147

Fractions (I)

Learning objectives:
Like and unlike fractions

Pupils will be able to:

- identify two or more like fractions and two or more unlike fractions
- differentiate a like fraction from an unlike fraction

Key concepts

- A fraction refers to a part of a whole.
- Like fractions are fractions with the same denominator.
- Unlike fractions are fractions with different denominators.

Thinking Skill

Comparing

What you will need

Fraction discs (see Photocopy master 4 on pp 321 to 322)

Additional activity

Ask pupils to work in pairs. One pupil picks up a fraction disc from a set of given fraction discs. Their partner then picks up a like fraction disc and an unlike fraction disc from the set. Then pupils swap roles.

Teaching sequence

a

- Use fraction discs provided on Photocopy master 4 to show two like fractions with the same denominator, $\frac{2}{5}$ and $\frac{3}{5}$. Explain to pupils why these fractions are called **like** fractions.
- Ask a pupil to pick up two like fraction discs and display them. Highlight to pupils that like fractions have the same denominator.

b

- Show two unlike fractions with different denominators, $\frac{2}{3}$ and $\frac{3}{4}$, using two fraction discs. Explain to pupils why these fractions are unlike fractions.
- Ask a pupil to pick up two unlike fraction discs and display them. Highlight the fact that unlike fractions have different denominators.

Unit

3 Fractions (I)

Let's Learn!

Like and unlike fractions

1 a Jack had $\frac{2}{5}$ of a biscuit.

Ella had $\frac{3}{5}$ of a biscuit.

 $\frac{2}{5}$ and $\frac{3}{5}$ are **like fractions**.
They have the same denominator, 5.

b Peter had $\frac{2}{3}$ of a pizza.

Ruby had $\frac{3}{4}$ of a pizza.

$\frac{2}{3}$ and $\frac{3}{4}$ are **unlike fractions**.
They have different denominators, 3 and 4.

70

Learning objectives: Adding unlike fractions

Pupils will be able to:

- list the multiples of the denominators of two unlike fractions and find the lowest common multiple from the lists
- add two unlike fractions using the above strategy
- draw a model to show equivalent fractions in the addition of unlike fractions

Key concepts

- Fractions are equivalent when they show the same parts of the whole.
- Fractions can be added when they are expressed as like fractions.

Heuristics for problem solving

- Make a systematic list
- Guess and check

What you will need

Fraction discs (see Photocopy master 4 on pp 321 to 322)

Additional activity

Revise addition of like fractions which has been taught previously. If necessary, use fraction discs to illustrate the addition.

Let's Learn!

Adding unlike fractions

1. $\frac{1}{2}$ of a stick is painted red. $\frac{1}{3}$ of the stick is painted green. What fraction of the stick is painted red and green?

$\frac{1}{2} + \frac{1}{3} = ?$

> Add $\frac{1}{2}$ and $\frac{1}{3}$.
> To add, convert $\frac{1}{2}$ and $\frac{1}{3}$ to like fractions.

List the multiples of the denominators, 2 and 3.

Multiples of 2: **2** , **4** , **6** , **8** , ...

Multiples of 3: **3** , **6** , **9** , **12**, ...

6 is the lowest common multiple of 2 and 3.

$\times 3$
$\frac{1}{2} = \frac{3}{6}$
$\times 3$

$\times 2$
$\frac{1}{3} = \frac{2}{6}$
$\times 2$

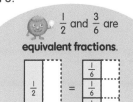

> $\frac{1}{2}$ and $\frac{3}{6}$ are **equivalent fractions**.

$\frac{1}{2} = \frac{3}{6}$ $\frac{1}{3} = \frac{2}{6}$

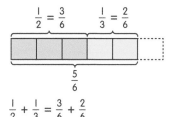

$\frac{5}{6}$

> As 6 is the lowest common multiple, I draw a model with 6 units.

$\frac{1}{2} + \frac{1}{3} = \frac{3}{6} + \frac{2}{6}$

$\qquad = \frac{5}{6}$

$\frac{5}{6}$ of the stick is painted red and green.

Teaching sequence

1

- Read and explain the question. Pupils should add the two fractions based on the part-whole concept.
- Use the concept of multiples to explain and show the procedure to find the common denominator:

  (a) Make a list of the multiples of the first denominator, 2.

  (b) Make a list of the multiples of the second denominator, 3.

  (c) Compare the two sets of multiples. Identify and select the lowest common number from the two sets of multiples.

- Ask pupils to recall what equivalent fractions are.
- Explain the procedure to change the two unlike fractions to like fractions by converting them to equivalent fractions with 6 as the common denominator. Highlight to pupils that the two equivalent fractions must come from the same whole or identical wholes.
- Then explain the method of adding the two fractions using model drawing.

Teaching sequence

- Use this question to informally assess whether pupils can add two unlike fractions. Remind pupils to find the lowest common multiple of the two denominators.

- Some pupils may notice that multiplying 2 and 7 gives 14, which is the lowest common multiple of the two denominators. Explain that this pattern only applies to some cases.

- See if pupils can solve the problem without listing the multiples of 3 and 4. They may make a guess of one multiple and then check if this multiple is also a multiple of the second number. This method helps to speed up the process of finding the common multiple. For example, pupils can guess 6 which is a multiple of 3, but it is not a multiple of 4. Next they can guess 12, which is a multiple of 3 and 4, so it is the lowest common multiple. Once the common denominator is found, pupils may use the equivalent fraction method to find the two fractions with the same denominator.

- This activity allows pupils to practise model drawing based on two fractions. However, they still need to find the lowest common multiple before they can draw the model. Use the method in ③ to find the lowest common multiple.

Unit 3 Fractions (I)

2 Add $\frac{1}{2}$ and $\frac{2}{7}$.

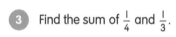

14 is the lowest common multiple of 2 and 7.

$$\frac{1}{2} = \frac{⑦}{14} \qquad \frac{2}{7} = \frac{④}{14}$$

$$\frac{1}{2} + \frac{2}{7} = \frac{⑦}{14} + \frac{④}{14}$$
$$= \frac{⑪}{⑭}$$

3 Find the sum of $\frac{1}{4}$ and $\frac{1}{3}$.

What is a common multiple of 4 and 3?

$$\frac{1}{4} = \frac{③}{⑫} \qquad \frac{1}{3} = \frac{④}{⑫}$$

$$\frac{1}{4} + \frac{1}{3} = \frac{③}{⑫} + \frac{④}{⑫}$$
$$= \frac{⑦}{⑫}$$

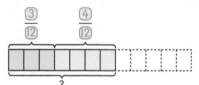

?

Activity

4 Draw bars to show the sum of these fractions. Then find the sum of the fractions.

    a $\frac{1}{2} + \frac{1}{4}$ $\frac{3}{4}$ **b** $\frac{1}{5} + \frac{3}{4}$ $\frac{19}{20}$ **c** $\frac{1}{4} + \frac{2}{3}$ $\frac{11}{12}$

72

Thinking Skill

Analysing parts and whole

Objective of activity

This *Maths Journal* enables pupils to reflect on the model method of adding fractions and recognise the common mistakes made in drawing models.

Independent work

- *Let's Practise!*
- Practice I in Practice Book 5A, pp 65 to 68.

Teaching sequence

5 *Maths Journal*

- This activity helps pupils to reflect on the methods of adding two unlike fractions and to relate the procedure to model drawing. Ask them to explain why the first two models are incorrect.

Maths Journal

5 One of the three models below shows the sum of $\frac{1}{2}$ and $\frac{1}{7}$. The other two models are incorrect. Explain why they are incorrect. Models I and 2 are incorrect.

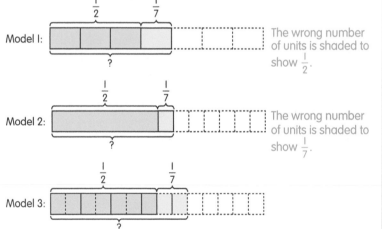

Model I: The wrong number of units is shaded to show $\frac{1}{2}$.

Model 2: The wrong number of units is shaded to show $\frac{1}{7}$.

Model 3:

Let's Practise!

6 Draw a model to find the sum of each pair of fractions.

a $\frac{1}{2}$ and $\frac{2}{5}$ $\frac{9}{10}$ b $\frac{1}{3}$ and $\frac{1}{4}$ $\frac{7}{12}$ c $\frac{3}{5}$ and $\frac{1}{3}$ $\frac{14}{15}$

7 Add. Express the answer in its simplest form where necessary.

a $\frac{2}{3} + \frac{1}{8}$ $\frac{19}{24}$ b $\frac{2}{3} + \frac{1}{12}$ $\frac{3}{4}$ c $\frac{1}{5} + \frac{3}{10}$ $\frac{1}{2}$ d $\frac{1}{4} + \frac{1}{6}$ $\frac{5}{12}$

Practice Book 5A, p.65

73

Learning objectives: Subtracting unlike fractions

Pupils will be able to:

- list the multiples of the denominators of two unlike fractions and find the lowest common multiple from the lists
- subtract two unlike fractions without regrouping
- draw a model to show equivalent fractions in the subtraction of unlike fractions

Key concept

Two fractions can be subtracted if they come from the same whole or from identical wholes.

Heuristics for problem solving

- Make a systematic list
- Guess and check

What you will need

Fraction discs (see Photocopy master 4 on pp 321 to 322)

Additional activity

Revise subtraction of like fractions which has been taught previously. If necessary, use fraction discs provided on Photocopy master 4 to illustrate this to pupils.

Teaching sequence

- Read and explain the question to pupils. Pupils should subtract the two fractions based on the taking away concept.
- Use the concept of multiples to explain and demonstrate the procedure for finding the common denominator:
  - (a) Make a list of the multiples of the first denominator, 4.
  - (b) Make a list of the multiples of the second denominator, 6.
  - (c) Compare the two sets of multiples. Identify and select the lowest common number from the two sets of multiples.
- Explain the procedure to change the two unlike fractions to like fractions by converting them to equivalent fractions with 12 as the common denominator. Highlight the fact that the two equivalent fractions must come from the same whole or identical wholes.
- Then explain the method of subtracting two fractions using model drawing.

Unit 3 Fractions (I)

Let's Learn!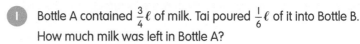

Subtracting unlike fractions

1. Bottle A contained $\frac{3}{4}\ell$ of milk. Tai poured $\frac{1}{6}\ell$ of it into Bottle B. How much milk was left in Bottle A?

$$\frac{3}{4} - \frac{1}{6} = ?$$

List the multiples of the denominators, 4 and 6.

> Subtract $\frac{1}{6}\ell$ from $\frac{3}{4}\ell$ of milk.
> To subtract, convert $\frac{1}{6}$ and $\frac{3}{4}$ to like fractions first.

Multiples of 4: **4** , **8** , **12** , **16** , …

Multiples of 6: **6** , **12** , **18** , **24** , …

12 is the lowest common multiple of 4 and 6.

 $\frac{3}{4} = \frac{9}{12}$ (× 3)

 $\frac{1}{6} = \frac{2}{12}$ (× 2)

$$\frac{3}{4} = \frac{9}{12}$$

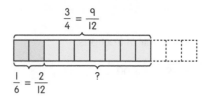

$\frac{1}{6} = \frac{2}{12}$?

$$\frac{3}{4} - \frac{1}{6} = \frac{9}{12} - \frac{2}{12}$$

$$= \frac{7}{12}\ell$$

$\frac{7}{12}\ell$ of milk was left in Bottle A.

> As 12 is the lowest common multiple, I draw a model with 12 units.

74

Additional activity

Ask pupils to find the lowest common multiple of the following pairs: 2 and 6, 3 and 4, 3 and 9, 4 and 12, 3 and 5. Encourage pupils to talk about how they found the lowest common multiples, and any generalisations they can make. For example, when one of the numbers is a multiple of the other (e.g. 9 is a multiple of 3), the lower number in the pair is the lowest common multiple. When the higher number in the pair is not a multiple of the lower number, a common multiple can be found by multiplying the two numbers.

Note

Some pupils may notice that multiplying 5 and 3 gives 15, which is the lowest common multiple of the two denominators. This pattern only applies to some cases and will not apply to the following case. For denominators 3 and 9, the first common denominator is not $3 \times 9 = 27$.
9 is the first common denominator.

Teaching sequence

2

- Use this question to informally assess whether pupils can subtract two unlike fractions. Remind them to find the lowest common multiple of the two denominators.

3

- Ask pupils to compare the denominators of this question with that of the previous question and find the difference between the two sets of denominators.

- Use this question to test if they can solve the problem without listing the multiples of 6 and 9. They may make a guess of one multiple and then check if this multiple is also a multiple of the second number. This method helps to speed up the process of finding the common multiple. For example, they can guess 12 which is a multiple of 6, but it is not a multiple of 9. Next they can guess 18, which is a multiple of 6 and 9, so it is the lowest common multiple of 6 and 9. Once the common denominator is found, pupils may use the equivalent fraction method to find the two fractions with the same denominator.

4

- This activity allows pupils to practise model drawing based on two fractions. They still need to find the lowest common multiple before they can draw the model. Use the method in **3** to find the lowest common multiple.

Fractions (I) **Unit 3**

2 Subtract $\frac{1}{5}$ from $\frac{2}{3}$.

$\frac{1}{5} = \frac{\boxed{3}}{15}$ ($\times \boxed{3}$)

$\frac{2}{3} = \frac{\boxed{10}}{15}$ ($\times \boxed{5}$)

$\frac{2}{3} - \frac{1}{5} = \frac{\boxed{10}}{15} - \frac{\boxed{3}}{15}$

$= \frac{\boxed{7}}{15}$

15 is the lowest common multiple of 3 and 5.

$\frac{2}{3} = \frac{\boxed{10}}{15}$

$\frac{1}{5} = \frac{\boxed{3}}{15}$

3 Find the difference between $\frac{5}{6}$ and $\frac{5}{9}$.

$\frac{5}{6} = \frac{\boxed{15}}{\boxed{18}}$

$\frac{5}{9} = \frac{\boxed{10}}{\boxed{18}}$

$\frac{5}{6} - \frac{5}{9} = \frac{\boxed{15}}{\boxed{18}} - \frac{\boxed{10}}{\boxed{18}}$

$= \frac{\boxed{5}}{\boxed{18}}$

What is the lowest common multiple of 6 and 9?

$\frac{\boxed{15}}{\boxed{18}}$

$\frac{\boxed{10}}{\boxed{18}}$

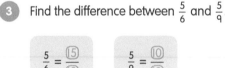

Activity

4 Draw bars to show the difference between the fractions. Then find the difference between the fractions.

a $\frac{1}{2} - \frac{2}{7} \quad \frac{3}{14}$

b $\frac{5}{6} - \frac{4}{9} \quad \frac{7}{18}$

c $\frac{3}{4} - \frac{3}{5} \quad \frac{3}{20}$

75

Independent work

- *Let's Practise!*
- Practice 2 and *Maths Journal*
  in Practice Book 5A, pp 69 to 72.

Let's Practise!

5 Complete the model with the fractions $\frac{1}{2}$, $\frac{3}{10}$ and $\frac{4}{5}$. Then write two subtraction sentences.

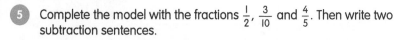

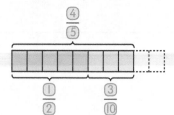

Answers vary.
Example:

$$\frac{4}{5} - \frac{1}{2} = \frac{3}{10}$$

$$\frac{8}{10} - \frac{5}{10} = \frac{3}{10}$$

6 Subtract. Draw models to help you.

a $\frac{5}{8} - \frac{1}{2} = \frac{5}{8} - \frac{4}{8}$

$= \frac{1}{8}$

b $\frac{4}{5} - \frac{1}{4} = \frac{16}{20} - \frac{5}{20}$

$= \frac{11}{20}$

7 Subtract. Express your answer in its simplest form.

a $\frac{5}{6} - \frac{1}{12}$ $\frac{3}{4}$

b $\frac{9}{10} - \frac{3}{5}$ $\frac{3}{10}$

c $\frac{8}{9} - \frac{5}{6}$ $\frac{1}{18}$

d $\frac{11}{12} - \frac{7}{8}$ $\frac{1}{24}$

e $\frac{4}{5} - \frac{2}{7}$ $\frac{18}{35}$

f $\frac{7}{9} - \frac{3}{4}$ $\frac{1}{36}$

g $\frac{4}{7} - \frac{1}{6}$ $\frac{17}{42}$

h $\frac{2}{3} - \frac{3}{8}$ $\frac{7}{24}$

Practice Book 5A, p.69

76

Learning objectives: Fractions and division

Pupils will be able to:

- associate fractions with division
- use 'conversion of improper fraction to mixed number' to express division as a mixed number
- use the long division method to express an improper fraction as a mixed number

Key concept

A whole number when divided by another whole number can result in:

(a) a whole number with or without remainder
(b) a proper fraction
(c) a mixed number.

What you will need

Fraction discs (see Photocopy master 4 on pp 321 to 322)

Thinking skills

- Relating part-whole concept to fractions
- Identifying patterns and relationships

Teaching sequence

- Work through this example: *"Divide 9 identical cakes among 3 pupils. How many cakes does each pupil get?"*
- Show concrete representation of each person getting 3 cakes.
- Ask pupils to divide 2 identical pizzas equally among 3 pupils. Ask pupils to give suggestions on how to divide the pizzas.
- Explain the procedure of dividing the pizzas into smaller pieces. Explain that the smaller pieces of pizza are fractional units. The strategy is to divide each pizza equally into the number of parts which represent the number of pupils, i.e. 3.
- Use the pictures in the textbook to illustrate that a pizza can be divided into 3 equal pieces. 6 pieces of pizza divided by 3 pupils means that each pupil gets 2 pieces of pizza. As each pizza comprises 3 equal pieces, each pupil gets $\frac{2}{3}$ of a pizza.

- Ask pupils to discuss the question and work in groups. Give each group copies of fraction discs provided on Photocopy master 4.
- Invite volunteers to explain how to get the answer. Prompt pupils by asking them how many pieces each muffin should be divided into and to explain why. Guide them to use the answer to find the fraction of a muffin each child received.

Fractions (I) **Unit 3**

Let's Learn!

Fractions and division

1 2 identical pizzas are shared equally among 3 pupils. What fraction of a pizza will each pupil get?

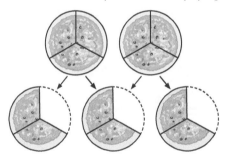

Each pizza is divided into 3 parts equally.
Each part is $\frac{1}{3}$ of a pizza.

$2 \div 3 = \frac{2}{3}$

Each pupil will get $\frac{2}{3}$ of a pizza.

2 divided by 3 is the same as $\frac{2}{3}$.

2 3 identical muffins were cut and shared among 4 children after dinner. What fraction of a muffin did each child get?

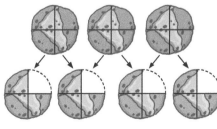

Each muffin is divided into ④ equal parts.

Each part is $\frac{①}{④}$ of a muffin.

$3 \div 4 = \frac{③}{④}$

Each child got $\frac{③}{④}$ of a muffin.

77

Unit 3: Fractions (I)   123

Teaching sequence

Arrange pupils into groups.
Guide them in exploring the
pattern of division as a fraction
by giving them some pieces of
paper strips to divide among
the groups.

What you will need

Paper strips of the same size
and length (see Photocopy
master 5 on p 323)

Teaching sequence

- Give pupils paper strips
provided on Photocopy
master 5. Use this activity to
assess whether pupils have
understood the concept of
division as a fraction and/or
to reinforce what they have
learnt. At this stage, they
should see the relationship
between division and fractions
i.e. dividing 2 by 5 gives $\frac{2}{5}$ and
dividing 4 by 9 gives $\frac{4}{9}$.

- Use these questions as
practice in expressing division
as a fraction. By now, pupils
should have observed the
pattern they have derived in
3 . Help pupils to apply this
pattern to obtain the answers.

- Use these questions as
practice in expressing a
fraction as a division sentence,
the reverse of 4 .

Unit 3 Fractions (I)

Activity

3 Work in groups of five.
Each group will need some paper strips of the same size and length.
The number of paper strips must be fewer than the number of pupils
in your group.

  1 Cut the strips into equal pieces so that each pupil gets the same
  number of pieces.

  Example Your group has two strips.

  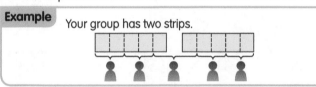

  2 Write the fraction of a strip that each one of you gets. For the
  example in I, write: 2 ÷ 5 = $\frac{2}{5}$

4 Find the value of each of the following. Express your answer as a fraction.

  a $4 \div 5 = \frac{④}{⑤}$

  b $7 \div 9 = \frac{⑦}{⑨}$

  c $5 \div 8 = \frac{⑤}{⑧}$

  d $7 \div 11 = \frac{⑦}{⑪}$

5 Express each fraction as a division sentence.

  a $\frac{3}{7} = \boxed{3} \div \boxed{7}$

  b $\frac{8}{12} = \boxed{8} \div \boxed{12}$

  c $\frac{3}{10} = \boxed{3} \div \boxed{10}$

  d $\frac{5}{6} = \boxed{5} \div \boxed{6}$

78

What you will need

Fraction discs (see Photocopy master 4 on pp 32I to 322)

Additional activity

Ask pupils to work in groups of five. Ask the groups to divide 9 squares among 5 pupils. How many squares will each pupil get? Ask them to explain to the other groups how they got the answer.

Teaching sequence

6

- Ask pupils to read the question and compare with **1**. Ask them to explain the difference between the two questions.
- Use fraction discs provided on Photocopy master 4 to review the example mentioned at the start of Teaching sequence **1** of dividing 9 identical cakes among 3 pupils to help the pupils conceptualise the division of a whole number by a smaller whole number.
- Next ask pupils to divide 5 identical pancakes equally among 4 pupils. Ask the pupils to give suggestions on how to divide the pancakes.
- Then explain the procedure of dividing each pancake into 4 parts to represent the number of pupils, i.e. 4. Use the pictures in the textbook to illustrate that a pancake can be divided into 4 equal pieces.
- Explain to pupils that division of a whole number by a smaller whole number can be expressed as an improper fraction.

Method I: Revise the partition method to convert an improper fraction to a mixed number with pupils, i.e. by breaking the improper fraction $\frac{5}{4}$ into a whole and part of a whole.

Method 2: Revise the long division method to convert an improper fraction to a mixed number with pupils and guide pupils to see that there is a whole and I quarter in $\frac{5}{4}$.

Fractions (I) **Unit 3**

6 5 identical pancakes are divided equally among 4 pupils. How many pancakes does each pupil get?

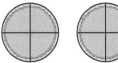

Each pancake is divided into 4 parts equally.

Method I

$5 \div 4 = \frac{5}{4}$

$= \frac{4}{4} + \frac{1}{4}$

$= 1\frac{1}{4}$

Recall that:

$\frac{5}{4}$ = 5 fourths

= 4 fourths + I fourth

$= \frac{4}{4} + \frac{1}{4}$

$= 1\frac{1}{4}$

We usually call fourths, **quarters**.

Method 2

$4 \overline{)5}$
$\underline{-4}$
1

$5 \div 4 = 1\frac{1}{4}$

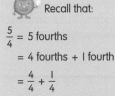

5 divided by 4 is the same as $\frac{5}{4}$ or $1\frac{1}{4}$.

Each pupil gets $1\frac{1}{4}$ pancakes.

79

Additional activity

Ask pupils to explore if there is any difference:

(a) if the improper fraction is not simplified

(b) if the improper fraction is simplified.

Will both (a) and (b) give the same answer?

What you will need

Paper strips of the same size and length (see Photocopy master 5 on p 323)

Teaching sequence

- Note that this activity is similar to ③ except that the number of paper strips given is more than the number of pupils sharing the paper strips.
- Use this activity to assess whether pupils have understood the concept of division as a fraction and reinforce what they have learnt. Help them to first carry out the activity with concrete representation before relating it to the algorithm method.

8

- Explain to pupils that this question is similar to ⑥. Emphasise that they need to simplify the improper fraction using the cancellation method, before expressing it as a mixed number using the long division method.

Activity

7 Work in groups.
Each group will need some paper strips of the same size and length. The number of paper strips must be one more than the number of pupils in your group. For example, if your group has three pupils, the group should get four paper strips.

1 Cut the strips into equal pieces so that each of you gets the same number of pieces.

> **Example**
>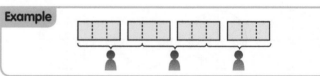

2 First write a division sentence and express it as a fraction to show what each of you gets. Then write the fraction as a mixed number.
For the example in **1**, write: $4 \div 3 = \frac{4}{3}$
$$= 1\frac{1}{3}$$

8 Express $14 \div 4$ as a fraction in its simplest form. Then change the fraction to a mixed number.

$$14 \div 4 = \frac{\overset{7}{\cancel{14}}}{\underset{2}{\cancel{4}}}$$
$$= \frac{7}{2}$$
$$= 3\frac{1}{2}$$

$$\begin{array}{r} 3 \\ 2{\overline{\smash{)}\,7}} \\ \underline{-6} \\ 1 \end{array}$$

80

Independent work

- *Let's Practise!*
- Practice 3 in Practice Book 5A, pp 73 to 76.

 **Calculator tip**

Note that the fraction button, display, and steps to type in fractions may be slightly different depending on the model of the calculator your school has adopted. For example, some calculators display $2\frac{3}{5}$ as 2⌋3 ⌋5.

Fractions (I) **Unit 3**

9 Express each division sentence as a fraction in its simplest form. Then change the fraction to a mixed number.

a $19 \div 2$ b $43 \div 4$ c $49 \div 5$ d $20 \div 8$

     $9\frac{1}{2}$ $10\frac{3}{4}$ $9\frac{4}{5}$ $2\frac{1}{2}$

10 Follow the steps to type in fractions and mixed numbers on your calculator.

Turn your calculator on.

To type in $\frac{1}{2}$, press: ① [aᵇ/c] ②

To clear the display on your calculator, press: [C]

To type in $2\frac{3}{5}$, press: ② [aᵇ/c] ③ [aᵇ/c] ⑤

 Display

0
$\frac{1}{2}$
0
$2\frac{3}{5}$

Let's Practise!

11 Find the value of each of the following. Express your answer as a fraction in its simplest form or as a mixed number.

a $10 \div 12 = \dfrac{\boxed{10}}{\boxed{12}}$

         $= \dfrac{\boxed{5}}{\boxed{6}}$

b $3 \div 2 = \dfrac{3}{2}$

         $= \dfrac{\boxed{2}}{\boxed{2}} + \dfrac{\boxed{1}}{\boxed{2}}$

         $= \boxed{1}\dfrac{\boxed{1}}{\boxed{2}}$

c $7 \div 3 \quad 2\frac{1}{3}$ d $\dfrac{11}{4} \quad 2\frac{3}{4}$ e $\dfrac{25}{7} \quad 3\frac{4}{7}$

 Practice Book 5A, p.73

81

Teaching sequence

9

- Ask pupils to work on these questions as an informal assessment. Ask pupils to practise expressing division as an improper fraction, and then simplifying the improper fractions using either the partition method or long division method.

10

- Show pupils the steps to type in fractions and mixed numbers on their calculators.

Learning objectives: Converting fractions to decimals

Pupils will be able to:

- convert proper fractions, improper fractions and mixed numbers by changing the denominators to 10, 100 or 1000
- convert proper fractions, improper fractions and mixed numbers using long division
- convert proper fractions, improper fractions and mixed numbers using a calculator

Key concepts

- Fractions and decimals are interchangeable.
- Decimals are a special type of fractions with denominators in tens, hundreds and thousands.

Thinking skill

Comparing

Teaching sequence

 and **2**

- Help pupils to recall the work from Unit 9 in Pupil Textbook 4B where the method of converting fractions to decimals was introduced. In these questions pupils convert $\frac{2}{5}$ and $\frac{9}{20}$ into tenths and hundredths so that

they can be expressed as decimals.

- Use the fraction bar and number line to revise how fractions with denominators that can be expressed as 10 and 100 can be written as decimals, by finding their respective equivalent fractions.

3

- Explain that 8 is a factor of 1000. Guide pupils to recognise that 8 × 125 = 1000. Demonstrate and explain to pupils that fractions with denominator 8 can be converted to decimals by expressing them as equivalent fractions with denominator 1000.

Unit 3 Fractions (I)

Let's Learn!

Converting fractions to decimals

Converting tenths, hundredths and thousandths

1 Express $\frac{2}{5}$ as a decimal.

$\frac{2}{5} = \frac{2 \times 2}{5 \times 2}$

$= \frac{4}{10}$

$= 0.4$

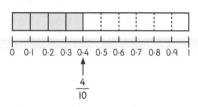

2 Express $\frac{9}{20}$ as a decimal.

$\frac{9}{20} = \frac{9 \times 5}{20 \times 5}$

$= \frac{45}{100}$

$= 0.45$

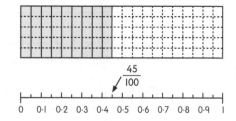

3 Express $\frac{1}{8}$ as a decimal.

$\frac{1}{8} = \frac{1 \times 125}{8 \times 125}$

$= \frac{125}{1000}$

$= 0.125$

8 is a factor of 1000.
8 × 125 = 1000

By converting $\frac{1}{8}$ to $\frac{125}{1000}$, we can express the fraction as a decimal easily.

82

Note

Emphasise to pupils that not all denominators can be expressed as 10, 100 or 1000. Emphasise to pupils that fractions with denominators that cannot be expressed as 10, 100 or 1000 can be converted using the long division method.

Additional activity

Ask pupils to work in groups of four. Shuffle the numbered cards and give four cards to each player and put the rest in a pile facing down. One of the players turns over the top card from the pile. If the number on the card multiplied with any of the players' four cards makes a number in tens, hundreds or thousands, the first person who calls "*Catch!*" will get the card. The player who finishes pairing all their cards first is the winner.

What you will need

Three sets of numbered cards comprising of 2, 4, 5, 8, 10, 20, 25, 50, 100, 125, 250, 400 and 500.

Fractions (I) **Unit 3**

4 Convert each fraction to a decimal.

a $\frac{4}{5} = \frac{8}{10} = \boxed{0.8}$

b $\frac{7}{20} = \frac{35}{100} = \boxed{0.35}$

c $\frac{2}{8} = \boxed{} \quad \frac{250}{1000} = 0.25$

d $\frac{6}{8} = \boxed{} \quad \frac{750}{1000} = 0.75$

Converting using long division

5 Express $\frac{3}{7}$ as a decimal. Round your answer to 2 decimal places.

$\frac{3}{7} = 3 \div 7$

≈ 0.43

$$\begin{array}{r} 0.428 \\ 7\overline{)\ 3} \\ -2\,8 \\ \hline 20 \\ -1\,4 \\ \hline 60 \\ -56 \\ \hline 4 \end{array}$$

Why do we need to find the answer to 3 decimal places first?

6 Express $\frac{2}{9}$ as a decimal. Round your answer to 2 decimal places.

$\frac{2}{9} = 2 \div 9$

$\approx \boxed{0.22}$

$$\begin{array}{r} 0.22\,\boxed{2} \\ 9\overline{)\ 2} \\ -1\,8 \\ \hline 20 \\ -1\,8 \\ \hline 2\,\boxed{0} \\ -\boxed{1}\,\boxed{8} \\ \hline \boxed{2} \end{array}$$

7 Convert each fraction to a decimal. Round your answers to 2 decimal places.

a $\frac{5}{7} \approx \boxed{0.71}$

b $\frac{1}{6} \approx \boxed{0.17}$

c $\frac{2}{3} \approx \boxed{0.67}$

d $\frac{8}{9} \approx \boxed{0.89}$

83

Teaching sequence

4

• Ask pupils to practise conversion of fractions to decimals using equivalent fractions with denominators 10, 100 or 1000. They should recognise at the end of this question that only certain fractions can be converted to equivalent fractions with tens, hundreds and thousands as denominators.

5

• Explain and show the strategy to convert a proper fraction to a decimal using long division. Emphasise that if it is required to express the decimal to a certain number of decimal places, the long division should be done to 1 more decimal place than the number required. For example, if 2 decimal places are required, they should do long division up to 3 decimal places before rounding to 2 decimal places.

6

• Ask pupils to work on this question as an informal assessment. Check if pupils can follow the procedure to use long division to express a fraction as a decimal.

7

• Ask pupils to practise the above strategy. They should first find the answers to 3 decimal places and then round the answers to 2 decimal places.

Teaching sequence

Additional activity

Ask pupils to work in pairs. Pupil A calls out a fraction, while Pupil B guesses whether the fraction expressed as a decimal will give 1, 2 or 3 decimal places. Pupil B gets a point if their guess is correct. Pupil A can use a calculator to check the answer. Then pupils A and B swap roles. After 10 rounds, the pupil who has the most points wins.

What you will need

Scientific calculator

8

- The objective of the activity is to familiarise pupils with the use of calculators in division and fractions.
- Pupils can convert each fraction to a decimal by dividing the numerator by the denominator on their calculator.
- The activity gets pupils to explore the various types of fractions that have 1, 2, 3, or more decimal places when expressed as decimals.
- It also helps pupils to recognise which fractions will provide decimals with 1, 2, 3, or more decimal places.

9

- Ask pupils to use their calculators to express fractions as decimals and round to 2 decimal places.
- Discuss how converting fractions into decimals can help us to arrange fractions in order of size.

10 and **11**

- Explain to pupils that they should first express the improper fraction as a mixed number.
- Then they will need to use long division to convert the fractional part to a decimal.
- Finally they should add the whole number to the decimal equivalent of the proper fraction to obtain the decimal value of the improper fraction.

Unit 3 Fractions (1)

Activity

8 These are some proper fractions.

$$\frac{1}{2}, \frac{2}{3}, \frac{3}{4}, \frac{3}{5}, \frac{5}{6}, \frac{2}{7}, \frac{7}{8}, \frac{2}{9}, \frac{3}{10}, \frac{6}{11}, \frac{11}{12}$$

 Use your calculator to find the fractions that have:

a 1, 2 or 3 decimal places when expressed as decimals $\frac{1}{2}, \frac{3}{4}, \frac{3}{5}, \frac{7}{8}, \frac{3}{10}$

b more than 3 decimal places when expressed as decimals. $\frac{2}{3}, \frac{5}{6}, \frac{2}{7}, \frac{2}{9}, \frac{6}{11}, \frac{11}{12}$

9 Write the following as decimals. Round your answers to 2 decimal places if necessary.

a $\frac{3}{11}$ **b** $\frac{7}{15}$ **c** $\frac{2}{13}$ **d** $\frac{11}{21}$

      0·27   0·47   0·15   0·52

Converting improper fractions and mixed numbers

10 Express $9 \div 6$ as a decimal.

$$9 \div 6 = \frac{9}{6}$$
$$= 1 + \frac{3}{6}$$
$$= 1·5$$

$$\begin{array}{r} 0·5 \\ 6\overline{)\,3} \\ -3\,0 \\ \hline 0 \end{array}$$

11 Express $2\frac{1}{7}$ as a decimal. Round your answer to 2 decimal places.

$$2\frac{1}{7} = 2 + \frac{1}{7}$$
$$\approx 2 + 0·14$$
$$= 2·14$$

$$\begin{array}{r} 0·142 \\ 7\overline{)\,1} \\ -\ 7 \\ \hline 30 \\ -28 \\ \hline 20 \\ -14 \\ \hline 6 \end{array}$$

84

130   **Unit 3:** Fractions (1)

 **Calculator tip**

On some calculators, pupils may be able to obtain the decimal value directly by pressing the fraction button after they input the fraction into the calculator. Help pupils to explore their calculator's fraction function.

Fractions (I) **Unit 3**

12 Write the following as decimals. Round your answers to 2 decimal places if necessary.

a $12 \div 5$ 2·4   **b** $8 \div 3$ 2·67   **c** $3\frac{3}{5}$ 3·6   **d** $5\frac{7}{9}$ 5·78

13 Express the following as decimals. Round your answers to 2 decimal places if necessary.

a $\frac{13}{9} \approx 1\cdot44$

Turn your calculator on.

To convert $\frac{13}{9}$, press ① ③ ÷ ⑨ =

 **Display**
0
1·4444 . . .

b $5\frac{4}{7} = 5 + \frac{4}{7} \approx$ 5·57

To clear the display on your calculator, press ⒞

To convert $\frac{4}{7}$, press ④ ÷ ⑦ =

 Display
0
0·57142 . . .

14 Express the following as decimals. Round your answers to 2 decimal places if necessary.

a $\frac{19}{6}$ 3·17   **b** $7\frac{9}{17}$ 7·53   **c** $4\frac{5}{18}$ 4·28   **d** $10\frac{8}{23}$ 10·35

Let's Practise!

15 Express each fraction as a decimal.

a $\frac{3}{5}$ 0·6   **b** $\frac{17}{20}$ 0·85   **c** $\frac{5}{8}$ 0·625

85

Teaching sequence

12

- **a** and **b** involve expressing division as a decimal. **c** and **d** involve converting a mixed number to a decimal. At this stage, pupils are expected to use long division to convert fractions or mixed numbers to decimals. Remind pupils that they have to divide up to 3 decimal places so that they can round to 2 decimal places as required.

13

- Introduce the use of calculators to convert improper fractions and mixed numbers to decimals of up to 2 decimal places. Depending on the calculator, they may have to first get a fraction and then convert it to a decimal using the method shown. For mixed numbers, remind pupils that they can first convert the fractional part and then add on the whole number.

14

- Ask pupils to work on these questions as an informal assessment to check if pupils are able to input mixed numbers and then convert them to decimals.

Independent work

Practice 4 and *Maths Journal* in Practice Book 5A, pp 77 to 80.

What you will need

Scientific calculator

Unit 3 Fractions (I)

Let's Practise!

16 Convert the following fractions to decimals. Round your answers to 2 decimal places.

a $\frac{1}{9}$ 0·11

b $\frac{2}{7}$ 0·29

c $\frac{7}{11}$ 0·64

17 Read each question. Write a division sentence. Then solve the problem.

a 8 identical cakes were shared equally among 6 children. How many cakes did each child get? $1\frac{1}{3}$

b Jeff made 16 ℓ of lemonade in a big container. He then poured the lemonade equally into 5 jugs. How many litres of lemonade were there in each jug? Express your answer as:

i a mixed number $3\frac{1}{5}\ell$

ii a decimal. 3·2 ℓ

18 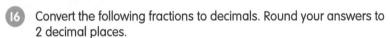 Find the value of each of the following. Express your answer as a mixed number and as a decimal correct to 2 decimal places.

a $7 \div 6$
$1\frac{1}{6}$, 1·17

b $13 \div 9$
$1\frac{4}{9}$, 1·44

c $\frac{14}{5}$
$2\frac{4}{5}$, 2·80

d $\frac{45}{11}$
$4\frac{1}{11}$, 4·09

19 Express each fraction or mixed number as a decimal. Round your answer to 2 decimal places where necessary.

a $\frac{7}{13}$ 0·54

b $\frac{21}{35}$ 0·6

c $\frac{22}{80}$ 0·28

d $3\frac{5}{18}$ 3·28

e $2\frac{7}{12}$ 2·58

f $5\frac{4}{15}$ 5·27

Practice Book 5A, p.77

86

Learning objectives: Adding mixed numbers

Pupils will be able to:

- add two mixed numbers with or without regrouping
- add two mixed numbers using a calculator

Key concepts

- A mixed number comprises a whole number and a proper fraction.
- Mixed numbers can be added like adding proper and improper fractions.

Thinking skill

Relating part-whole, adding on and comparing concepts to fractions.

Note

Remind pupils to always write their answers in the simplest form.

Fractions (I) **Unit 3**

Let's Learn!

Adding mixed numbers

1 Susie walked $1\frac{1}{2}$ km and jogged $2\frac{3}{4}$ km. How many kilometres did she walk and jog altogether?

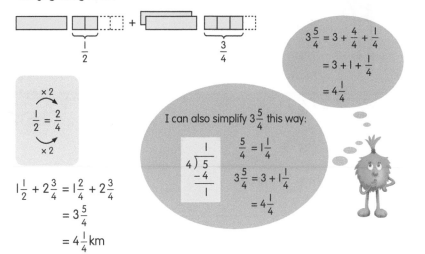

$$3\frac{5}{4} = 3 + \frac{4}{4} + \frac{1}{4}$$
$$= 3 + 1 + \frac{1}{4}$$
$$= 4\frac{1}{4}$$

I can also simplify $3\frac{5}{4}$ this way:

$$\begin{array}{r} 1 \\ 4\overline{)5} \\ -4 \\ \hline 1 \end{array}$$

$$\frac{5}{4} = 1\frac{1}{4}$$
$$3\frac{5}{4} = 3 + 1\frac{1}{4}$$
$$= 4\frac{1}{4}$$

$$\frac{1}{2} \xrightarrow{\times 2} \frac{2}{4} \xleftarrow{\times 2}$$

$$1\frac{1}{2} + 2\frac{3}{4} = 1\frac{2}{4} + 2\frac{3}{4}$$
$$= 3\frac{5}{4}$$
$$= 4\frac{1}{4} \text{ km}$$

Susie walked and jogged $4\frac{1}{4}$ km altogether.

2 Find the sum of $2\frac{2}{3}$ and $3\frac{5}{9}$.

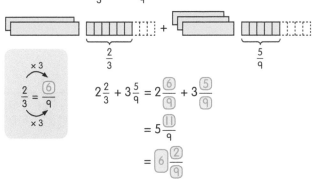

$$\frac{2}{3} \xrightarrow{\times 3} \frac{\boxed{6}}{9} \xleftarrow{\times 3}$$

$$2\frac{2}{3} + 3\frac{5}{9} = 2\frac{\boxed{6}}{9} + 3\frac{\boxed{5}}{9}$$
$$= 5\frac{\boxed{11}}{9}$$
$$= \boxed{6}\frac{\boxed{2}}{9}$$

87

Teaching sequence

1

- Explain the context as an addition of two distances. Relate the 'part-whole' concept in addition to these two mixed numbers. Explain that the principles underpinning the addition of fractions and mixed numbers are the same.

- Explain the steps in adding two mixed numbers:

  Step 1: Using pictorial representation, show that adding mixed numbers involves addition of the whole and the fractional parts separately, then regrouping them. In this example, add the two wholes 1 and 2. Then add the two fractional parts, $\frac{1}{2}$ and $\frac{3}{4}$.

  Step 2: Show the method of converting the two fractional parts to fractions with the same denominator.

  Step 3: Then add the wholes and the fractional parts accordingly.

2

- Ask pupils to work on this question as an informal assessment. Ensure that they use the strategy and the three steps given above.

Additional activity

Ask pupils to work in pairs. Ask them to think of two different ways to add two mixed numbers. Then compare the methods they have discovered with the other groups. Summarise the different methods to the whole class.

Note

Pupils are allowed to use calculators for addition of mixed numbers. However, for the purposes of explaining the concept, models are used to guide pupils in finding the answer.

Teaching sequence

- Explain to pupils that this question is similar to ① and ② except that the fractional parts are unlike fractions. Use the same strategy as in ①.

- Ask pupils to work on this question as an informal assessment. Ensure that they use the strategy and the 3 steps used in ①.

---

③ Ruby bought $2\frac{1}{5}$ kg of pears. She also bought $1\frac{1}{2}$ kg of grapes. What is the total mass of fruit that she bought?

$$2\frac{1}{5} + 1\frac{1}{2} = ?$$

First convert the fractional parts to like fractions. 10 is the lowest common multiple of 5 and 2. Then add the whole numbers before adding the fractional parts.

$$2\frac{1}{5} + 1\frac{1}{2} = 2\frac{2}{10} + 1\frac{5}{10}$$

$$= 3\frac{7}{10}\text{ kg}$$

Ruby bought $3\frac{7}{10}$ kg of fruit.

$\dfrac{1}{5}$ $\dfrac{1}{2}$

$\dfrac{1}{5} = \dfrac{2}{10}$ (×2) $\dfrac{1}{2} = \dfrac{5}{10}$ (×5)

④ Add $3\frac{1}{4}$ and $2\frac{5}{9}$.

$$3\frac{1}{4} + 2\frac{5}{9} = 3\frac{\boxed{}9}{\boxed{}36} + 2\frac{\boxed{}20}{\boxed{}36}$$

$$= \boxed{5}\ \frac{\boxed{}29}{\boxed{}36}$$

$\dfrac{1}{4}$ $\dfrac{5}{9}$

$\dfrac{1}{4} = \dfrac{\boxed{9}}{36}$ (×9) $\dfrac{5}{9} = \dfrac{\boxed{}20}{36}$ (×4)

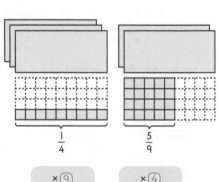

88

Additional activity

Ask pupils to work in groups of four. Ask the first two pupils to think of a mixed number that can be broken into two parts in many ways. The other two pupils think of different possible answers. The first two pupils check the answers with a calculator.

Calculator tip

- On some calculators, pupils may be able to obtain the decimal value by pressing the fraction button after they input the mixed number. Remind pupils that they can use this function to check their answers and assist them in conversion.

- On many calculators, pressing the shift key and the fraction button will convert mixed numbers to improper fractions and vice versa.

Fractions (I) **Unit 3**

Teaching sequence

5

- This is a reverse activity. Instead of asking pupils to add the numbers, they are expected to break them into two parts. The strategy is to look at the wholes and fractional parts separately. Using the number bond concept, they can find the parts that make the whole or the fractional part.

Activity

5 Work in pairs.

a Write two mixed numbers with denominator 3 that have a sum of $5\frac{2}{3}$.

$$\boxed{}\frac{\square}{3} + \boxed{}\frac{\square}{3} = 5\frac{2}{3}$$

Answers vary
Example: $3\frac{1}{3} + 2\frac{1}{3} = 5\frac{2}{3}$

b Write two mixed numbers with denominator 4 that have a sum of $3\frac{3}{4}$.

$$\boxed{}\frac{\square}{4} + \boxed{}\frac{\square}{4} = 3\frac{3}{4}$$

Answers vary
Example: $2\frac{1}{4} + 1\frac{2}{4} = 3\frac{3}{4}$

6

- In these questions, pupils are guided in learning to use their calculators to add two mixed numbers. You could ask pupils why they think the denominator of the answer is 40 and how it links to the fractions being added.

6 Find the sum of $3\frac{2}{5}$ and $4\frac{7}{8}$. Express your answer as:

a a mixed number **b** a decimal correct to 2 decimal places.

a $3\frac{2}{5} + 4\frac{7}{8} = ?$

The sum of $3\frac{2}{5}$ and $4\frac{7}{8}$ is $8\frac{11}{40}$.

b The sum of $3\frac{2}{5}$ and $4\frac{7}{8} \approx 8{\cdot}28$.

Press	Display
C	0
3 ab/c 2 ab/c 5	$3\frac{2}{5}$
+ 4 ab/c 7 ab/c 8	$4\frac{7}{8}$
=	$8\frac{11}{40}$

7

- Use these questions to assess if pupils can follow the procedure to use a calculator to add two mixed numbers.

7 Find the sum of the following mixed numbers. Express your answer as a mixed number and as a decimal correct to 2 decimal places.

a $2\frac{7}{9} + 5\frac{3}{11}$ $8\frac{5}{99}$, $8{\cdot}05$ **b** $4\frac{6}{7} + 9\frac{7}{12}$ $14\frac{37}{84}$, $14{\cdot}44$

89

- *Let's Practise!*
- Practice 5 in Practice Book 5A, pp 81 to 82.

Scientific calculator

Unit 3 Fractions (I)

Let's Practise!

8 Add. Express your answer in its simplest form. Then check your answer with a calculator.

a $5\frac{5}{6} + 3\frac{5}{12}$ $9\frac{1}{4}$

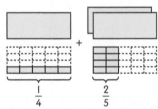

$\frac{5}{6}$ $\frac{5}{12}$

b $1\frac{1}{4} + 2\frac{2}{5}$ $3\frac{13}{20}$

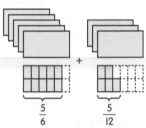

$\frac{1}{4}$ $\frac{2}{5}$

c $3\frac{3}{8} + 4\frac{1}{3}$ $7\frac{17}{24}$

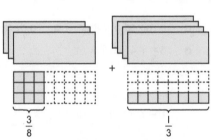

$\frac{3}{8}$ $\frac{1}{3}$

9 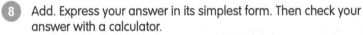 Find the sum of the mixed numbers. Express your answer as:

i   a mixed number   ii   a decimal correct to 2 decimal places.

a $1\frac{3}{5} + 2\frac{3}{8}$

b $3\frac{3}{4} + 5\frac{2}{7}$

c $5\frac{1}{6} + 2\frac{2}{9}$

$3\frac{39}{40}$, 3·98

$9\frac{1}{28}$, 9·04

$7\frac{7}{18}$, 7·39

Practice Book 5A, p.81

90

Learning objectives: Subtracting mixed numbers

Pupils will be able to:

- subtract a mixed number from another mixed number with or without regrouping
- subtract a mixed number from another mixed number using a calculator

Key concepts

- A mixed number comprises a whole number and a proper fraction.
- Mixed numbers can be subtracted like subtracting proper and improper fractions.

Thinking skill

Relating part-whole, taking away and comparing concepts to fractions.

Let's Learn!

 Subtracting mixed numbers

1. Tai bought $2\frac{3}{4}$ m of material. He cut $1\frac{1}{8}$ m to make a bag. How much material did he have left?

To subtract, change $\frac{1}{8}$ and $\frac{3}{4}$ to like fractions first.

$$\frac{3}{4} \overset{\times 2}{\underset{\times 2}{=}} \frac{6}{8}$$

$$2\frac{3}{4} - 1\frac{1}{8} = 2\frac{6}{8} - 1\frac{1}{8}$$
$$= 1\frac{5}{8} \text{ m}$$

Tai had $1\frac{5}{8}$ m of material left.

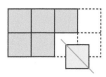

91

Teaching sequence

1

- Relate cutting some parts from a piece of material to the taking away concept and explain to pupils that this question involves subtraction.
- The first mixed number does not need to be regrouped as the numerator of its fractional part is sufficient for the subtraction.
- Explain the strategies in subtracting a mixed number from another mixed number:

  Step 1: Using pictorial representation, show that subtracting mixed numbers involves changing a fraction to its equivalent fraction so that both fractions have the same denominator.

  Step 2: Next subtract the wholes and fractional parts separately.

Note

The pictorial representations shown are provided to illustrate the concept. Pupils need to find the answers numerically here, rather than relying on the pictorial representations to solve the problem.

Teaching sequence

- Ask pupils to work on this question as an informal assessment. Ensure that pupils use the strategy and the two steps given in ❶.

- In this question, the first mixed number has to be regrouped as the numerator of its fractional part is not sufficient for the subtraction.

- Highlight to pupils that they should first express both fractions as equivalent fractions with the same denominator.

- You may need to revise finding a common denominator as the fractional parts are unrelated, using the following strategy:

  Step 1: Pick the greater denominator (i.e. 9)

  Step 2: Find the next multiple of 9, i.e. 9 × 2 = 18

  Step 3: Check whether this number is also a multiple of the smaller denominator. Since 18 is also a multiple of 6, 18 is the lowest common multiple of 6 and 9.

- Explain to pupils that the fractional parts are unrelated. Guide pupils to use the strategy in ❷ to find the lowest common multiple.

  Then proceed to subtract the wholes and fractional parts separately.

② Find the difference between $4\frac{5}{9}$ and $3\frac{5}{6}$.

$$4\frac{5}{9} - 3\frac{5}{6} = 4\frac{\bigcirc10}{\bigcirc18} - 3\frac{\bigcirc15}{\bigcirc18}$$

$$= 3\frac{\bigcirc28}{\bigcirc18} - 3\frac{\bigcirc15}{\bigcirc18}$$

$$= \frac{\bigcirc13}{\bigcirc18}$$

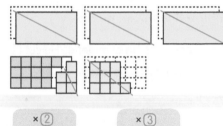

③ A bottle contained $3\frac{3}{8}\ell$ of water. Miya used $1\frac{1}{3}\ell$ of it. What was the volume of water left in the bottle?

$$3\frac{3}{8} - 1\frac{1}{3} = ?$$

To subtract, change the fractional parts to like fractions first. Then subtract the whole numbers before subtracting the fractional parts.

$$3\frac{3}{8} - 1\frac{1}{3} = 3\frac{9}{24} - 1\frac{8}{24}$$

$$= 2\frac{1}{24}\ell$$

The volume of water left was $2\frac{1}{24}\ell$.

Fractions (I) **Unit 3**

4 Subtract.

a $5\frac{5}{9} - 2\frac{1}{3} = 5\frac{\boxed{5}}{9} - 2\frac{\boxed{3}}{9}$

$= \boxed{3}\frac{\boxed{2}}{9}$

$\frac{1}{3} = \frac{\boxed{3}}{9}$

b $3\frac{4}{5} - 2\frac{1}{2} = \boxed{3}\frac{\boxed{8}}{10} - \boxed{2}\frac{\boxed{5}}{10}$

$= \boxed{1}\frac{\boxed{3}}{10}$

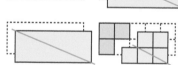

Activity

5 Work in pairs.

The difference between two mixed numbers is $3\frac{1}{4}$. What are the two mixed numbers?

 $= 3\frac{1}{4}$ Answers vary

Example: $4\frac{1}{2} - 1\frac{1}{4} = 3\frac{1}{4}$

Teaching sequence

4

- Ask pupils to work on these questions as an informal assessment. Guide pupils to see that in **a**, the denominators of the two fractions are related. However in **b**, the denominators are unrelated. In both, they are required to find equivalent fractions with the same denominators.

5

- This is a reverse activity. Instead of asking pupils to subtract a mixed number from another mixed number, they are expected to break them into two parts. The strategy is to look at the wholes and fractional parts separately. Using the number bond concept, they can find the parts that make the whole or the fractional part.

Teaching sequence

- Guide pupils to follow the steps shown to learn how to use their calculators to subtract a mixed number from another mixed number.

- Use this question to informally assess whether pupils can follow the procedure to use their calculators to subtract a mixed number from another mixed number.

Unit 3 Fractions (I)

Activity

6   Find the difference between $3\frac{5}{8}$ and $1\frac{3}{5}$.

$3\frac{5}{8} - 1\frac{3}{5} = ?$

Press	Display
C	0
3 a^b/c 5 a^b/c 8	$3\frac{5}{8}$
− 1 a^b/c 3 a^b/c 5	$1\frac{3}{5}$
=	$2\frac{1}{40}$

The difference between $3\frac{5}{8}$ and $1\frac{3}{5}$ is $2\frac{1}{40}$.

7   Subtract. Express your answer as a mixed number and as a decimal. Correct the decimal to 2 decimal places if necessary.

    a $5\frac{3}{11} - 4\frac{7}{8}$ $\frac{35}{88}$, 0·40

    b $9\frac{5}{12} - 3\frac{8}{9}$ $5\frac{19}{36}$, 5·53

Let's Practise!

8   Subtract without using a calculator. Then check your answer using a calculator.

    a $3\frac{3}{4} - 1\frac{1}{2}$ $2\frac{1}{4}$

What you will need
Scientific calculator

Independent work
Practice 6 in Practice Book 5A,
pp 83 to 84.

Fractions (I) **Unit 3**

Let's Practise!

b $5\frac{5}{6} - 2\frac{2}{3}$ $3\frac{1}{6}$

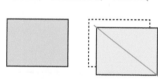

c $3\frac{1}{3} - 2\frac{1}{4}$ $1\frac{1}{12}$

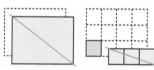

d $2\frac{3}{4} - 1\frac{3}{8}$ $1\frac{3}{8}$

9 🖩 Subtract. Express your answer as a mixed number and a decimal.
Correct the decimal to 2 decimal places if necessary.

a $6\frac{1}{10} - 3\frac{1}{5}$
   $2\frac{9}{10}$, 2·9

b $4\frac{1}{2} - 1\frac{7}{8}$
   $2\frac{5}{8}$, 2·63

c $5\frac{1}{4} - 2\frac{1}{3}$
   $2\frac{11}{12}$, 2·92

d $7\frac{2}{3} - 4\frac{1}{2}$
   $3\frac{1}{6}$, 3·17

e $9\frac{4}{7} - 2\frac{1}{3}$
   $7\frac{5}{21}$, 7·24

f $12\frac{7}{12} - 5\frac{8}{9}$
   $6\frac{25}{36}$, 6·69

Practice Book 5A, p.83

95

Teaching sequence

9 *Let's Practise!*

- Pupils can use division in order
  to express the numbers as
  decimals or they can use the
  fraction key on the calculator.
  You could ask pupils: "*Which
  fraction in question 9 does
  not need to be rounded to 2
  decimal places? How can you
  tell before you express it as a
  decimal?*"

Learning objectives:
Word problems

Pupils will be able to:

- solve word problems by relating to concepts in addition and subtraction
- solve word problems using models

Key concepts

The following concepts are applied to fractions: part-whole concepts in addition and subtraction, comparison concept, adding-on in addition, taking-away in subtraction and division concept.

Thinking skills

- Relating concepts in addition and subtraction
- Comparing

Teaching sequence

- Explain to pupils that it is necessary to divide each cake into smaller pieces in order for the 5 cakes to be divided equally into 3 equal portions.
- Explain the strategy to work on this problem:

  Step 1: Express the division sentence as a fraction, i.e. $5 \div 3 = \frac{5}{3}$.

  Step 2: Use the long division method to find the mixed number which is the equal portion of the three portions.

- Use this question as an informal assessment to check whether pupils can answer the 2-step problem.

Unit 3 Fractions (I)

Let's Learn!

Word problems

1 Mr Newman baked 5 cakes of the same size. He divided the cakes equally into 3 portions. How many cakes were there in each portion?

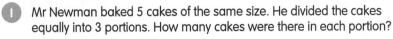

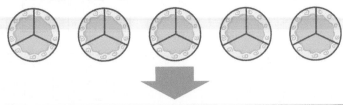

$5 \div 3 = \frac{5}{3} = 1\frac{2}{3}$ cakes

There were $1\frac{2}{3}$ cakes in each portion.

$$\begin{array}{r} 1 \\ 3{\overline{)5}} \\ -3 \\ \hline 2 \end{array}$$

2 Alisha had 17 ℓ of fruit juice. She gave 5 ℓ of fruit juice to her sister. The remaining fruit juice was poured equally into 5 bottles. How much fruit juice did each bottle contain?

$17 - 5 = \boxed{12}\,\ell$

She had $\boxed{12}\,\ell$ of fruit juice left.

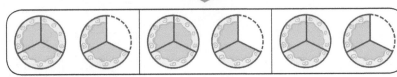

Each bottle contained $\boxed{2}\dfrac{\boxed{2}}{\boxed{5}}\,\ell$ of fruit juice.

96

3 Hardeep was given $\frac{4}{5}$h to complete his homework. He completed it in $\frac{3}{4}$h.
How much spare time did he have left after he completed his homework?

$\frac{4}{5}$h

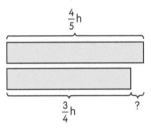

$\frac{3}{4}$h ?

$\frac{4}{5} - \frac{3}{4} = \frac{16}{20} - \frac{15}{20} = \frac{1}{20}$h

Hardeep had $\frac{1}{20}$h left after he completed his homework.

4 Isabel spent $\frac{1}{6}$ of her money on food. She also spent $\frac{5}{8}$ of her money on
a present. What fraction of Isabel's money was left?

$\frac{\boxed{1}}{\boxed{6}} = \frac{\boxed{4}}{\bigcirc 24}$ $\frac{\boxed{5}}{\boxed{8}} = \frac{\bigcirc 15}{\bigcirc 24}$

 First find the amount of money Isabel spent on the food and present altogether.

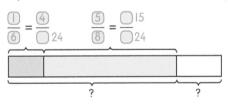

? ?

$\frac{\boxed{1}}{\boxed{6}} + \frac{\boxed{5}}{\boxed{8}} = \frac{\bigcirc 19}{\bigcirc 24}$

Isabel spent $\frac{\bigcirc 19}{\bigcirc 24}$ of her money on the food and present altogether.

$\boxed{1} - \frac{\bigcirc 19}{\bigcirc 24} = \frac{\boxed{5}}{\bigcirc 24}$

$\frac{\boxed{5}}{\bigcirc 24}$ of Isabel's money was left.

97

Additional activity

Ask pupils to work in groups of four. Ask the first two pupils to draw a part-whole model that is the result of subtraction of two mixed numbers. They must also provide some information relating to the model. The other two pupils write a 2-step word problem using the model as a guide. The first two pupils check the answer.

Teaching sequence

3

- The context in this question is related to the 'part-whole' concept in subtraction. Explain that the whole is the given time to complete the homework. The part given is the time that Hardeep took to complete his homework. The part that needs to be found is the unused time. Relate this context to the model to show the whole and the parts. Encourage pupils to write down the subtraction sentence and complete the solution.

4

- Use this question to informally assess whether pupils are able to apply the 'part-whole' concept to solve fraction word problems. If necessary, guide pupils to see that this is a 2-step word problem. There are two fractional parts and a whole in this 'part-whole' model.

Ask pupils to work in groups of four. Ask the first two pupils to draw a comparison model that is the result of subtraction of two mixed numbers. They must also provide some information relating to the model. The other two pupils write a 2-step word problem using the model as a guide. The first two pupils check the answer.

Scientific calculator

Teaching sequence

- The context in this question is related to the 'part-whole' concept in addition. Explain to pupils that the whole is the total amount of squash bought by Lisa and Ravi. The parts are the individual amounts of squash bought by each person. Relate this concept to the model to show the whole and the parts. Guide pupils to write down the addition sentence and complete the solution.

- This question is a 2-step problem that involves both addition and subtraction. The context is related to the comparison model concept.

- Encourage pupils to differentiate this problem from ③. Highlight the different presentation of the models. Explain that in a comparison model, it is easier to visualise by placing one bar above and the other below.

- Some pupils may be able to express their answer to this question in hours and minutes. Ask them how they can use the calculator to perform this conversion.

Unit 3 Fractions (I)

⑤ Lisa bought $1\frac{2}{9}\ell$ of orange squash. Ravi gave Lisa another $2\frac{1}{6}\ell$ of orange squash. How many litres of orange squash did Lisa have altogether?

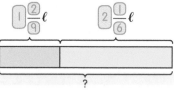

$1\frac{\boxed{2}}{\boxed{9}} + 2\frac{\boxed{1}}{\boxed{6}} = 1\frac{\boxed{4}}{\boxed{18}} + 2\frac{\boxed{3}}{\boxed{18}} = 3\frac{\boxed{7}}{\boxed{18}}\ell$

Lisa had $3\frac{\boxed{7}}{\boxed{18}}\ell$ of orange squash altogether.

⑥ Claire took $2\frac{1}{4}$ h to finish reading a book. Her brother, Dan, took $\frac{2}{3}$ h less to finish reading his book. How long did they spend to finish reading their books altogether?

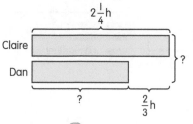

First find the time Dan took to read the book.

$2\frac{1}{4} - \frac{2}{3} = 1\frac{\boxed{7}}{\boxed{12}}$ h

Dan finished reading his book in $1\frac{7}{12}$ h.

$2\frac{1}{4} + 1\frac{7}{12} = 3\frac{\boxed{5}}{\boxed{6}}$ h

Claire and Dan spent $3\frac{\boxed{5}}{\boxed{6}}$ h to finish reading their books altogether.

98

What you will need

Scientific calculator

Independent work

- *Let's Practise!*
- Practice 7 & 8 in Practice Book 5A, pp 85 to 92.

Let's Practise!

Solve these word problems. Show your workings clearly.

7 Ethan had 5 bags of green beans, each with a mass of 7 kg. He divided all the beans equally into 3 portions. What was the mass of the beans in each portion? $11\frac{2}{3}$ kg

8 Rosa cuts a 15 m length of the string into 4 equal pieces. What is the length of each piece of string? $3\frac{3}{4}$ m

9 Sian spent $\frac{1}{4}$ of her money on Monday and $\frac{7}{10}$ of it on Tuesday. What fraction of Sian's money was spent during the two days? $\frac{19}{20}$

Solve these word problems. You can use your calculator in this section.

10 Serge runs $1\frac{7}{8}$ km. Sam runs $\frac{1}{2}$ km less than Serge. How many kilometres does Sam run? $1\frac{3}{8}$ km

11 George drank $1\frac{5}{9}\ell$ of water per day. Harry drank $\frac{5}{12}\ell$ of water less than George per day. How many litres of water did Harry drink per day? $1\frac{5}{36}\ell$

12 Sophie bought $2\frac{5}{6}$ kg of flour. Ali bought $\frac{5}{9}$ kg more flour than Sophie. How many kilograms of flour did Ali buy? $3\frac{7}{18}$ kg

13 Mr Lee poured out $2\frac{1}{2}\ell$ of apple juice. He gave $\frac{7}{8}\ell$ of the juice to Selina and $\frac{5}{12}\ell$ to Rosalind. How many litres of apple juice did Mr Lee have left? $1\frac{5}{24}\ell$

14 Mr Taylor sold $5\frac{2}{3}$ kg of sugar in the morning. He sold $\frac{11}{12}$ kg less sugar in the afternoon. How many kilograms of sugar did Mr Taylor sell in the morning and afternoon altogether? $10\frac{5}{12}$ kg

Practice Book 5A, p.85 and p.89

99

Teaching sequence

10 to **14** *Let's Practise!*

- Use your judgement on whether pupils should use their calculators for these questions.

Objective of activity

This journal enables pupils to reflect on the concept of adding fractions and recognise the common mistakes that they might make.

What you will need

Scientific calculator

Independent work

Maths Journal in Practice Book 5A, p 93.

Teaching sequence

15 *Maths Journal*

- This journal requires pupils to explain the mistakes Sarah and Ava made while adding two fractions.
- In the process of looking for the mistakes, pupils reflect on the concepts they have learnt and their understanding is reinforced.

Let's Wrap It Up!

- Review each bullet point in *Let's Wrap It Up!* with pupils. This helps them to see if they have already mastered the current topic.
- You may ask pupils to think of an example question for each bullet point in *Let's Wrap It Up!* Invite some pupils to present their questions and answers to the class.

Maths Journal

15 Sarah, Ava and Hannah worked out the following:

$$\frac{5}{6} + \frac{7}{9} = ?$$

Sarah's answer: $\frac{12}{15}$ Ava's answer: $2\frac{9}{18}$ Hannah's answer: $1\frac{11}{18}$

Two of the three answers are incorrect.

a Whose answers are incorrect? Sarah's and Ava's answers are incorrect.

b Explain why.
Sarah added the numerators and denominators of the fractions.
Ava misread the fraction $\frac{29}{18}$ as a mixed number $2\frac{9}{18}$.

Let's Wrap It Up!

You have learnt to:

- identify like fractions, which have the same denominator
- identify unlike fractions, which have different denominators
- add and subtract unlike fractions by converting them to like fractions
- express division as a fraction and vice versa
- convert proper fractions, improper fractions and mixed numbers to decimals by:
  - (a) converting to tenths, hundredths and thousandths
  - (b) using long division
  - (c) using a calculator
- add and subtract mixed numbers using a calculator.

Let's Revise!

Anna took $1\frac{2}{5}$ h to paint a cupboard and $1\frac{2}{3}$ h to paint a bookshelf.
Jacob took $\frac{2}{3}$ h less than Anna to paint a similar cupboard and bookshelf.

100

Objective of activity
Pupils will be able to draw a comparison model and use the before-after concept to find the solution to the problem posed.

Thinking skill
Analysing parts and whole

Heuristics for problem solving
- Draw a model
- Use before-after concept

Independent work
Challenging Practice in Practice Book 5A, p 94.

Fractions (I) **Unit 3**

Let's Wrap It Up!

a How long did Anna take to paint both the cupboard and bookshelf?

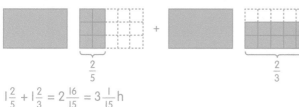

$1\frac{2}{5} + 1\frac{2}{3} = 2\frac{16}{15} = 3\frac{1}{15}$ h

Anna took $3\frac{1}{15}$ h to paint the cupboard and bookshelf.

b How long did Jacob spend to paint a similar cupboard and bookshelf?

$3\frac{1}{15} - \frac{2}{3} = 2\frac{6}{15} = 2\frac{2}{5}$ h

Jacob took $2\frac{2}{5}$ h to paint a similar cupboard and bookshelf.

Put On Your Thinking Caps!

16 Jack had two identical bottles. The first bottle contained 1 ℓ of water. The second bottle contained $\frac{5}{9}$ ℓ of water.

What amount of water must Jack pour from the first bottle into the second bottle so that both bottles contain the same amount of water?

Express your answer as a fraction.

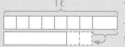

4 units ÷ 2 = 2 units
Jack must pour $\frac{2}{9}$ ℓ of water from the first bottle into the second bottle.

Practice Book 5A, p.94

101

Teaching sequence

Let's Wrap It Up!
- Go through the worked example with pupils. Use the question to assess whether pupils have understood the concepts learnt in this unit and whether they can relate these to the worked example.

16 *Put On Your Thinking Caps!*
- This question requires pupils to present the context using a model so that they are able to see the changes before and after pouring the water.
- First ask pupils to show the model representing 1 ℓ and $\frac{5}{9}$ ℓ. Then ask them to visualise movement of some units from the longer bar to the shorter bar so that they are equal in length after the movement.

Unit 3: Fractions (I) 147

Unit 3 Fractions (I)

Date: _____

Practice I   Adding unlike fractions

I Find two equivalent fractions for each of the following:
Accept any correct answers.

Example

$$\frac{2}{3} = \frac{4}{6} = \frac{6}{9}$$

a $\frac{3}{4} = \frac{6}{8} = \frac{9}{12}$

b $\frac{2}{5} = \frac{4}{10} = \frac{6}{15}$

c $\frac{5}{6} = \frac{10}{12} = \frac{15}{18}$

2 Express each fraction in its simplest form.

a $\frac{6}{8} = \frac{3}{4}$

b $\frac{8}{20} = \frac{2}{5}$

c $\frac{10}{15} = \frac{2}{3}$

d $\frac{9}{21} = \frac{3}{7}$

3 For each pair of fractions, change the denominator of one fraction so that both fractions have the same denominator.

Example

$$\frac{1}{2}, \frac{3}{4} \quad\rightarrow\quad \frac{2}{4}, \frac{3}{4}$$

a $\frac{1}{4}, \frac{5}{12} \quad\rightarrow\quad \frac{3}{12}, \frac{5}{12}$

b $\frac{1}{10}, \frac{2}{5} \quad\rightarrow\quad \frac{1}{10}, \frac{4}{10}$

c $\frac{5}{9}, \frac{2}{3} \quad\rightarrow\quad \frac{5}{9}, \frac{6}{9}$

4 Write equivalent fractions for each fraction below. Then find a common denominator of the fractions.

a
$\frac{1}{2} = \frac{2}{4} = \frac{3}{6}$

$\frac{2}{3} = \frac{4}{6}$

A common denominator is $\underline{6}$.

b
$\frac{2}{3} = \frac{4}{6} = \frac{6}{9} = \frac{8}{12}$

$\frac{3}{4} = \frac{6}{8} = \frac{9}{12}$

A common denominator is $\underline{12}$.

5

a The model has been shaded to show $\frac{1}{2}$ and $\frac{1}{3}$. Look at the model and complete the addition sentence.

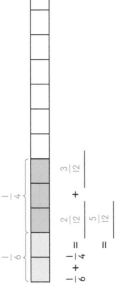

$\frac{1}{2}$ $\frac{1}{3}$

$\frac{1}{2} + \frac{1}{3} = \frac{3}{6} + \frac{2}{6}$

$= \frac{5}{6}$

b Shade to show $\frac{1}{5}$ and $\frac{1}{2}$ on the model. Then complete the addition sentence.

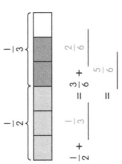

$\frac{1}{5}$ $\frac{1}{2}$

$\frac{1}{5} + \frac{1}{2} = \frac{2}{10} + \frac{5}{10}$

$= \frac{7}{10}$

c Shade to show $\frac{1}{6}$ and $\frac{1}{4}$ on the model. Then complete the addition sentence.

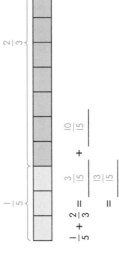

$\frac{1}{6}$ $\frac{1}{4}$

$\frac{1}{6} + \frac{1}{4} = \frac{2}{12} + \frac{3}{12}$

$= \frac{5}{12}$

d Shade to show $\frac{1}{5}$ and $\frac{2}{3}$ on the model. Then complete the addition sentence.

$\frac{1}{5}$ $\frac{2}{3}$

$\frac{1}{5} + \frac{2}{3} = \frac{3}{15} + \frac{10}{15}$

$= \frac{13}{15}$

6 Look at the model below. Then write two addition sentences.

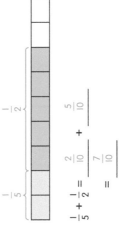

Addition sentence 1:

$\boxed{\frac{3}{12}} + \boxed{\frac{8}{12}} = \frac{11}{12}$

Addition sentence 2 (fractions in their simplest form):

$\frac{1}{4} + \frac{2}{3} = \frac{11}{12}$ Answers vary

Date: _____

Practice 2 | Subtracting unlike fractions

1. Here are two fractions: $\frac{1}{2}$ and $\frac{1}{3}$. Convert them to fractions with the same denominator.

What is the first common multiple of 2 and 3?

$$\times 3 \quad \frac{1}{2} \quad \times 3 \quad \frac{3}{6}$$

$$\times 2 \quad \frac{1}{3} \quad \times 2 \quad \frac{2}{6}$$

Write the equivalent fractions of $\frac{1}{2}$ and $\frac{1}{3}$ in the boxes.

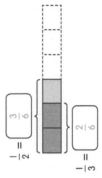

$$\frac{1}{2} = \frac{3}{6}$$

$$\frac{1}{3} = \frac{2}{6}$$

Now complete this subtraction sentence.

$$\frac{1}{2} - \frac{1}{3} = \frac{3}{6} - \frac{2}{6}$$

$$= \frac{1}{6}$$

---

7. Add. Express your answer in its simplest form where necessary.

a
$$\frac{1}{3} + \frac{1}{9} = \frac{3}{9} + \frac{1}{9}$$
$$= \frac{4}{9}$$

b
$$\frac{1}{8} + \frac{2}{4} = \frac{1}{8} + \frac{4}{8}$$
$$= \frac{5}{8}$$

c
$$\frac{1}{3} + \frac{3}{8} = \frac{8}{24} + \frac{9}{24}$$
$$= \frac{17}{24}$$

d
$$\frac{4}{8} + \frac{1}{5} = \frac{20}{40} + \frac{8}{40}$$
$$= \frac{28}{40}$$
$$= \frac{7}{10}$$

e
$$\frac{1}{2} + \frac{3}{7} = \frac{7}{14} + \frac{6}{14}$$
$$= \frac{13}{14}$$

f
$$\frac{1}{6} + \frac{3}{10} = \frac{5}{30} + \frac{9}{30}$$
$$= \frac{14}{30}$$
$$= \frac{7}{15}$$

g
$$\frac{2}{3} + \frac{2}{10} = \frac{20}{30} + \frac{6}{30}$$
$$= \frac{26}{30}$$
$$= \frac{13}{15}$$

h
$$\frac{3}{9} + \frac{1}{7} = \frac{21}{63} + \frac{9}{63}$$
$$= \frac{30}{63}$$
$$= \frac{10}{21}$$

4 Subtract. Express your answer in its simplest form where necessary.

a $\dfrac{7}{12} - \dfrac{2}{4} = \dfrac{7}{12} - \dfrac{6}{12}$
$= \dfrac{1}{12}$

b $\dfrac{7}{9} - \dfrac{1}{3} = \dfrac{7}{9} - \dfrac{3}{9}$
$= \dfrac{4}{9}$

c $\dfrac{5}{6} - \dfrac{1}{12} = \dfrac{10}{12} - \dfrac{1}{12}$
$= \dfrac{9}{12}$
$= \dfrac{3}{4}$

d $\dfrac{4}{5} - \dfrac{1}{3} = \dfrac{12}{15} - \dfrac{5}{15}$
$= \dfrac{7}{15}$

e $\dfrac{2}{3} - \dfrac{3}{8} = \dfrac{16}{24} - \dfrac{9}{24}$
$= \dfrac{7}{24}$

f $\dfrac{7}{9} - \dfrac{1}{4} = \dfrac{28}{36} - \dfrac{9}{36}$
$= \dfrac{19}{36}$

g $\dfrac{8}{10} - \dfrac{3}{4} = \dfrac{16}{20} - \dfrac{15}{20}$
$= \dfrac{1}{20}$

h $\dfrac{5}{12} - \dfrac{1}{9} = \dfrac{15}{36} - \dfrac{4}{36}$
$= \dfrac{11}{36}$

---

2 Here are two fractions: $\dfrac{1}{3}$ and $\dfrac{1}{4}$. Convert them to fractions with the same denominator. Write their equivalent fractions in the boxes.

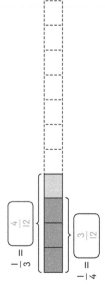

$\dfrac{1}{3} = \dfrac{4}{12}$

$\dfrac{1}{4} = \dfrac{3}{12}$

Now complete this subtraction sentence.

$\dfrac{1}{3} - \dfrac{1}{4} = \dfrac{4}{12} - \dfrac{3}{12}$
$= \dfrac{1}{12}$

3 Here are two fractions: $\dfrac{1}{2}$ and $\dfrac{1}{5}$. Convert them to fractions with the same denominator. Write their equivalent fractions in the boxes.

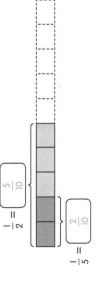

$\dfrac{1}{2} = \dfrac{5}{10}$

$\dfrac{1}{5} = \dfrac{2}{10}$

Now complete this subtraction sentence.

$\dfrac{1}{2} - \dfrac{1}{5} = \dfrac{5}{10} - \dfrac{2}{10}$
$= \dfrac{3}{10}$

Practice 3 — Fractions and division

Date: _____

1 Look at the picture. Then write a division sentence and a fraction.

a

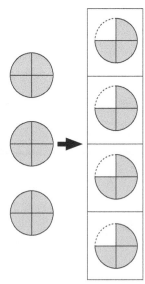

$$3 \div 4 = \boxed{3} \; \boxed{4}$$

b

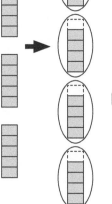

$$4 \div 5 = \dfrac{\boxed{4}}{\boxed{5}}$$

Maths Journal

Date: _____

1 Millie drew a model to find $\frac{4}{5} - \frac{1}{2}$.

She drew the model incorrectly. Explain her mistakes. Then draw the correct model to find the answer.

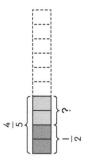

$\frac{4}{5}$? $\frac{1}{2}$

Millie's model is wrong because:

$\frac{4}{5} = \frac{8}{10}$

8 out of 10 parts should be shaded instead.

$\frac{1}{2} = \frac{5}{10}$

5 out of 10 parts should be taken away.

The correct model is:

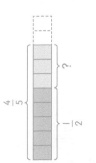

$\frac{4}{5}$? $\frac{1}{2}$

Total = 10 parts

Remainder = 3 parts

Answer = $\frac{3}{10}$

b

$3 \div 2 = \dfrac{3}{2} = 1\dfrac{1}{2}$

5 Complete the following:

a $7 \div 4 = \dfrac{7}{4} = \dfrac{4}{4} + \dfrac{3}{4}$
$= 1 + \dfrac{3}{4}$
$= 1\dfrac{3}{4}$

b $35 \div 11 = \dfrac{35}{11} = \dfrac{33}{11} + \dfrac{2}{11}$
$= 3 + \dfrac{2}{11}$
$= 3\dfrac{2}{11}$

---

2 Write each division sentence as a fraction. Fill in the spaces.

a $5 \div 7 = \dfrac{5}{7}$

b $3 \div 10 = \dfrac{3}{10}$

c $4 \div 9 = \dfrac{4}{9}$

d $2 \div 11 = \dfrac{2}{11}$

3 Write each fraction as a division sentence. Fill in the spaces.

a $\dfrac{7}{8} = 7 \div 8$

b $\dfrac{5}{12} = 5 \div 12$

c $\dfrac{1}{10} = 1 \div 10$

d $\dfrac{6}{7} = 6 \div 7$

4 Look at the picture. Then write a division sentence, an improper fraction and a mixed number.

a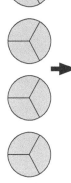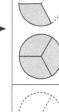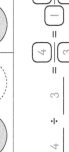

$4 \div 3 = \dfrac{4}{3} = 1\dfrac{1}{3}$

Practice 4 Converting fractions to decimals

1 Write each fraction as a decimal.

a $\dfrac{3}{5} = \dfrac{\boxed{6}}{\boxed{10}}$
$= 0.6$

b $\dfrac{13}{20} = \dfrac{\boxed{65}}{\boxed{100}}$
$= 0.65$

c $\dfrac{3}{8} = \dfrac{\boxed{375}}{\boxed{1000}}$
$= 0.375$

d $\dfrac{4}{8} = \dfrac{\boxed{500}}{\boxed{1000}}$
$= 0.5$

2 Write each fraction as a decimal. Round your answers to 2 decimal places.

a $\dfrac{5}{6} = 5 \div 6$

```
  0.833
6)5
 -48
   20
  -18
    20
   -18
     2
```
≈ 0.83

b $\dfrac{7}{9} = 7 \div 9$

```
  0.777
9)7
 -63
   70
  -63
    70
   -63
     7
```
≈ 0.78

c $\dfrac{4}{7} = 4 \div 7$

```
  0.571
7)4
 -35
   50
  -49
    10
   -7
     3
```
≈ 0.57

d $\dfrac{9}{11} = 9 \div 11$

```
   0.818
11)9
  -88
    20
   -11
     90
    -88
      2
```
≈ 0.82

3 Express each division sentence as an improper fraction and as a decimal correct to 2 decimal places where necessary.

Division Sentence	Express the Division Sentence as:	
	an Improper Fraction	a Decimal
a $8 \div 5$	$\dfrac{8}{5}$	1·60
b $7 \div 3$	$\dfrac{7}{3}$	2·33
c $12 \div 7$	$\dfrac{12}{7}$	1·71

---

6 Divide using long division. Express your answer as a mixed number.

a $5 \div 3 = 1\dfrac{\boxed{2}}{\boxed{3}}$

```
   1
3)5
 -3
  2
```

b $7 \div 2 = 3\dfrac{\boxed{1}}{\boxed{2}}$

```
   3
2)7
 -6
  1
```

c $9 \div 4 = 2\dfrac{1}{4}$

```
   2
4)9
 -8
  1
```

d $18 \div 5 = 3\dfrac{3}{5}$

```
   3
5)18
 -15
   3
```

7 Write each fraction in its simplest form. Then divide to express your answer as a mixed number.

a $18 \div 4 = \dfrac{\boxed{18}}{\boxed{4}}$
$= \dfrac{\boxed{9}}{\boxed{2}}$
$= \boxed{4}\dfrac{\boxed{1}}{\boxed{2}}$

```
   4
2)9
 -8
  1
```

b $22 \div 6 = \dfrac{\boxed{22}}{\boxed{6}}$
$= \dfrac{\boxed{11}}{\boxed{3}}$
$= \boxed{3}\dfrac{\boxed{2}}{\boxed{3}}$

```
   3
3)11
 -9
  2
```

4 Express each division sentence as a mixed number and as a decimal correct to 2 decimal places where necessary.

Division Sentence	Express the Division Sentence as:	
	an Improper Fraction	a Decimal
a $12 \div 5$	$2\frac{2}{5}$	$2 \cdot 40$
b $7 \div 2$	$3\frac{1}{2}$	$3 \cdot 50$
c $9 \div 4$	$2\frac{1}{4}$	$2 \cdot 25$
d $11 \div 6$	$1\frac{5}{6}$	$1 \cdot 83$

5 Express each improper fraction as a decimal correct to 2 decimal places.

a $\frac{40}{15} \approx \underline{2 \cdot 67}$ **b** $\frac{53}{13} \approx \underline{4 \cdot 08}$ **c** $\frac{43}{21} \approx \underline{2 \cdot 05}$

d $\frac{65}{17} \approx \underline{3 \cdot 82}$ **e** $\frac{65}{14} \approx \underline{4 \cdot 64}$ **f** $\frac{35}{13} \approx \underline{2 \cdot 69}$

6 Express each mixed number as a decimal correct to 2 decimal places.

a $2\frac{3}{21} \approx \underline{2 \cdot 14}$ **b** $5\frac{4}{13} \approx \underline{5 \cdot 31}$ **c** $7\frac{9}{34} \approx \underline{7 \cdot 26}$

d $3\frac{5}{17} \approx \underline{3 \cdot 29}$ **e** $4\frac{11}{14} \approx \underline{4 \cdot 79}$ **f** $6\frac{15}{27} \approx \underline{6 \cdot 56}$

Unit 3: Fractions (I)

78

7 A coil of rope 217 m long is cut into 9 equal pieces. What is the length of each piece? Express your answer as a mixed number and as a decimal correct to 2 decimal places.

$217 \div 9 = \frac{217}{9} = 24\frac{1}{9} \approx 24 \cdot 11$ m

Each piece is 24·11 m long.

8 A chef bought $8\frac{1}{2}$ kg of apples for £20. Find the cost of 1 kg of apples.

$8\frac{1}{2}$ kg $\rightarrow$ £20

1 kg $\rightarrow$ £20 $\div$ $8\frac{1}{2}$ kg

$= 20 \div \frac{17}{2}$

$= 20 \times \frac{2}{17}$

$=$ £2·35 (to 2 decimal places)

9 Simon bought $47\frac{2}{5}$ kg of meat. He cut the meat into 15 pieces of the same mass. Find the mass of each piece of meat correct to 2 decimal places.

15 pieces $\rightarrow 47\frac{2}{5}$ kg

1 piece $\rightarrow 47\frac{2}{5} \div 15$

$= \frac{237}{5} \times \frac{1}{15}$

$= 3 \cdot 16$ kg

Unit 3: Fractions (I)

79

Maths Journal

Date: _____

In a mathematics competition, Daniel and Monica computed the following with their calculators. Circle the incorrect answers. Explain their mistakes.

1

Division	Express the Answer to 2 Decimal Places.	
	Daniel	Monica
$\frac{13}{8}$	(1·62)	1·63

Reason for the mistake:

Daniel did not round the answer correctly. He should have rounded up the answer, instead of rounding down.

2

Division	Express the Answer to 2 Decimal Places.	
	Daniel	Monica
$\frac{14}{9}$	1·56	(1·556)

Reason for the mistake:

Monica expressed the answer to 3 decimal places instead of 2 decimal places.

Date: _____

Practice 5   Adding mixed numbers

1 Add. Express your answer in its simplest form.

a $3\frac{5}{8} + 2\frac{1}{4}$

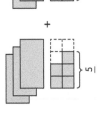 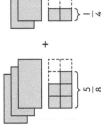

$= 3\,\dfrac{\boxed{5}}{\boxed{8}} + 2\,\dfrac{\boxed{2}}{\boxed{8}}$

$= 5\,\dfrac{\boxed{7}}{\boxed{8}}$

b $1\frac{2}{3} + 2\frac{1}{4}$

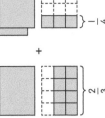 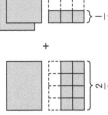 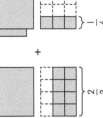 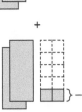

$= 1\,\dfrac{\boxed{8}}{\boxed{12}} + 2\,\dfrac{\boxed{3}}{\boxed{12}}$

$= 3\,\dfrac{\boxed{11}}{\boxed{12}}$

c $2\frac{1}{5} + 3\frac{1}{2}$

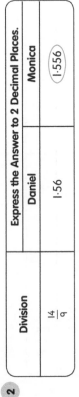  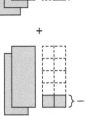

$= 2\,\dfrac{\boxed{2}}{\boxed{10}} + 3\,\dfrac{\boxed{5}}{\boxed{10}}$

$= 5\,\dfrac{\boxed{7}}{\boxed{10}}$

Date: _____

Practice 6 Subtracting mixed numbers

1. Subtract. Express your answer in its simplest form.

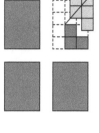

a $3\frac{2}{3} - \frac{5}{12}$

$= 3\frac{\boxed{8}}{12} - \frac{5}{12}$

$= 3\frac{\boxed{3}}{12}$

$= 3\frac{\boxed{1}}{\boxed{4}}$

b $4\frac{8}{9} - 3\frac{1}{3}$

$= 4\frac{8}{9} - 3\frac{\boxed{3}}{\boxed{9}}$

$= 1\frac{\boxed{5}}{\boxed{9}}$

    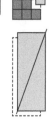 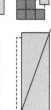

c $3\frac{7}{12} - 2\frac{3}{8}$

$= 3\frac{\boxed{14}}{\boxed{24}} - 2\frac{\boxed{9}}{\boxed{24}}$

$= 1\frac{\boxed{5}}{\boxed{24}}$

---

2. Add. Express your answer in its simplest form.

a $1\frac{4}{5} + 2\frac{1}{3} = 4\frac{\boxed{2}}{\boxed{15}}$

b $3\frac{5}{12} + 1\frac{2}{3} = 5\frac{1}{12}$

c $2\frac{3}{4} + 3\frac{2}{5} = 6\frac{3}{20}$

d $2\frac{5}{9} + 1\frac{5}{6} = 4\frac{7}{18}$

e $4\frac{2}{3} + 2\frac{1}{4} = 6\frac{11}{12}$

f $5\frac{7}{12} + 1\frac{3}{4} = 7\frac{1}{3}$

3. Add. Express your answer as a mixed number and as a decimal correct to 2 decimal places.

a $6\frac{3}{5} + 4\frac{5}{6}$

$= 11\frac{\boxed{13}}{\boxed{30}} \approx 11.43$

b $5\frac{7}{8} + 2\frac{2}{7}$

$= 8\frac{\boxed{9}}{\boxed{56}} \approx 8.16$

c $9\frac{6}{7} + 7\frac{5}{12}$

$= 17\frac{\boxed{23}}{\boxed{84}} \approx 17.27$

d $4\frac{7}{12} + 10\frac{5}{9}$

$= 15\frac{\boxed{5}}{\boxed{36}} \approx 15.14$

Practice 7 Word problems (I)

Solve these word problems. Show your workings clearly.

1 Rajesh baked 12 flapjacks of the same size. He gave an equal amount of the flapjacks to 5 friends. How many flapjacks did he give each friend?

$12 \div 5 = 2\frac{2}{5}$ flapjacks

Rajesh gave each friend $2\frac{2}{5}$ flapjacks.

2 Mrs Little had a ball of string 26 m long. She cut 5 m of string to tie up some parcels. The remaining string was then cut into 4 equal pieces. What is the length of each piece of string?

$26 - 5 = 21$ m

$21 \div 4 \approx 5\frac{1}{4}$ m or 5·25 m

The length of each piece of string is $5\frac{1}{4}$ m or 5·25 m.

---

2 Subtract. Express your answer as a mixed number.

a $3\frac{1}{4} - 1\frac{7}{8} = \boxed{1}\ \boxed{3}\atop\boxed{8}$

b $5\frac{1}{3} - 3\frac{5}{12} = 1\frac{11}{12}$

c $4\frac{1}{5} - 1\frac{1}{3} = 2\frac{13}{15}$

d $6\frac{3}{8} - 3\frac{5}{6} = 2\frac{13}{24}$

e $7\frac{1}{4} - 5\frac{1}{12} = 2\frac{1}{6}$

f $8\frac{1}{3} - 4\frac{3}{4} = 3\frac{7}{12}$

3 Subtract. Express your answer as a mixed number and as a decimal correct to 2 decimal places.

a $7\frac{2}{9} - 2\frac{5}{12}$

$= \boxed{4}\ \boxed{29}\atop\boxed{36} \approx 4·81$

b $5\frac{2}{7} - 2\frac{7}{8}$

$= \boxed{2}\ \boxed{23}\atop\boxed{56} \approx 2·41$

c $12\frac{2}{5} - 8\frac{7}{12}$

$= \boxed{3}\ \boxed{49}\atop\boxed{60} \approx 3·82$

d $20\frac{4}{11} - 5\frac{7}{9}$

$= \boxed{14}\ \boxed{58}\atop\boxed{99} \approx 14·59$

3 Mr Dee bought 57 kg of sugar. He packed an equal amount of sugar into 6 bags and had 4 kg of sugar left. What is the mass of sugar in each bag? Express your answer as a decimal correct to 2 decimal places.

$57 - 4 = 53\,kg$

$53 \div 6 \approx 8.83\,kg$

The mass of sugar in each bag is 8.83 kg.

4 A water bill showed that 7700 ℓ of water was used in a household of 8 adults in a week. If each member of the family used the same amount of water each day, how many litres of water were used by each person in a day?

$7700 \div 7 = 1100\,\ell$

1100 ℓ of water was used by the family each day.

$1100 \div 8 = \frac{1100}{8}$

$\qquad = 137\frac{1}{2}\,\ell$

$137\frac{1}{2}\,\ell$ of water were used by each person in a day.

5 Sharon puts an empty container under a leaking tap. In the first hour, $\frac{3}{8}\,\ell$ of water is collected. In the second hour, $\frac{1}{6}\,\ell$ of water is collected. How much water is collected in the container in the two hours?

$\frac{3}{8} + \frac{1}{6} = \frac{9}{24} + \frac{4}{24}$

$\qquad = \frac{13}{24}\,\ell$

$\frac{13}{24}\,\ell$ of water is collected in the container in the two hours.

6 Jamie bought $\frac{8}{9}$ kg of minced meat. He used $\frac{3}{4}$ kg of the minced meat to make some meatballs. How many kilograms of minced meat was left?

$\frac{8}{9} - \frac{3}{4} = \frac{32}{36} - \frac{27}{36}$

$\qquad = \frac{5}{36}\,kg$

$\frac{5}{36}$ kg of minced meat was left.

Practice 8   Word problems (2)

Solve these word problems. Show your workings clearly.

1 Mrs Quick bought $1\,\ell$ of milk. Michael drank $\frac{2}{7}\,\ell$ of it and Joel drank $\frac{1}{3}\,\ell$ of it. How many litres of milk were left?

$\frac{2}{7} + \frac{1}{3} = \frac{6}{21} + \frac{7}{21}$
$\qquad\quad = \frac{13}{21}\,\ell$

Michael and Joel drank $\frac{13}{21}\,\ell$ of milk.

$1 - \frac{13}{21} = \frac{21}{21} - \frac{13}{21}$
$\qquad\quad = \frac{8}{21}\,\ell$

There were $\frac{8}{21}\,\ell$ of milk left.

2 Suzanne and Imaan each bought 4 identical cakes. They cut the cakes into equal pieces. The pieces of cake were shared equally among 5 friends. How many cakes did each friend get?

$4 + 4 = 8$
Suzanne and Imaan had 8 cakes altogether.

$8 \div 5 = 1\frac{3}{5}$ cakes
Each friend got $1\frac{3}{5}$ cakes.

---

7 A snail was at the bottom of a well. In the first 10 minutes, the snail climbed $2\frac{7}{12}$ m. In the next 10 minutes, it climbed $1\frac{5}{7}$ m. How far was the snail from the bottom of the well after 20 minutes?

$2\frac{7}{12} + 1\frac{5}{7} = 4\frac{25}{84}$ m
The snail was $4\frac{25}{84}$ m from the bottom of the well after 20 minutes.

8 John is jogging along a track. He has already jogged $5\frac{2}{3}$ km. How many more kilometres does he have to jog to complete the track of $9\frac{1}{4}$ km?

$9\frac{1}{4} - 5\frac{2}{3} = 9\frac{3}{12} - 5\frac{8}{12}$
$\qquad\qquad\; = 8\frac{15}{12} - 5\frac{8}{12}$
$\qquad\qquad\; = 3\frac{7}{12}$ km

John has to jog $3\frac{7}{12}$ km more.

3 May had 5 pieces of paper. She cut each piece into 3 identical rectangles. The rectangular pieces of paper were shared equally among 6 pupils. How many rectangular pieces of paper did each pupil get?

$5 \times 3 = 15$
May cut out 15 rectangles altogether.

$15 \div 6 = 2\frac{3}{6}$
$= 2\frac{1}{2}$

Each pupil got $2\frac{1}{2}$ rectangular pieces.

4 Joe bought a plot of land. He planted tomatoes on $\frac{5}{9}$ of the land and broad beans on $\frac{1}{12}$ of the land. He planted potatoes on the remaining plot of land. What fraction of the land was planted with potatoes?

$\frac{5}{9} + \frac{1}{12} = \frac{20}{36} + \frac{3}{36}$
$= \frac{23}{36}$

Joe planted tomatoes and broad beans on $\frac{23}{36}$ of the land.

$1 - \frac{23}{36} = \frac{36}{36} - \frac{23}{36}$
$= \frac{13}{36}$

Joe planted potatoes on $\frac{13}{36}$ of the land.

5 A tin contains three types of biscuits. The mass of chocolate biscuits is $1\frac{2}{9}$ kg. The mass of ginger biscuits is $2\frac{5}{6}$ kg. The total mass of biscuits is 5 kg. What is the mass of the three types of shortbread biscuits?

$1\frac{2}{9} + 2\frac{5}{6} = 1\frac{4}{18} + 2\frac{15}{18}$
$= 3\frac{19}{18}$
$= 4\frac{1}{18}$ kg

The total mass of chocolate and ginger biscuits is $4\frac{1}{18}$ kg.

$5 - 4\frac{1}{18} = 4\frac{18}{18} - 4\frac{1}{18}$
$= \frac{17}{18}$ kg

The total mass of shortbread biscuits is $\frac{17}{18}$ kg.

6 Bella and Victor go for a walk every morning. Bella walks $2\frac{1}{6}$ km. Victor walks $1\frac{3}{8}$ km less than Bella. What is the total distance they walk every morning?

$2\frac{1}{6} - 1\frac{3}{8} = 2\frac{4}{24} - 1\frac{9}{24}$
$= 1\frac{28}{24} - 1\frac{9}{24}$
$= \frac{19}{24}$ km

Victor walks $\frac{19}{24}$ km every morning.

$2\frac{1}{6} + \frac{19}{24} = 2\frac{4}{24} + \frac{19}{24}$
$= 2\frac{23}{24}$ km

They walk $2\frac{23}{24}$ km every morning.

Maths Journal

Date: _____

1 Tai found the answer to the following without using a calculator.

$$\frac{1}{8} + \frac{2}{3} = ?$$

Explain the steps used to add $\frac{1}{8}$ and $\frac{2}{3}$. Then work out the correct answer. You may use drawings to show how to work it out.

$\frac{1}{8}$ $\frac{2}{3}$

First find the first common multiple of the denominators, 8 and 3.

Next find the equivalent fractions of $\frac{1}{8}$ and $\frac{2}{3}$ using the first common multiple of the denominators.

Finally add the fractions.

$\frac{1}{8} + \frac{2}{3} = \frac{3}{24} + \frac{16}{24}$

$\qquad\quad = \frac{19}{24}$

The correct answer is $\frac{19}{24}$.

---

7 Alice uses $\frac{3}{4}\ell$ of paint to colour her drawing. Belinda uses $\frac{4}{5}\ell$ more than Alice to colour her drawing. How many litres of paint do they use altogether?

$\frac{3}{4} + \frac{4}{5} = \frac{15}{20} + \frac{16}{20}$

$\qquad\quad = \frac{31}{20}$

$\qquad\quad = 1\frac{11}{20}\ell$

$\frac{3}{4} + 1\frac{11}{20} = \frac{15}{20} + 1\frac{11}{20}$

$\qquad\qquad = 1\frac{26}{20}$

$\qquad\qquad = 2\frac{6}{20}$

$\qquad\qquad = 2\frac{3}{10}\ell$

Belinda uses $1\frac{11}{20}\ell$ of paint.

They use $2\frac{3}{10}\ell$ of paint altogether.

8 A squirrel climbs $3\frac{3}{5}$m up a tree 10m high. It rests for a while and continues to climb another $4\frac{2}{3}$m up the tree. How many more metres must the squirrel climb to reach the top of the tree?

$3\frac{3}{5} + 4\frac{2}{3} = 3\frac{9}{15} + 4\frac{10}{15}$

$\qquad\qquad = 7\frac{19}{15}$

$\qquad\qquad = 8\frac{4}{15}$m

The squirrel climbed $8\frac{4}{15}$m up the tree.

$10 - 8\frac{4}{15} = 9\frac{15}{15} - 8\frac{4}{15}$

$\qquad\qquad = 1\frac{11}{15}$m

The squirrel must climb $1\frac{11}{15}$m more to reach the top of the tree.

Challenging Practice

1. Ruby, Miya and Jack had a total of 25 similar square tiles to place over a square grid. Ruby used $\frac{8}{25}$ of the square tiles. Miya used $\frac{1}{5}$ of the square tiles. Shade the 5 × 5 square grid below to show how Ruby and Miya could have placed the square tiles. What fraction of the square grid must Jack place the tiles on so that $\frac{1}{5}$ of the square grid is **not** covered?

Answers vary

$\frac{8}{25} + \frac{1}{5} + \frac{1}{5} = \frac{18}{25}$

$1 - \frac{18}{25} = \frac{7}{25}$

Jack must place the tiles over $\frac{7}{25}$ of the square grid.

Unit 4: Fractions (2)

Week	Learning Objectives	Thinking Skills	Resources
1	**(1) Product of proper fractions** Pupils will be able to: • conceptualise the meaning of multiplying two proper fractions with concrete representation • use the cancellation (simplification) method to compute the product of two proper fractions • explore and compare the product of two whole numbers and the product of two proper fractions *Let's Explore!* Pupils are expected to identify that the product of two whole numbers is always greater than each of the two whole numbers, whereas the product of two proper fractions is always less than each of the two proper fractions.	• Comparing • Identifying patterns	• Pupil Textbook 5A, pp 102 to 104 • Practice Book 5A, pp 95 to 96 • Teacher's Guide 5A, pp 168 to 170
1	**(2) Word problems (1)** Pupils will be able to solve up to 2-step word problems involving fractions using: • model drawing and the unitary method • the product of two fractions	• Applying multiplying concept to fractions	• Pupil Textbook 5A, pp 105 to 109 • Practice Book 5A, pp 97 to 102 • Teacher's Guide 5A, pp 171 to 175

Unit 4: Fractions (2)

Week	Learning Objectives	Thinking Skills	Resources
1 – 2	**(3) Product of an improper fraction and a proper or improper fraction** Pupils will be able to: • conceptualise the meaning of multiplying an improper fraction by another proper or improper fraction with concrete representation • use the cancellation (simplification) method to compute the product of two fractions • use a calculator to compute the above	• Comparing	• Pupil Textbook 5A, pp 110 to 111 • Practice Book 5A, pp 103 to 104 • Teacher's Guide 5A, pp 176 to 177
2	**(4) Product of a mixed number and a whole number** Pupils will be able to: • conceptualise the meaning of multiplying a mixed number by a whole number • use the regrouping process to compute the product of a mixed number and a whole number • use a calculator to compute a mixed number with a whole number	• Comparing	• Pupil Textbook 5A, pp 112 to 115 • Practice Book 5A, pp 105 to 106 • Teacher's Guide 5A, pp 178 to 181

Unit 4: Fractions (2)

Medium-term plan

Week	Learning Objectives	Thinking Skills	Resources
2	**(5) Word problems (2)** Pupils will be able to solve up to 2-step word problems by applying the concept of multiplication and product of a whole number and a mixed number.	• Applying concepts of the four operations including multiplication	• Pupil Textbook 5A, pp 116 to 118 • Practice Book 5A, pp 107 to 108 • Teacher's Guide 5A, pp 182 to 184
2 – 3	**(6) Dividing a fraction by a whole number** Pupils will be able to: • understand the meaning of dividing a fraction by a whole number • use three different methods to divide a fraction by a whole number	• Comparing • Analysing parts and whole	• Pupil Textbook 5A, pp 119 to 123 • Practice Book 5A, pp 109 to 112 • Teacher's Guide 5A, pp 185 to 189

Unit 4: Fractions (2)

Week	Learning Objectives	Thinking Skills	Resources
3	**(7) Word problems (3)** Pupils will be able to solve up to 2-step word problems with the use of multiplication and division in fractions. *Maths Journal* Pupils will be able to reflect on their understanding of division of a fraction by a whole number and the product of proper fractions through identification of mistakes made. *Let's Wrap It Up!* Emphasise the key concepts, skills and processes that have been taught in the unit. Discuss the worked example with pupils to assess whether they have mastered these concepts, skills and processes.	• Comparing • Applying the concepts of four operations • Analysing parts and whole	• Pupil textbook 5A, pp 124 to 131 • Practice Book 5A, pp 113 to 116 • Teacher's Guide 5A, pp 190 to 197
3	*Put On Your Thinking Caps!* Pupils will be able to make use of the strategies of looking for patterns and drawing models to solve challenging problems related to fractions.	• Identifying patterns and relationships • Visualisation Heuristics for problem solving: • Look for a pattern • Draw a model	• Pupil textbook 5A, p 132 • Practice Book 5A, pp 117 to 118 • Teacher's Guide 5A, p 198
	Review 2		Practice Book 5A, pp 119 to 132

Summative assessment opportunities

Assessment Book 5, Test 2, pp 7 to 12
For extension, Assessment Book 5, Challenging Problems 1, pp 13 to 14
Assessment Book 5, Check-up 1, pp 15 to 26

Fractions (2)

Learning objectives: Product of proper fractions

Pupils will be able to:

- conceptualise the meaning of multiplying two proper fractions with concrete representation

- use the cancellation (simplification) method to compute the product of two proper fractions

- explore and compare the product of two whole numbers and the product of two proper fractions

Key concept

Multiplying two fractions is the same as finding the fractional part of another fraction.

Thinking skill

Comparing

Additional activity

Ask pupils to work in pairs. Pupil A thinks of two proper fractions and follows the method in to find the product of the two fractions. Pupil B reverses the order of the two proper fractions and finds the product.

Teaching sequence

- Ask pupils the following questions:

  (a) *"Which is greater? 2, 3 or 2 × 3?"*

  (b) *"Which is greater? $\frac{1}{2}$, $\frac{1}{3}$ or $\frac{1}{2} \times \frac{1}{3}$?"*

  (c) *"Will the results for both (a) and (b) be the same?"*

- Explain and follow the procedures given in the book to show the result of $\frac{1}{2} \times \frac{3}{5}$ using concrete representation.

- Do the same for $\frac{3}{5} \times \frac{1}{2}$.

- From the demonstration above, guide pupils to understand that:

  (a) the product of two proper fractions is smaller than each of the two fractions

  (b) the product of two proper fractions and the reverse order in both cases have the same value (commutative property of multiplication).

Unit 4 Fractions (2)

Let's Learn!

Product of proper fractions

 Ella draws a rectangle and colours $\frac{3}{5}$ of it blue.

She then draws red stripes over $\frac{1}{2}$ of the coloured parts.

$\frac{1}{2}$ of $\frac{3}{5}$

$\frac{1}{2}$ of $\frac{3}{5} = \frac{1}{2} \times \frac{3}{5}$

$= \frac{1 \times 3}{2 \times 5}$

$= \frac{3}{10}$

Jack draws an identical rectangle and colours $\frac{1}{2}$ of it blue.

$\frac{1}{2}$

He then draws red stripes over $\frac{3}{5}$ of the coloured parts.

$\frac{3}{5}$ of $\frac{1}{2}$

$\frac{3}{5}$ of $\frac{1}{2} = \frac{3}{5} \times \frac{1}{2}$

$= \frac{3 \times 1}{5 \times 2}$

$= \frac{3}{10}$

Do Ella and Jack get the same answer? Yes

We say $\frac{1}{2}$ of $\frac{3}{5}$ $=$ $\frac{3}{5}$ of $\frac{1}{2}$.

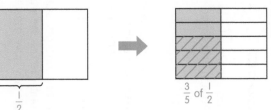
There are ⑩ parts in each of Ella's and Jack's rectangles. ③ coloured parts in each rectangle have red stripes.

$\frac{③}{⑩}$ of each rectangle has red stripes.

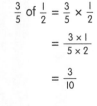

102

What you will need
- Sheets of square grid paper (see p 330)
- Coloured pencils

Additional activity
Ask pupils to work in pairs. Ask them to think of two pairs of fractions and find the product of the first pair of fractions using the multiplication method. Then, find the product of the second pair of fractions by using the cancellation method.

Teaching sequence

- Revise the multiplication and cancellation methods learnt previously in Pupil Textbook 4A under 'Fractions of a set', p 104.
- The objective of this question is to teach pupils how to use the multiplication and cancellation methods to find the product of two proper fractions in its simplest form.
- Explain and show that the multiplication method involves multiplying the corresponding numerators and denominators of the two fractions and then expressing the answer in its simplest form.
- Explain and show the cancellation method to simplify the two proper fractions before multiplying them together.

- Use this question to informally assess whether pupils can follow the procedure to multiply two proper fractions. Remind pupils to check if the two proper fractions can be simplified.

- Give each pair a copy of the square grid paper provided on p 330. This activity helps to reinforce the concept of multiplying two proper fractions. At the end of the activity, invite pupils to present their results to the class.

Fractions (2) **Unit 4**

② Find the product.

Method 1

$$\frac{3}{4} \times \frac{8}{9} = \frac{3 \times 8}{4 \times 9}$$

$$= \frac{24}{36}$$

$$= \frac{2}{3}$$

Method 2

$$\frac{3}{4} \times \frac{8}{9} = \frac{\cancel{3}}{4} \times \frac{8}{\cancel{9}_3}$$ ← Divide both the numerator and denominator by the common factor, 3.

$$= \frac{\cancel{3}^{1}}{\cancel{4}_1} \times \frac{\cancel{8}^{2}}{\cancel{9}_3}$$ ← Divide both the numerator and denominator by the common factor, 4.

$$= \frac{1 \times 2}{1 \times 3}$$

$$= \frac{2}{3}$$

③ Find the product.

a $\frac{3}{10}$ of $\frac{5}{9} = \frac{\boxed{}}{\boxed{6}}$

b $\frac{4}{10} \times \frac{5}{12} = \frac{\boxed{}}{\boxed{6}}$

Activity

④ Work in pairs.

Each group will need a sheet of grid paper.

1   Draw a rectangle on the grid paper.
2   Divide the rectangle into 4 equal parts. Colour $\frac{3}{4}$ of it.
3   Draw crosses on $\frac{1}{4}$ of the coloured parts.

How many coloured parts have crosses on them? 3

How many parts are there altogether? 16

What fraction of the whole rectangle has crosses on it?

$\frac{1}{4}$ of $\frac{3}{4} = \frac{\boxed{}3}{\boxed{}16}$

4   Now draw a rectangle identical to the first one.
5   Colour $\frac{1}{4}$ of it.

103

Objective of activity

Pupils are expected to identify that the product of two whole numbers is always greater than each of the two whole numbers, whereas the product of two proper fractions is always less than each of the proper fractions.

Thinking skill

Identifying patterns

Independent work

- *Let's Practise!*
- Practice I in Practice Book 5A, pp 95 to 96.

Teaching sequence

5 *Let's Explore!*

- Pupils should be able to make the following conclusions after the activity (excluding the use of zero):
  (a) The product of two whole numbers is greater than each of the two whole numbers.
  (b) The product of two proper fractions is less than each of the two proper fractions.

- Explain the multiplying method again so that pupils understand why the product of two whole numbers is greater than each of the two whole numbers.

- Then explain the concept of fractions and relate the product of two proper fractions to finding a fractional part of another fraction. A proper fraction is always less than I, so a fractional part of a proper fraction will always be smaller than the original value.

Activity

6 Draw crosses on $\frac{3}{4}$ of the coloured parts.

How many coloured parts have crosses on them? 3

How many parts are there altogether? I6

What fraction of the whole rectangle has crosses on it?

$\frac{3}{4}$ of $\frac{I}{4}$ = $\dfrac{\bigcirc\,3}{\bigcirc\,I6}$

Do you get the same answer in both cases? Yes

What can you say about $\frac{I}{4}$ of $\frac{3}{4}$ and $\frac{3}{4}$ of $\frac{I}{4}$? They are equal.

Let's Explore!

5 Find the product of the following whole numbers.

$3 \times 4 =$ ⬚ 12 $\quad$ $5 \times I7 =$ ⬚ 85 $\quad$ $9 \times 8 =$ ⬚ 72 $\quad$ $I2 \times 7 =$ ⬚ 84

What do you notice about each product? The product is always more than the 2 original whole numbers.

Is it greater than each of the whole numbers used to find the product?

Explain why. Yes, because multiplying 2 whole numbers always makes a larger number than the original whole numbers.

Next find the product of the following fractions.

$\frac{I}{2} \times \frac{3}{4} =$ ⬚ $\frac{3}{8}$ $\quad$ $\frac{3}{4} \times \frac{4}{5} =$ ⬚ $\frac{3}{5}$ $\quad$ $\frac{2}{7} \times \frac{3}{4} =$ ⬚ $\frac{3}{14}$ $\quad$ $\frac{I}{6} \times \frac{5}{9} =$ ⬚ $\frac{5}{54}$

What do you notice about each product? The product is always less than the 2 original fractions.

Is it greater than each of the fractions used to find the product?

Explain why. $\frac{I}{2}$ of $\frac{3}{4}$ is only half of the fraction, so the product is always

less than the original $\frac{3}{4}$.

Let's Practise!

6 Find the value of each product in its simplest form.

a $\frac{7}{10}$ of $\frac{5}{10}$ $\frac{7}{20}$ $\quad$ **b** $\frac{3}{8}$ of $\frac{4}{6}$ $\frac{I}{4}$ $\quad$ **c** $\frac{I}{3} \times \frac{6}{7}$ $\frac{2}{7}$ $\quad$ **d** $\frac{6}{8} \times \frac{4}{9}$ $\frac{I}{3}$

I04

Practice Book 5A, p.95

Learning objectives: Word problems (I)

Pupils will be able to solve up to 2-step word problems involving fractions using:

- model drawing and the unitary method
- the product of two fractions

Key concept

The product of two proper fractions is the fractional part of another fraction.

Thinking skill

Applying multiplying concept to fractions

Let's Learn!

Word problems (I)

① Peter had $\frac{3}{4}\ell$ of vegetable stock. He used $\frac{2}{3}$ of it to make some soup.

   a   How much vegetable stock did he use to make the soup?

   b   How much vegetable stock did he have left?

Method I

4 units ⟶ 1ℓ

1 unit ⟶ $\frac{1}{4}\ell$

2 units ⟶ $\frac{1}{2}\ell$

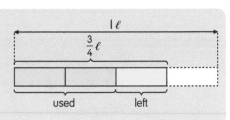

The model above shows that:

   a   Peter used $\frac{1}{2}\ell$ of vegetable stock to make the soup.

   b   He had $\frac{1}{4}\ell$ of vegetable stock left.

Method 2

a $\frac{\overset{1}{\cancel{2}}}{\underset{1}{\cancel{3}}} \times \frac{\overset{1}{\cancel{3}}}{\underset{2}{\cancel{4}}} = \frac{1}{2}\ell$

   Peter used $\frac{1}{2}\ell$ of vegetable stock to make the soup.

b $\frac{3}{4} - \frac{1}{2} = \frac{3}{4} - \frac{2}{4}$

               $= \frac{1}{4}\ell$

   He had $\frac{1}{4}\ell$ of vegetable stock left.

105

Teaching sequence

①

- Explain to pupils the context of the question and relate it to finding the product of two proper fractions. The fundamental principle of this question is to get a fractional part of a quantity which is measured in a fractional form.

Method I: Draw a model showing 4 equal units and use the unitary method to solve the problem. Explain that 4 units represent 1ℓ.

3 units represent $\frac{3}{4}\ell$. From the model, we can see that $\frac{2}{3}$ of 3 units is equivalent to $\frac{1}{2}\ell$.

Method 2: Use the cancellation method to find the product of two proper fractions. Pupils should be able to relate the context of finding a fractional part of a fractional quantity to the product of two proper fractions to solve the problem.

Additional activity

Ask pupils to work in pairs. Each pair thinks of two proper fractions and writes a 1-step word problem and another 2-step word problem using these fractions. They swap their questions with another group and check if the questions are workable. They then solve the questions.

Teaching sequence

- Use these questions as an informal assessment to find out if the pupils have understood the meaning of the product of two proper fractions and are able to follow the method they learnt in ❶.

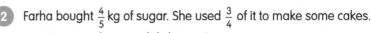

❷ Farha bought $\frac{4}{5}$ kg of sugar. She used $\frac{3}{4}$ of it to make some cakes.

a   How much sugar did she use?

b   How much sugar was left?

Method 1

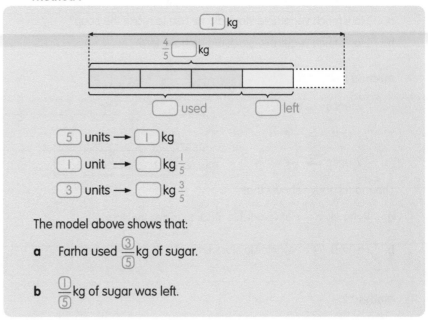

The model above shows that:

a   Farha used $\frac{③}{⑤}$ kg of sugar.

b $\frac{①}{⑤}$ kg of sugar was left.

Method 2

a $\frac{3}{4} \times \frac{④}{⑤} = \frac{③}{⑤}$ kg   b $\frac{4}{5} - \frac{③}{⑤} = \frac{①}{⑤}$ kg

Farha used $\frac{③}{⑤}$ kg of sugar. $\frac{①}{⑤}$ kg of sugar was left.

106

Additional activity

Ask pupils to work in pairs. Each pair thinks of two fractions and draws a model to show how these two fractions can fit into the model based on the example in ③ . Emphasise to pupils that these two fractions do not come from the same whole number.

③ Miya had a sum of money. She saved $\frac{1}{4}$ of it. She spent $\frac{4}{9}$ of the remainder on a football.

a What fraction of her money was spent on the football?

b What fraction of her money was left?

Method 1

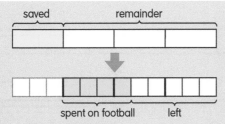

saved   remainder

spent on football   left

The model above shows that:
Number of units spent on football = 4
Number of units left = 5
Total number of units in 1 whole = 12

a Fraction of money spent on football = $\frac{4}{12} = \frac{1}{3}$
$\frac{1}{3}$ of her money was spent on the football.

b $\frac{5}{12}$ of her money was left.

Method 2

a $1 - \frac{1}{4} = \frac{3}{4}$ (remainder)

$\frac{\cancel{4}^{\,1}}{\cancel{9}_{\,3}} \times \frac{\cancel{3}^{\,1}}{\cancel{4}_{\,1}} = \frac{1}{3}$

$\frac{1}{3}$ of her money was spent on the football.

b $\frac{3}{4} - \frac{1}{3} = \frac{9}{12} - \frac{4}{12}$

$= \frac{5}{12}$

$\frac{5}{12}$ of her money was left.

107

Teaching sequence

• Explain the difference in the context of this question and ❶ . Here, pupils are only given the fractional remainder. By contrast, ❶ gives the original amount in fraction form.

Method 1: Explain that $\frac{1}{4}$ refers to the fractional part of a whole and $\frac{4}{9}$ is a fractional part of another whole which is made up from the remainder of the first whole. Explain to pupils that they have to divide the remaining $\frac{3}{4}$ into 9 units to find $\frac{4}{9}$ of it. Guide them to sub-divide the 3 parts into 9 units.

Method 2: Use the cancellation method to find $\frac{4}{9} \times \frac{3}{4}$.

Additional activity
If pupils were not ready to do
the additional activity on the
previous page, ask them to do
the same activity after ④.

Teaching sequence

- Use this question as an
informal assessment to find
out if pupils can follow the
methods they learnt in ③ to
solve the problem.

Unit 4 Fractions (2)

④ Hardeep cut $\frac{3}{5}$ of a pie for his friends. He gave $\frac{3}{4}$ of the remainder
to his brother.

a What fraction of the pie did he give to his brother?

b What fraction of the pie did he have left?

Method 1

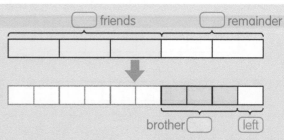

friends ⬜   remainder ⬜

brother ⬜   left ⬜

The model above shows that:
Number of units given to Hardeep's brother = ⬜ 3
Total number of units in 1 whole = ⬜ 10

a He gave $\frac{\square 3}{\bigcirc 10}$ of the pie to his brother.

b He had $\frac{\square 1}{\bigcirc 10}$ of the pie left.

Method 2

a $1 - \frac{③}{⑤} = \frac{②}{⑤}$ (remainder)

$\frac{3}{4} \times \frac{②}{⑤} = \frac{\square 3}{\bigcirc 10}$

He gave $\frac{\square 3}{\bigcirc 10}$ of the pie to
his brother.

b $1 - \frac{③}{⑤} - \frac{\square 3}{\bigcirc 10} = \frac{\square 1}{\bigcirc 10}$

He had $\frac{\square 1}{\bigcirc 10}$ of the pie left.

108

- *Let's Practise!*
- Practice 2 in Practice Book 5A, pp 97 to 102.

Let's Practise!

Solve these word problems. Draw models to help you where necessary.

5 Mrs Smith had a plot of land. She planted flowering plants on $\frac{3}{4}$ of the land. $\frac{2}{3}$ of the flowering plants were sunflowers. What fraction of the land was planted with sunflowers? $\frac{1}{2}$

6 Matt spent $\frac{7}{9}$ of his time in the morning studying French and English. He spent $\frac{4}{7}$ of this time studying French. What fraction of the total time did he spend studying English? $\frac{1}{3}$

7 Ruby has a piece of string $\frac{5}{6}$m in length. She cuts $\frac{3}{5}$ of it to tie some papers together. What is the length of string left? $\frac{1}{3}$ m

8 A farmer sold $\frac{7}{12}$ of his animals. Of his remaining animals, $\frac{3}{5}$ were chickens and the rest were ducks. What fraction of all the animals were the unsold ducks? $\frac{1}{6}$

9 Michael ate $\frac{1}{6}$ of a cake. He gave $\frac{1}{5}$ of the remainder to his friend. He kept the rest of the cake. What fraction of the cake did he keep? $\frac{2}{3}$

10 Mrs Lim used $\frac{1}{3}$ of a pack of butter to make some biscuits. Then she used $\frac{5}{8}$ of the remaining butter to make some tarts. What fraction of the butter was left? $\frac{1}{4}$

11 Lisa spent $\frac{2}{5}$ of her money on a jacket. She then spent $\frac{4}{9}$ of her remaining money on a pair of shoes. What fraction of her money was left? $\frac{1}{3}$

Practice Book 5A, p.97

109

Learning objectives:
Product of an improper fraction and a proper or improper fraction

Pupils will be able to:

- conceptualise the meaning of multiplying an improper fraction by another proper or improper fraction with concrete representation
- use the cancellation (simplification) method to compute the product of two fractions
- use a calculator to compute the above

Teaching sequence

1

- Revise the 'Product of proper fractions' work learnt earlier and explain that $\frac{6}{5} \times \frac{3}{4} = \frac{3}{4} \times \frac{6}{5}$ which has been explored previously.

- Use the following procedure to explain $\frac{6}{5} \times \frac{3}{4}$:

  Step 1: Show $\frac{6}{5}$ with the model and explain that it is more than 1 whole, which is why two rectangles are used to represent this fraction.

  Step 2: Explain that to show $\frac{3}{4}$ of $\frac{6}{5}$, $\frac{3}{4}$ of the blue shaded parts should be further shaded with the red lines.

  Step 3: The number of squares shaded with the red line is 18. 1 whole contains 20 units, so the fraction representing $\frac{6}{5} \times \frac{3}{4}$ is $\frac{18}{20}$ which can be simplified to $\frac{9}{10}$.

- Work through the procedure to use a calculator to find the answer.

Key concept

Multiplying a fraction and another fraction is the same as finding the fractional part of another fraction.

Thinking skill

Comparing

What you will need

Scientific calculator

Additional activity

Ask pupils to practise using the calculator to find the answers to:

(a) $\frac{5}{3} \times \frac{8}{11}$

(b) $\frac{12}{9} \times \frac{19}{10}$

Unit 4 Fractions (2)

Let's Learn!

Product of an improper fraction and a proper or improper fraction

1 Find the product of $\frac{6}{5}$ and $\frac{3}{4}$.

$\frac{6}{5} \times \frac{3}{4}$

$\frac{6}{5} \times \frac{3}{4} = \frac{6^{\,3}}{5} \times \frac{3}{4_{\,2}}$

$= \frac{3 \times 3}{5 \times 2}$

$= \frac{9}{10}$

$\frac{18}{20} = \frac{9}{10}$

We can also find the answer using a calculator.

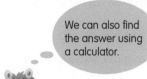

Press	Display
C	0
6 [a^{b}c] 5	$\frac{6}{5}$
× 3 [a^{b}c] 4	$\frac{3}{4}$
=	$\frac{9}{10}$

Fractions (2) **Unit 4**

2 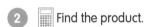 Find the product.

a $\frac{2}{7} \times \frac{21}{12}$ $1\frac{1}{2}$

b $\frac{16}{3} \times \frac{9}{4}$ 12

c $\frac{3}{7} \times \frac{14}{5}$ $1\frac{1}{5}$

d $\frac{7}{6} \times \frac{3}{11}$ $\frac{7}{22}$

e $\frac{9}{4} \times \frac{10}{3}$ $7\frac{1}{2}$

f $\frac{7}{5} \times \frac{9}{2}$ $6\frac{3}{10}$

Let's Practise!

3  Find the product.

a $\frac{1}{3} \times \frac{7}{5}$ $\frac{7}{15}$

b $\frac{15}{6} \times \frac{4}{5}$ 2

c $\frac{21}{8} \times \frac{10}{7}$ $3\frac{3}{4}$

d $\frac{32}{12} \times \frac{15}{4}$ 10

e $\frac{17}{3} \times \frac{22}{5}$ $24\frac{14}{15}$

f $\frac{14}{9} \times \frac{11}{3}$ $5\frac{19}{27}$

g $\frac{28}{11} \times \frac{43}{12}$ $9\frac{4}{33}$

h $\frac{23}{13} \times \frac{11}{3}$ $6\frac{19}{39}$

Practice Book 5A, p.103

Teaching sequence
2
- Assess pupils informally to see if they can use a calculator to find the product of an improper fraction and a proper fraction or improper fraction.

3 *Let's Practise!*
- You could lead pupils to see that in **b** and **d** one numerator is a multiple of a denominator. So the product is a whole number.

III

Unit 4: Fractions (2) **177**

Learning objectives: Product of a mixed number and a whole number

Pupils will be able to:

- conceptualise the meaning of multiplying a mixed number by a whole number
- use regrouping process to compute the product of a mixed number and a whole number
- use a calculator to compute a mixed number with a whole number

Key concept

The product of a whole and a mixed number refers to the group and item multiplication concept.

Thinking skill

Comparing

What you will need

- Fraction discs (see Photocopy master 4 on pp 321 to 322)
- Scientific calculator

Teaching sequence

- Use fraction discs provided on Photocopy master 4 to show that $6 \times 1\frac{1}{2}$ is the same as $1\frac{1}{2} \times 6$. Relate the commutative property of multiplication to this word problem. Explain that $6 \times 1\frac{1}{2}$ is the same as 6 groups of $1\frac{1}{2}$.
- Use fraction discs to show that $6 \times 1\frac{1}{2} = 6 \times \frac{3}{2} = 9$ as shown in the textbook.
- Explain and show how to use a calculator to compute the product of a whole number and a mixed number.

Unit 4 Fractions (2)

Let's Learn!

| Product of a mixed number and a whole number |

1 There are 6 children in the Walker family. Each child is given $1\frac{1}{2}$ sandwiches. How many sandwiches did they get altogether?

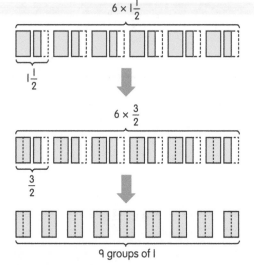

$6 \times 1\frac{1}{2}$

$1\frac{1}{2}$

$6 \times \frac{3}{2}$

$\frac{3}{2}$

9 groups of 1

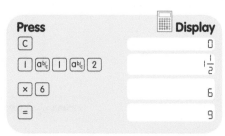

Press	Display
C	0
1 a^b_c 1 a^b_c 2	$1\frac{1}{2}$
× 6	6
=	9

They got 9 sandwiches altogether.

$1\frac{1}{2} = \frac{3}{2}$

$1\frac{1}{2} \times 6$ is the same as 6 groups of $1\frac{1}{2}$.

Use a calculator to find the product.

112

Fractions (2) **Unit 4**

2 Find the product of $2\frac{1}{3}$ and 5.

$5 \times 2\frac{1}{3}$

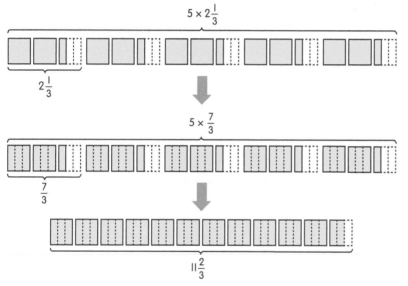

$2\frac{1}{3}$

$5 \times \frac{7}{3}$

$\frac{7}{3}$

$11\frac{2}{3}$

$2\frac{1}{3} \times 5 = \frac{\boxed{7}}{\boxed{3}} \times 5$

$= \frac{\boxed{}\,35}{\boxed{3}}$

$= \frac{33}{3} + \frac{\boxed{2}}{\boxed{3}}$

$= 11 + \frac{\boxed{2}}{\boxed{3}}$

$= \boxed{11}\frac{\boxed{2}}{\boxed{3}}$

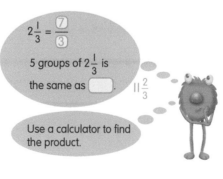

$2\frac{1}{3} = \frac{\boxed{7}}{\boxed{3}}$

5 groups of $2\frac{1}{3}$ is the same as $\boxed{}$. $11\frac{2}{3}$

Use a calculator to find the product.

113

Teaching sequence

2

- Use this question to assess if pupils can multiply a mixed number and a whole number using pictorial representation.
- The following steps may be used to explain the process to pupils:

  Step 1: First convert the mixed number to an improper fraction.

  Step 2: Multiply the numerator and the whole number, keeping the denominator the same.

  Step 3: Regroup the improper fraction to a whole and a proper fraction.

  Step 4: Recombine them to make a mixed number.

- Reinforce the concept of commutativity by checking together that the same answer of $11\frac{2}{3}$ can be obtained from: $5 \times 2 + 5 \times \frac{1}{3}$.

  Pupils could use a calculator to check the answer in this way.

Ask pupils to work in pairs. Each pupil thinks of two sets each containing a whole number and a mixed number. The product of the first set must be a whole number. The product of the second set must not be a whole number. Invite the pairs to explain why the product of the first set is a whole number whereas the product of the second set is not a whole number.

Teaching sequence

a

- Give pupils squares of paper provided on Photocopy master 6. The purpose here is to reinforce pupils' understanding of the concept of multiplying a whole by a mixed number with a concrete activity.

b

- Rearranging the product helps pupils to see the relationship between the product and the results.

- You can explain at the end of the activity that $4 \times 3\frac{1}{2}$ can be divided into 2 parts: 4×3 and $4 \times \frac{1}{2}$. There are 12 wholes in 4×3 and 2 wholes in $4 \times \frac{1}{2}$. So the total is 14 wholes in $4 \times 3\frac{1}{2}$.

4

- This is a reverse activity that helps pupils to understand the concept of multiplying a whole number by a mixed number.

Unit 4 Fractions (2)

Activity

3 You will need some pieces of paper that represent 1 whole.

To represent $\frac{1}{2}$, fold a piece of paper into two and cut it into equal halves.

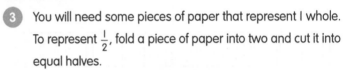

I whole $\frac{1}{2}$

a Use these pieces of paper to show the following:

   i $3\frac{1}{2}$ **ii** $4 \times 3\frac{1}{2}$ **iii** $3\frac{1}{2} \times 5$

b Rearrange the pieces of paper representing $4 \times 3\frac{1}{2}$. How many wholes are there in $4 \times 3\frac{1}{2}$? 14

4

Look at this diagram showing $4\frac{1}{2}$.
Express this as a product of another mixed number and a whole number.

$$4\frac{1}{2} = \boxed{2}\frac{\boxed{1}}{\boxed{4}} \times 2$$

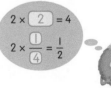
$2 \times \boxed{2} = 4$
$2 \times \frac{\boxed{1}}{\boxed{4}} = \frac{1}{2}$

Use the same method to find the missing number below.

$$8\frac{1}{4} = \boxed{4}\frac{\boxed{1}}{\boxed{8}} \times 2$$

114

Let's Practise!

5 Find the product without using a calculator. Then check your answer using a calculator. Express your answer as a mixed number.

a $1\frac{1}{2} \times 3 = \boxed{4}\boxed{\frac{1}{2}}$

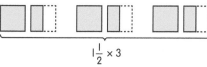

$1\frac{1}{2} \times 3$

b $2\frac{1}{3} \times 2 = \boxed{4}\boxed{\frac{2}{3}}$

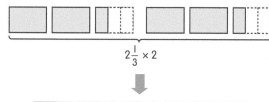

$2\frac{1}{3} \times 2$

6 Find the product. Express your answer as a whole number or a mixed number.

a $3\frac{9}{11} \times 33$ 126   b $14 \times 2\frac{3}{5}$ $36\frac{2}{5}$ c $38 \times 5\frac{2}{7}$ $200\frac{6}{7}$

Practice Book 5A, p.105

115

Teaching sequence

6 *Let's Practise!*

• You could ask pupils how they can tell that the answer for part **a** would be a whole number and that the answers for **b** and **c** would not be whole numbers.

Unit 4: Fractions (2)   **181**

Learning objective:
Word problems (2)

Pupils will be able to solve up to 2-step word problems by applying the concept of multiplication and product of a whole number and a mixed number.

Key concept

Use the group and item multiplication concept to find the product of a whole number and a mixed number.

Thinking Skill

Applying concepts of the four operations including multiplication

What you will need

Scientific calculator

Teaching sequence

- Explain the context of this question which requires pupils to apply the group and item multiplication concept to multiplication of a whole number and a mixed number.
- The unitary method is used in finding the solution. Calculators are allowed to be used for pupils to find the product of a mixed number and a whole number.
- Ask pupils if they can find another way to multiply the numbers and fractions here without using a calculator.

- Ask pupils to work on this question as an informal assessment to check if they are able to use the unitary method and carry out multiplication of a mixed number and a whole number.

Let's Learn!

Word problems (2)

🖩 You can use your calculator in this section.

① During an art class, Miss Brook asked her pupils to cut out $1\frac{1}{2}$ circles each from pieces of paper. There were 24 pupils in the class altogether. Miss Brook then arranged the cut-outs to make whole circles. How many whole circles were there?

I pupil   ⟶ $1\frac{1}{2}$ circles

24 pupils ⟶ $24 \times 1\frac{1}{2}$

         = 36 circles

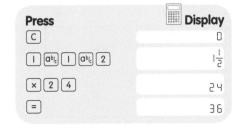

Press	Display
C	0
1 a^b_c 1 a^b_c 2	$1\frac{1}{2}$
× 2 4	24
=	36

There were 36 whole circles.

② There were 40 guests at a party. Each guest ate $2\frac{3}{4}$ mini pizzas. How many mini pizzas did the guests eat altogether?

I guest   ⟶ $2\frac{3}{4}$ mini pizzas

40 guests ⟶ $40 \times 2\frac{3}{4}$

         = 110 mini pizzas

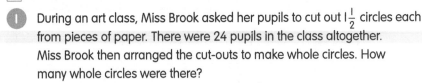

The guests ate 110 mini pizzas altogether.

You can use a calculator to find the answer.

116

Additional activity

Ask pupils to work in pairs to think of another real-life context which allows them to use multiplication of a whole number and a mixed number. Invite some pairs to present their answers to the class.

Fractions (2) **Unit 4**

3 An allotment plot has a length of $12\frac{3}{4}$ m and a width of 7 m.
Find the area of this plot. Express your answer as a decimal.

Area of plot = length × width

$12\frac{3}{4}$ = ◯ × 7

= ◯ m² 89·25

4 Lucy bought 4 bags of potatoes. The mass of each bag of potatoes was $2\frac{3}{5}$ kg. Each kilogram of potatoes cost £2. How much did Lucy pay for the 4 bags of potatoes?

1 bag of potatoes ⟶ $2\frac{3}{5}$ kg

4 bags of potatoes ⟶ $4 \times 2\frac{3}{5}$

= $10\frac{2}{5}$ kg

The mass of 4 bags of potatoes was $10\frac{2}{5}$ kg.

1 kg of potatoes ⟶ £2

$10\frac{2}{5}$ kg of potatoes ⟶ $10\frac{2}{5} \times £2$

= £20·80

Lucy paid £20·80 for the 4 bags of potatoes.

117

Teaching sequence

3

- The context of this problem relates to finding the area of a rectangle by calculating the product of a mixed number and a whole number. Revise with pupils the formula for finding the area of a rectangle.

4

- This 2-step word problem requires pupils to conceptualise two contexts. One context is on the mass of 4 bags of potatoes and the other context is on the cost of potatoes given the cost for 1 kg of potatoes.

- In both contexts, pupils can use the unitary method and apply multiplication of a mixed number and a whole number.

Independent work
- *Let's Practise!*
- Practice 5 in Practice Book 5A, pp 107 to 108.

What you will need
Scientific calculator

Teaching sequence

- Ask pupils to work on this question as an informal assessment to check they are able to solve a 2-step word problem using the product of a whole number and a mixed number to find:

  (a) the amount of syrup in the 3 bottles

  (b) the total cost of the 3 bottles of syrup.

6 to **9** *Let's Practise!*

- You could allow pupils who are confident in performing calculations without a calculator to do so for these questions.

Unit 4 Fractions (2)

5 Tom used 3 bottles of syrup to make some desserts. Each bottle contained $1\frac{1}{2}$ ℓ of syrup. The cost of 1 ℓ of syrup was £5. Find the total cost of the syrup he used.

1 bottle ⟶ ◯ ℓ $1\frac{1}{2}$

3 bottles ⟶ 3 × ◯ ℓ $1\frac{1}{2}$

= ◯ ℓ $4\frac{1}{2}$

3 bottles contained ◯ ℓ of syrup. $4\frac{1}{2}$

1 ℓ of syrup ⟶ £5

◯ ℓ of syrup ⟶ ◯ × £5 $4\frac{1}{2}$
$4\frac{1}{2}$

= £◯ 22·50

The total cost of the syrup he used was £◯. 22·50

Let's Practise!

⊞ Solve these word problems. Show your workings clearly.

6 Ben has 6 children. He gives each child $2\frac{1}{3}$ sandwiches. How many sandwiches does he need? 14 sandwiches

7 Amy cuts a ball of string into 15 equal pieces. The length of each piece of string is $15\frac{1}{4}$ cm. What is the total length of the string? $228\frac{3}{4}$ cm

8 Mr Peters buys 9 packs of meat. Each pack of meat weighs $7\frac{1}{2}$ kg. The cost of 1 kg of meat is £3. How much does he pay for all the meat he buys? £202·50

9 Miss Owen bought a plot of land 12 m long and $5\frac{2}{5}$ m wide. The cost of 1 m² of land is £2200. How much did Miss Owen pay for the whole plot of land? £142 560

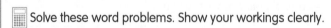

Practice Book 5A, p.107

118

Learning objectives:
Dividing a fraction by
a whole number

Learning objectives:
Dividing a fraction by
a whole number

Pupils will be able to:

- understand the meaning of dividing a fraction by a whole number
- use three different methods to divide a fraction by a whole number

Key concept

Division in fractions is dividing each fractional part into smaller equal parts/units.

Thinking Skills

- Comparing
- Analysing parts and whole

Teaching sequence

1

- Explain the context of the question and help pupils to understand that dividing a fraction by a whole number will only give a fractional piece.

Method 1: Draw a model showing 2 equal units, where 1 unit represents $\frac{1}{2}$ of a cottage pie. Next draw another model showing 3 equal units to correspond with 1 unit in the first model to represent sharing $\frac{1}{2}$ a cottage pie among 3 children.

Method 2: Emphasise that $\frac{1}{2} \div 3$ is to be interpreted as $\frac{1}{3}$ of $\frac{1}{2}$. Then use the product of two proper fractions to find the answer of $\frac{1}{6}$.

Method 3:
As $\frac{1}{3} \times \frac{1}{2} = \frac{1}{2} \times \frac{1}{3}$, we can write:
$\frac{1}{2} \div 3 = \frac{1}{2} \times \frac{1}{3} = \frac{1}{6}$
This is the concept of 'invert and multiply'. That is, dividing by 3 is the same as multiplying by $\frac{1}{3}$.

Fractions (2) **Unit 4**

Let's Learn!

Dividing a fraction by a whole number

1 Half of a cottage pie is shared equally among 3 children. What fraction of the cottage pie will each child get?

Method 1

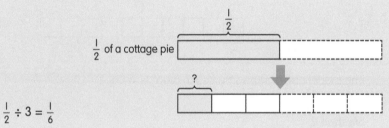

$\frac{1}{2} \div 3 = \frac{1}{6}$

The model above shows that each child will get $\frac{1}{6}$ of the cottage pie.

Method 2

$\frac{1}{2} \div 3 = \frac{1}{3}$ of $\frac{1}{2}$

$\qquad = \frac{1}{3} \times \frac{1}{2}$

$\qquad = \frac{1}{6}$

Each child will get $\frac{1}{3}$ of $\frac{1}{2}$ of the cottage pie.

Each child will get $\frac{1}{6}$ of the cottage pie.

Method 3

$\frac{1}{2} \div 3 = \frac{1}{2} \times \frac{1}{3}$

$\qquad = \frac{1}{6}$

Multiply $\frac{1}{2}$ by $\frac{1}{3}$.

Each child will get $\frac{1}{6}$ of the cottage pie.

119

Teaching sequence

- Ask pupils to work on this question as an informal assessment to check if they are able to follow and use the three methods shown in ① to solve the problem.

Unit 4 Fractions (2)

② A coil of wire, $\frac{3}{5}$m long, is cut into 6 equal pieces. How long is each piece of the wire?

Method 1

$\frac{3}{5} \div 6 = \frac{\bigcirc}{\bigcirc}$ m $\frac{1}{10}$

The model above shows that each piece is $\frac{\bigcirc}{\bigcirc}$ m. $\frac{1}{10}$

Method 2

$\frac{3}{5} \div 6 = \frac{1}{6}$ of $\frac{3}{5}$

$= \frac{\text{①}}{\text{⑥}} \times \frac{\text{③}}{\text{⑤}}$

$= \frac{\bigcirc}{\bigcirc}$ m $\frac{1}{10}$

Each piece is $\frac{\bigcirc}{\bigcirc}$ m. $\frac{1}{10}$

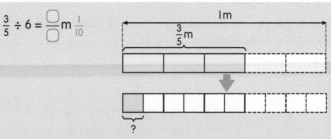

Each piece is $\frac{\text{①}}{\text{⑥}}$ of $\frac{3}{5}$m.

Method 3

$\frac{3}{5} \div 6 = \frac{3}{5} \times \frac{\text{①}}{\text{⑥}}$

$= \frac{\bigcirc}{\bigcirc}$ m $\frac{1}{10}$

Each piece is $\frac{\bigcirc}{\bigcirc}$ m. $\frac{1}{10}$

120

Additional activity

If pupils were not ready to carry out the activity on the previous page, they may be asked to do it at this stage.

Teaching sequence

3

- Encourage pupils to use (a) model drawing and the unitary method and (b) the invert and multiply method to solve problems involving division of a fraction by a whole number.

4

- Assess pupils further to check that they are able to use different methods to divide a fraction by a whole number.

3 A watermelon with a mass of $\frac{4}{7}$ kg is cut into 2 equal pieces. What is the mass of each piece of watermelon?

Method 1

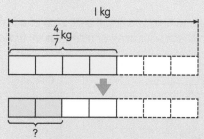

The model above shows that the mass of each piece of watermelon is $\frac{2}{7}$ kg.

Method 2

$$\frac{4}{7} \div 2 = \frac{4}{7} \times \frac{1}{2}$$

$$= \frac{2}{7} \text{ kg}$$

The mass of each piece of watermelon is $\frac{2}{7}$ kg.

4 Find the value of $\frac{9}{11} \div 3$.

Method 1

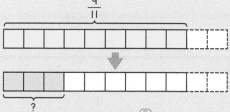

The model above shows that $\frac{9}{11} \div 3 = \frac{③}{⑪}$

Method 2

$$\frac{9}{11} \div 3 = \frac{9}{11} \times \frac{①}{③}$$

$$= \frac{③}{⑪}$$

121

Independent work

Let's Practise!

Teaching sequence

- This activity reinforces solving problems involving division of a fraction by a whole number using:
  (a) the model drawing and unitary method
  (b) the invert and multiply concept.

Activity

5 Work in pairs.

Use the models to help you find the division of a fraction by a whole number. Then check your answer using the multiplication method.

a Divide $\frac{1}{4}$ by 3.

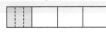

b Divide $\frac{1}{3}$ by 5.

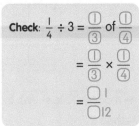

Check: $\frac{1}{4} \div 3 = \frac{\bigcirc}{\textcircled{3}}$ of $\frac{\bigcirc}{\textcircled{4}}$

$= \frac{\bigcirc}{\textcircled{3}} \times \frac{\bigcirc}{\textcircled{4}}$

$= \frac{\bigcirc}{\bigcirc}\frac{1}{12}$

Let's Practise!

6 Divide.

a $\frac{2}{7} \div 4 = \frac{2}{7} \times \frac{1}{4}$

$= \frac{\bigcirc}{\bigcirc}\frac{1}{14}$

b $\frac{2}{3} \div 8 = \frac{2}{3} \times \frac{1}{8}$

$= \frac{\bigcirc}{\bigcirc}\frac{1}{12}$

c $\frac{3}{4} \div 12 \frac{1}{16}$

d $\frac{6}{7} \div 9 \frac{2}{21}$

7 Draw a model to solve each division sentence.

a $\frac{6}{11} \div 3 \frac{2}{11}$

b $\frac{8}{9} \div 4 \frac{2}{9}$

c $\frac{2}{5} \div 4 \frac{1}{10}$

d $\frac{3}{7} \div 2 \frac{3}{14}$

8 Solve these word problems. Draw models to help you where necessary.

a A box contained red and green apples. $\frac{4}{5}$ of the apples were red. The red apples were shared equally among 8 children. What fraction of all the apples from the box did each child get? $\frac{1}{10}$

Teaching sequence

8 *Let's Practise!*

• For part **g** you could allow pupils who are confident in performing calculations without a calculator to do so.

Let's Practise!

b Hardeep cut out $\frac{9}{10}$ of a cake. This portion of the cake was shared equally among Tai, Miya and Omar. What fraction of the cake did each of them get? $\frac{3}{10}$

c The area of a rectangular piece of material is $\frac{4}{9}$ m². Julie cuts the material into 3 smaller pieces of the same size. What is the area of each small piece of material? $\frac{4}{27}$ m²

d A plank of wood $\frac{3}{5}$ m long is cut into 4 pieces of the same length. Find the length of each piece of wood. $\frac{3}{20}$ m or 15 cm

e Mrs Ford gave $\frac{1}{3}$ of her savings to Lisa and $\frac{5}{12}$ of her savings to James. Then she deposited the rest of her savings equally in 3 accounts. What fraction of her savings did she put in each account? $\frac{1}{12}$

f Sophia bought $\frac{3}{8}$ ℓ of blackcurrant squash. She poured the squash equally into 6 identical cups. Find the amount of squash in litres:

   i in each cup $\frac{1}{16}$ ℓ

   ii in 5 cups. $\frac{5}{16}$ ℓ

g   Christine bought $\frac{5}{9}$ kg of mixed spice. She repacked it equally into 15 packets.

   i Find the mass of 1 packet of mixed spice in kilograms. $\frac{1}{27}$ kg

   ii She sold 7 packets of mixed spice. How many kilograms of mixed spice did she sell? $\frac{7}{27}$ kg

Practice Book 5A, p.109

123

Learning objective:
Word problems (3)

Pupils will be able to solve up to 2-step word problems with the use of multiplication and division in fractions.

Key concept

The concepts of the four operations and division of a fraction are applied.

Thinking skills

- Comparing
- Applying the concepts of four operations
- Analysing parts and whole

Teaching sequence

- Explain to pupils that this problem embodies the part-whole concept. The whole is the set of all the apples, and the parts are the apples sold to Chris and Jenny and the apples that were not sold.

  Method 1: Draw a model showing the 3 parts of the whole: the apples sold to Chris and Jenny, and the apples that were not sold. Next use the unitary method to relate the number of units to the number of apples.

  Method 2: The part-whole concept is used to find the fractional parts sold by using addition. Then apply the fraction of a set method to find the amounts that correspond to the sold and unsold parts.

  Method 3: This method is similar to Method 2 except that the fraction of a set method is applied to find the number of apples bought by each individual, before applying the part-whole concept to find the number of apples unsold. This method is the reverse of Method 2.

Unit 4 Fractions (2)

Let's Learn!

Word problems (3)

① Ron had 240 apples. He sold $\frac{1}{2}$ of them to Chris and $\frac{1}{3}$ to Jenny.

  a How many apples did Ron sell altogether?

  b How many apples did he have left?

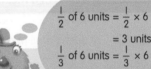
$\frac{1}{2}$ of 6 units $= \frac{1}{2} \times 6$
$= 3$ units
$\frac{1}{3}$ of 6 units $= \frac{1}{3} \times 6$
$= 2$ units

Method 1

6 is a common multiple of 2 and 3. Draw a model with 6 equal units.

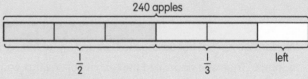

The model above shows that:

6 units ⟶ 240 apples

I unit ⟶ $240 \div 6 = \boxed{40}$ apples

5 units ⟶ $5 \times \boxed{40} = 200$ apples

a Ron sold 200 apples. **b** He had 40 apples left.

Method 2

$\frac{1}{2} = \frac{3}{6}$ $\frac{1}{3} = \frac{2}{6}$

Fraction of apples sold is $\frac{3}{6} + \frac{2}{6} = \frac{5}{6}$.

$\frac{5}{6}$ of 240 $= \frac{5}{6} \times 240 = 200$ apples

a Ron sold 200 apples.

b He had $240 - 200$
$= 40$ apples left.

Method 3

$\frac{1}{2} \times 240 = 120$

$\frac{1}{3} \times 240 = 80$

a Ron sold $120 + 80 = 200$ apple

b He had $240 - 200$
$= 40$ apples left.

124

Fractions (2) **Unit 4**

2 🖩 Kim planted 312 carrots, tomatoes, and pumpkins in her garden. $\frac{2}{3}$ of her plants were carrots and $\frac{1}{4}$ of them were tomatoes. The rest of the plants were pumpkins. How many pumpkins did she plant?

Method 1

12 is a common multiple of 3 and 4. Draw a model with ⌈12⌉ equal units.

$\frac{2}{3}$ of 12 units $= \dfrac{②}{③} \times$ ⌈12⌉

$= $ ⌈8⌉ units

$\frac{1}{4}$ of 12 units $= \dfrac{①}{④} \times$ ⌈12⌉

$= $ ⌈3⌉ units

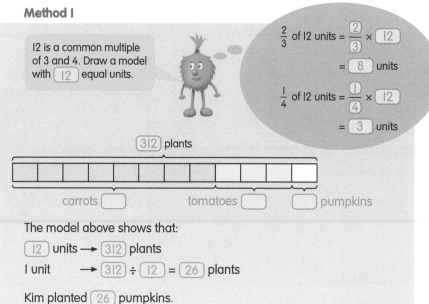

⌈312⌉ plants

carrots ⌈ ⌉   tomatoes ⌈ ⌉   ⌈ ⌉ pumpkins

The model above shows that:

⌈12⌉ units ⟶ ⌈312⌉ plants

1 unit ⟶ ⌈312⌉ ÷ ⌈12⌉ = ⌈26⌉ plants

Kim planted ⌈26⌉ pumpkins.

Method 2

$\frac{2}{3} = \dfrac{⑧}{⑫}$ $\frac{1}{4} = \dfrac{③}{⑫}$

$1 - \dfrac{⑧}{⑫} - \dfrac{③}{⑫} = \dfrac{①}{⑫}$

$\dfrac{①}{⑫}$ of 312 $= \dfrac{①}{⑫} \times 312$

$= $ ⌈26⌉ pumpkins

Kim planted ⌈26⌉ pumpkins.

125

Teaching sequence

2

• Ask pupils to work on this question as an informal assessment to check if they are able to apply the concepts and strategies used in **1** to solve similar problems. Pupils should be exposed to all the methods so that they may use any of them to tackle future problems.

• Pupils who are confident in using their knowledge of the 12 times table to perform long division, could be asked to show how they can use these methods to answer the question without using a calculator.

Ask pupils to think of two
fractions that fit into a model
with a context that is similar to
③. Highlight that there are two
wholes. The two fractions must
come from two different wholes.
Invite pupils to explain what
the two wholes are, how many
parts there are in each whole
and what the fractional part
concerned in each whole is.

Teaching sequence

③

- Ask pupils to read the
  question and compare with
  ①. Ask them what the
  similarities and differences
  between these two
  questions are.

- Pupils should be able to see
  that ① comprises fractions
  that come from one whole
  whereas ③ comprises
  fractions that come from
  two different wholes. In this
  question, the first whole is
  the amount of money Mrs
  Barlow had, and the second
  whole is the remaining
  amount of money after
  buying a game console.

- Explain and show the two
  different methods to solve the
  problem:

  (a) the model drawing and
  unitary method

  (b) the fraction of a set
  method.

Unit 4 Fractions (2)

③ Mrs Barlow had £480. She used $\frac{1}{3}$ of it to buy a game console. Then she spent
$\frac{1}{4}$ of the remainder on some games. How much money did she have left?

Method I

£480

| | | | | | |

console games   left

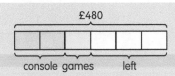

The model above shows that:

6 units ⟶ £480

I unit ⟶ £$\frac{480}{6}$ = £80

3 units ⟶ 3 × £80 = £240

She had £240 left.

First draw a model with
3 parts. Shade I part to show the
amount spent on the console.

console remainder

Then divide the model further to
show I part of the remainder is
spent on the games.

games

Method 2

$\frac{1}{3}$ of £480 = $\frac{1}{3}$ × £480

= £160

Mrs Barlow spent £160 on the console.

£480 − £160 = £320
After buying the console, she had £320 left.

$1 - \frac{1}{4} = \frac{3}{4}$

$\frac{3}{4}$ of £320 = $\frac{3}{4}$ × £320

= £240

She had £240 left.

126

---

(4) In a test consisting of Sections A, B and C, Peter spent $\frac{1}{5}$ of his time on Section A, $\frac{1}{3}$ of the remaining time on Section B and the rest of the time on Section C. If he spent 48 minutes on Section C, how much time did he take to complete the whole test?

Method 1

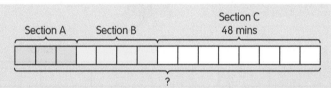

The model above shows that:

8 units ⟶ 48 mins

1 unit ⟶ 6 mins

15 units ⟶ 90 mins

Peter took 90 mins to complete the test.

Method 2

$\frac{1}{3} \times \frac{4}{5} = \frac{4}{15}$ (Section B)

$\frac{1}{5} + \frac{4}{15} = \frac{3}{15} + \frac{4}{15} = \frac{7}{15}$ (Sections A & B)

$1 - \frac{7}{15} = \frac{8}{15}$ (Section C)

$\frac{8}{15} \longrightarrow$ 48 mins

$\frac{15}{15} \longrightarrow$ 90 mins

Peter took 90 mins to complete the test.

127

Teaching sequence

(4)

- Ask pupils to read the question and compare it with (3). Then ask them what the similarities and differences between these two questions are.

- Pupils should be able to see that both questions comprise fractions that come from two different wholes. In this question, the remaining parts have to be divided into smaller units so that fractional parts of a whole can be obtained. However, for (3) dividing the parts of the remainder into smaller units is not required as it is possible to find the fraction of the whole.

- Explain and show the model drawing and unitary method to solve the problem.

Additional activity

Ask pupils to think of two fractions that fit into a model with a context similar to 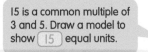 5 . Emphasise that there are two wholes. The two fractions must come from two different wholes. Encourage pupils to explain what the two wholes are, how many parts there are in each whole and what the fractional part concerned in each whole is.

Teaching sequence

5

- Use this question to informally assess whether pupils can understand the problem and apply the strategies and methods used in **3**.

6

- Ask pupils to work on this question as an informal assessment to check whether they can understand the problem and apply the strategy and method in **4** to solve a similar problem.

Unit 4 Fractions (2)

5 Tim prepared a mixture of apple, carrot and orange juice. $\frac{1}{3}$ of the mixture was apple juice and $\frac{2}{5}$ of the remainder was orange juice. 315 ml of the mixture was orange juice. What volume of the mixture was carrot juice?

15 is a common multiple of 3 and 5. Draw a model to show $\boxed{15}$ equal units.

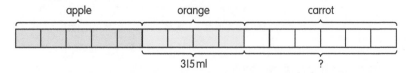

apple	orange	carrot

315 ml   ?

The model above shows that:

4 units ⟶ 315 ml

1 unit ⟶ 315 ÷ 4 = ⬚ ml $\frac{315}{4}$

6 units ⟶ 6 × ⬚ = ⬚ ml
$\frac{315}{4}$ $472\frac{1}{2}$

$472\frac{1}{2}$ ⬚ ml of the mixture was carrot juice.

6 Nick gave his cousin $\frac{1}{3}$ of his plastic bricks. He gave his sister $\frac{5}{6}$ of the remainder and had 80 bricks left. How many bricks did he have at first?

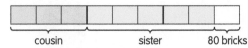

cousin   sister   80 bricks

The model above shows that:

1 unit ⟶ 80 bricks

9 units ⟶ 9 × 80 = 720 bricks

Nick had 720 bricks at first.

128

Fractions (2) **Unit 4**

Let's Practise!

Solve these word problems. Show your workings clearly.

7   Jane had 288 charity raffle tickets. She sold $\frac{2}{9}$ of the tickets to her relatives and $\frac{1}{3}$ of them to her friends.

   a   How many tickets were sold to her relatives and friends? 160 tickets
   b   How many tickets were not sold? 128 tickets

8   Miss Carpenter had £960. She spent $\frac{1}{4}$ of it on a holiday and $\frac{1}{6}$ of the remainder on a wetsuit. She kept the rest of the money. How much money did she keep? £600

9   Josh took 1h 40 mins to complete a 3-lap race. He took $\frac{1}{4}$ of the total time to run the first lap and $\frac{1}{3}$ of the remaining time to run the second lap. The rest of the time was used to run the third lap. How many minutes did he take to run the third lap of the race? 50 mins

10   Mr Young had a length of rope. He used $\frac{1}{4}$ of it to tie some boxes together. He then used $\frac{5}{9}$ of the remainder to make a skipping rope for his daughter. 120 cm of rope was left. What was the length of rope used to tie the boxes together? 90 cm

11   Jeremy had a total of 216 photos of butterflies, bees and beetles in his collection. $\frac{7}{12}$ of the photos were butterflies, $\frac{5}{9}$ of the remainder were bees and the rest were beetles. How many photos of beetles were there in his collection? 40 photos of beetles

129

Teaching sequence

11 *Let's Practise!*

- You could allow pupils who are confident in performing calculations without a calculator to do so for this question. They may need to work out

$$\frac{5}{27} \times 216 = \frac{5}{9} \times 72 = 5 \times 8 = 40.$$

Using model drawing here could help pupils to visualise the part-whole concept.

Objective of activity

Pupils will be able to reflect on their understanding of division of a fraction by a whole number and the product of proper fractions through identification of mistakes made.

Independent work

Practice 7 and *Maths Journal* in Practice Book 5A, pp 113 to 116.

Teaching sequence

13 *Maths Journal*

- This journal requires pupils to explain and correct the mistakes Tom and Selina made in their calculations.
- In the process of looking for the mistakes, pupils reflect on the concepts they have learnt and their understanding is reinforced.

Let's Wrap It Up!

- Review with pupils each bullet point in *Let's Wrap It Up!*
- This helps pupils to see if they have already mastered the current topic.
- You may ask pupils to think of an example question for each bullet point in *Let's Wrap It Up!* Invite some pupils to present their questions and answers to the class.

Let's Practise!

12 Rhys bought a bag of assorted berries containing strawberries, raspberries and blueberries. $\frac{1}{4}$ of the berries were strawberries, $\frac{2}{3}$ of the remainder were raspberries and the rest were blueberries. If there were 48 raspberries, how many blueberries were there?

24 blueberries

Practice Book 5A, p.113

Maths Journal

13 Tom and Selina did the following incorrectly. Explain and correct their mistakes.

a Tom: $\frac{2}{9} \div 3 = \frac{2}{3}$

He divided the denominator by 3. He should have multiplied the denominator by 3 instead.

b Selina: $\frac{2}{9} \times \frac{4}{11} = \frac{6}{20}$

She added the numerators and denominators separately. She should have multiplied the numerators and denominators separately.

Let's Wrap It Up!

You have learnt to:

- find the product of proper fractions
- find the product of an improper fraction and a proper or improper fraction
- find the product of a mixed number and a whole number using a calculator
- divide a proper fraction by a whole number.

130

Let's Wrap It Up!

Let's Revise!

Jody has a rectangular piece of material $\frac{7}{8}$ m long and $\frac{4}{5}$ m wide. She decides to share the rectangular piece of material equally with her friend.

a What is the area of the rectangular piece of material?

Method 1

$$\frac{7}{8} \times \frac{4}{5} = \frac{7 \times 4}{8 \times 5}$$

$$= \frac{28}{40}$$

$$= \frac{7}{10} \, m^2$$

The area of the rectangular piece of material is $\frac{7}{10}$ m².

Method 2

$$\frac{7}{8} \times \frac{4}{5} = \frac{7}{\cancel{8}_2} \times \frac{\cancel{4}^1}{5}$$

$$= \frac{7}{10} \, m^2$$

The area of the rectangular piece of material is $\frac{7}{10}$ m².

b What is the area of the piece of material her friend gets?

$$\frac{7}{10} \div 2 = \frac{7}{10} \times \frac{1}{2}$$

$$= \frac{7}{20} \, m^2$$

The area of the piece of material her friend gets is $\frac{7}{20}$ m².

131

Teaching sequence

Let's Wrap It Up!

- Go through the worked example question with the pupils. Use the question to test if pupils have understood the concepts learnt in this unit and whether they can relate them to the worked example question.

Objective of activity

Pupils will be able to make use of the strategies of looking for patterns and drawing models to solve challenging problems related to fractions.

Teaching sequence

14 *Put On Your Thinking Caps!*

- This question requires pupils to identify the pattern in a given set of measurements. Then using the pattern, the unknown value is determined.
- Notice that in **a**, each measurement value is obtained by multiplying the preceding value by 3. However, in **b** each measurement value is obtained by adding an increasing multiple of 4 to the preceding value.

15

- Pupils may use the model drawing and the unitary method to find the answer. To help pupils understand the concept, use the following number line:

Position: 1, 2, 3, …, 30, 31, …

- So $\frac{5}{9}$ of all the children is 30.

Using the unitary method:

5 units → 30
1 unit → 6
9 units → 54

The number of children is 54.

16

- Pupils need to understand and use the product of a mixed number and a whole number to find the number of cars Aisha had. Then by applying the unitary method, the cost of each toy car can be found.
- You could allow pupils who are confident in performing calculations without a calculator to do so for this question.

Thinking skills

- Identifying patterns and relationships
- Visualisation

Heuristics for problem solving

- Look for a pattern
- Draw a model

What you will need

Scientific calculator

Independent work

Challenging Practice, Problem Solving and Review 2 in Practice Book 5A, pp 117 to 132.

Put On Your Thinking Caps!

14 Find the missing mass in each pattern.

a   2000 g $\frac{1}{3}$ of 18 kg   18 000 g   ⌈ 54 ⌉ kg $\frac{1}{3}$ of 486 kg

        × 3   11 000   × 3   × 3   × 3

b   7000 g   [ ] g $\frac{1}{12}$ of 228 kg   31 kg $1\frac{1}{4}$ of 37 600 g

        + 4 kg   + 8 kg   + 12 kg   + 16 kg

15 In a race, Daniel was in 31st position. His position in the group was just behind $\frac{5}{9}$ of the children. How many children were in the race?

54 children

16 Keith bought 10 identical toy cars. Aisha bought $1\frac{1}{2}$ times as many of these toy cars as Keith. The total cost of the toy cars the two children had was £75. What was the cost of each toy car?

$1\frac{1}{2} \times 10 = 15$

Total number of toy cars: 10 + 15 = 25

25 toy cars → £75
1 toy car → £75 ÷ 25 = £3

The cost of each toy car was £3.

| Practice Book 5A, p.117 | Practice Book 5A, p.118 |

132

Unit 4 Fractions (2)

Product of proper fractions

Practice 1

1 Look at the diagram. Then fill in the spaces.

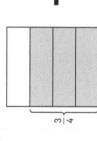

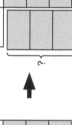

$\dfrac{3}{4}$

$\dfrac{1}{2}$ of $\dfrac{3}{4}$ = $\boxed{1}$ $\times$ $\boxed{3}$

= $\dfrac{\boxed{3}}{\boxed{8}}$

2 Find the value of each of the following:

a $\dfrac{1}{3}$ of $\dfrac{5}{8}$ = $\boxed{1}$ $\times$ $\boxed{5}$

= $\dfrac{\boxed{5}}{\boxed{24}}$

b $\dfrac{2}{7}$ of $\dfrac{9}{11}$ = $\boxed{2}$ $\times$ $\boxed{9}$

= $\dfrac{\boxed{18}}{\boxed{77}}$

Practice 2 | Word problems (1)

Solve these word problems. Show your workings clearly.

1 Susie finished a job in $\frac{3}{4}$ h. Megan finished it in $\frac{4}{5}$ of the time Susie took. How long did Megan take to finish the job?

$$\frac{{}^1\cancel{4}}{5} \times \frac{3}{\cancel{4}_1} = \frac{3}{5}\,h$$

Megan took $\frac{3}{5}$ h to finish the job.

2 Ben had a bottle containing $\frac{7}{8}$ ℓ of milk. He poured $\frac{4}{5}$ of it into a bowl. What volume of milk did he pour into the bowl?

$$\frac{4}{5} \times \frac{7}{\cancel{8}_2} = \frac{7}{10}\,\ell$$

Ben poured $\frac{7}{10}$ ℓ of milk into the bowl.

3 Anna ran $\frac{3}{4}$ km in a race. Jess ran $\frac{2}{9}$ of the distance that Anna had run. What was the distance that Jess ran?

$$\frac{\cancel{2}}{\cancel{9}_3} \times \frac{\cancel{3}}{\cancel{4}_2} = \frac{1}{6}\,km$$

Jess ran $\frac{1}{6}$ km.

---

3 Find the value of each of the following. Express your answer in its simplest form.

a
$$\frac{2}{5} \text{ of } \frac{7}{10} = \frac{{}^1\cancel{2}}{5} \times \frac{7}{\cancel{10}_5}$$
$$= \frac{7}{25}$$

b
$$\frac{3}{4} \text{ of } \frac{8}{9} = \frac{{}^1\cancel{3}}{\cancel{4}_1} \times \frac{{}^2\cancel{8}}{\cancel{9}_3}$$
$$= \frac{2}{3}$$

4 Find the value of each of the following:

a $\dfrac{3}{8} \times \dfrac{1}{2} = \dfrac{3}{16}$

b $\dfrac{5}{12} \times \dfrac{7}{8} = \dfrac{35}{96}$

5 Find the value of each of the following:

a
$$\frac{2}{11} \times \frac{7}{12} = \frac{{}^1\cancel{2}}{11} \times \frac{7}{\cancel{12}_6}$$
$$= \frac{7}{66}$$

b

$$\frac{3}{8} \times \frac{4}{9} = \frac{{}^1\cancel{3}}{\cancel{8}_2} \times \frac{{}^1\cancel{4}}{\cancel{9}_3}$$
$$= \frac{1}{6}$$

Solve these word problems. Show your workings clearly. Draw models to help you where necessary.

4 Meena bought some pieces of fruit. $\frac{4}{5}$ of her pieces of fruit were apples. $\frac{1}{2}$ of the apples she bought were red. What fraction of the pieces of fruit were red apples?

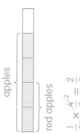

apples

red apples

$\frac{1}{2} \times \frac{4^2}{5} = \frac{2}{5}$

$\frac{2}{5}$ of the pieces of fruit were red apples.

5 Richard worked in a factory packing computers. He packed $\frac{1}{3}$ of all the computers in the morning. $\frac{1}{2}$ of the computers he packed were shipped out immediately after packing. What fraction of all the computers in the factory was shipped out after packing?

$\frac{1}{3}$ packed

$\frac{1}{2}$ shipped out

$\frac{1}{2} \times \frac{1}{3} = \frac{1}{6}$

$\frac{1}{6}$ of all the computers was shipped out after packing.

6 Mrs Mackay had some eggs in a basket. She took out $\frac{3}{5}$ of the eggs to bake some muffins and egg tarts. She used $\frac{2}{3}$ of the eggs taken out to bake muffins. What fraction of the total number of eggs was used to bake muffins?

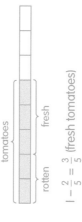

muffins and egg tarts

muffins

$\frac{2}{3_1} \times \frac{3^1}{5} = \frac{2}{5}$

Mrs Mackay used $\frac{2}{5}$ of the eggs that she had to bake muffins.

7 Hardeep bought $\frac{5}{8}$ kg of tomatoes to make a salad. $\frac{2}{5}$ of the tomatoes were rotten and the rest were fresh. What was the mass of fresh tomatoes?

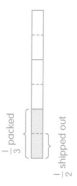

tomatoes

rotten   fresh

$1 - \frac{2}{5} = \frac{3}{5}$ (fresh tomatoes)

$\frac{3}{5_1} \times \frac{5^1}{8} = \frac{3}{8}$ kg

The mass of fresh tomatoes was $\frac{3}{8}$ kg.

Solve these word problems. Show your workings clearly. You may use your calculator where necessary.

10 Sonia had shells of three different sizes. $\frac{4}{9}$ of the shells were big and $\frac{2}{5}$ of the remainder were medium-sized. The rest of the shells were small. What fraction of the shells were small?

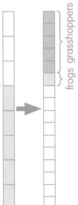

big shells | remainder

medium-sized shells | small shells

$1 - \frac{4}{9} = \frac{5}{9}$ (remainder)

$\frac{2}{5} \times \frac{5}{9} = \frac{2}{9}$ (medium-sized shells)

$\frac{5}{9} - \frac{2}{9} = \frac{3}{9} = \frac{1}{3}$

$\frac{1}{3}$ of the shells were small.

11 Millie made some origami animals. $\frac{5}{8}$ of them were birds and $\frac{1}{6}$ of the remainder were frogs. The rest were grasshoppers. What fraction of the origami animals were grasshoppers?

birds | remainder

frogs grasshoppers

$1 - \frac{5}{8} = \frac{3}{8}$ (remainder)

$\frac{1}{6} \times \frac{3}{8} = \frac{1}{16}$ (frogs)

$\frac{3}{8} - \frac{1}{16} = \frac{5}{16}$

$\frac{5}{16}$ of the origami animals were grasshoppers.

---

8 Jenny gave $\frac{1}{6}$ of her pocket money to her brother and spent $\frac{2}{5}$ of her remaining pocket money. What fraction of her total pocket money did she spend?

Method 1

gave to brother | remaining pocket money

spent

From the model we see that:
Total pocket money = 6 units
Amount spent = 2 units
Fraction of pocket money spent = $\frac{2}{6} = \frac{1}{3}$

Method 2

$1 - \frac{1}{6} = \frac{5}{6}$ (remaining pocket money)

$\frac{2}{5} \times \frac{5}{6} = \frac{1}{3}$

$\frac{1}{3}$ of her total pocket money was spent.

9 In a class, $\frac{3}{4}$ of the pupils liked football. $\frac{1}{3}$ of the pupils who did not like football were boys. What fraction of all the pupils were boys who did not like football?

Method 1

pupils who liked football | pupils who did not like football

boys

From the model we see that:
Total number of pupils = 12 units
Number of boys who did not like football = 1 unit
Fraction of boys who did not like football = $\frac{1}{12}$

Method 2

$1 - \frac{3}{4} = \frac{1}{4}$ (pupils who did not like football)

$\frac{1}{3} \times \frac{1}{4} = \frac{1}{12}$

$\frac{1}{12}$ of all the pupils were boys who did not like football.

Practice 3

Product of an improper fraction and a proper or improper fraction

1 Look at the diagram. Then fill in the boxes.

a

$$\frac{3}{2} \times \frac{1}{2} = \frac{3}{4}$$

b

$$\frac{8}{3} \times \frac{1}{4} = \frac{2}{3}$$

2 Find the product.

 $$\frac{11}{12} \times \frac{1}{3}$$

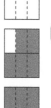

$$\frac{11}{12} \times \frac{1}{3} = \frac{5}{6} \quad \frac{1}{6}$$

---

12 $\frac{2}{3}$ of the flowers in a garden were roses. $\frac{5}{12}$ of the roses were yellow and the rest were red. What fraction of the flowers were red?

$$1 - \frac{5}{12} = \frac{7}{12}$$

$$\frac{7}{12} \times \frac{2}{3} = \frac{7}{18}$$

$\frac{7}{18}$ of the flowers in the garden were red roses.

13 Karen has a pile of coins. $\frac{1}{4}$ of her coins are European coins. $\frac{2}{9}$ of the European coins are euros. What fraction of the European coins are not euros?

$$1 - \frac{2}{9} = \frac{7}{9}$$

$$\frac{7}{9} \times \frac{1}{4} = \frac{7}{36}$$

$\frac{7}{36}$ of the European coins are not euros.

Date: _____

Practice 4

Product of a mixed number and a whole number

1 Look at the diagram. Then fill in the boxes.

a

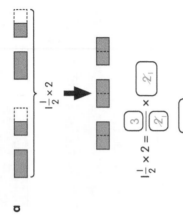

$1\frac{1}{2} \times 2$

$1\frac{1}{2} \times 2 = \dfrac{3}{2} \times \dfrac{2}{1}$

$= 3$

b

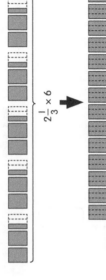

$2\frac{1}{3} \times 6$

$2\frac{1}{3} \times 6 = \dfrac{7}{3} \times \dfrac{6}{1}$

$= 14$

 Check your answers using a calculator.

---

3 Find the product of the fractions. Express your answer in its simplest form.

a $\dfrac{8}{3} \times \dfrac{3}{10} = \dfrac{4}{5}$

b $\dfrac{15}{9} \times \dfrac{3}{20} = \dfrac{1}{4}$

c $\dfrac{2}{5} \times \dfrac{15}{4} = 1\dfrac{1}{2}$

d $\dfrac{16}{7} \times \dfrac{21}{2} = 24$

e $\dfrac{7}{4} \times \dfrac{1}{3} = \dfrac{7}{12}$

f $\dfrac{9}{8} \times \dfrac{2}{7} = \dfrac{9}{28}$

4 Find the product of the fractions.

a $\dfrac{15}{12} \times \dfrac{5}{8} = \dfrac{25}{32}$

b $\dfrac{32}{9} \times \dfrac{36}{8} = 16$

c $\dfrac{7}{8} \times \dfrac{6}{5} = 1\dfrac{1}{20}$

d $\dfrac{11}{12} \times \dfrac{28}{3} = 8\dfrac{5}{9}$

e $\dfrac{21}{5} \times \dfrac{15}{6} = 10\dfrac{1}{2}$

f $\dfrac{25}{4} \times \dfrac{18}{10} = 11\dfrac{1}{4}$

g $\dfrac{30}{9} \times \dfrac{7}{2} = 11\dfrac{2}{3}$

h $\dfrac{14}{8} \times \dfrac{5}{3} = 21\dfrac{11}{12}$

Practice 5 Word problems (2)

Solve these word problems. You may use your calculator in this section.

1 At a party, there were 8 guests. Each guest ate $2\frac{1}{4}$ oranges. How many oranges did the 8 guests eat in total?

1 guest → $2\frac{1}{4}$ oranges

8 guests → $8 \times 2\frac{1}{4}$

= $\underline{18}$ oranges

The 8 guests ate a total of 18 oranges.

2 One kilogram of chicken cost £3. Tim bought $8\frac{2}{3}$ kg of chicken. How much did Tim pay for the chicken?

1 kg → £3

$8\frac{2}{3}$ kg → $8\frac{2}{3} \times £3$

= £26

Tim paid £26 for the chicken.

3 Omar tied up a parcel with $2\frac{1}{4}$ m of string. He tied up a total of 20 of these parcels. How many metres of string did he use?

1 parcel → $2\frac{1}{4}$ m

20 parcels → $20 \times 2\frac{1}{4}$

= 45 m

He used 45 m of string.

2 Find the product.

a $4\frac{1}{5} \times 15 = \boxed{63}$

b $2\frac{3}{7} \times 28 = \boxed{68}$

c $24 \times 1\frac{5}{6} = \boxed{44}$

d $21 \times 2\frac{5}{9} = \boxed{53}\ \boxed{\tfrac{2}{3}}$

e $14 \times 2\frac{7}{9} = \boxed{38}\ \boxed{\tfrac{8}{9}}$

f $26 \times 1\frac{1}{6} = \boxed{30}\ \boxed{\tfrac{1}{3}}$

3 Find the product.

a $4\frac{1}{2} \times 18 = \underline{81}$

b $2\frac{3}{4} \times 16 = \underline{44}$

c $32 \times 3\frac{1}{8} = \underline{100}$

d $1\frac{4}{5} \times 12 = \underline{21\tfrac{3}{5}}$

e $15 \times 2\frac{3}{7} = \underline{36\tfrac{3}{7}}$

f $12 \times 2\frac{3}{8} = \underline{28\tfrac{1}{2}}$

g $9 \times 2\frac{1}{3} = \underline{21}$

h $7 \times 2\frac{1}{4} = \underline{15\tfrac{3}{4}}$

Practice 6 Dividing a fraction by a whole number

1 Shade parts of the model to show the division. Then fill in the answers.

a $\frac{1}{3} \div 2$

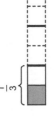

$\boxed{1}$ is shaded.
$\boxed{6}$

$\frac{1}{3} \div 2 = \underline{\frac{1}{6}}$

b $\frac{1}{6} \div 3$

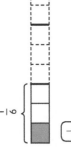

$\boxed{1}$ is shaded.
$\boxed{18}$

$\frac{1}{6} \div 3 = \underline{\frac{1}{18}}$

---

4 The length of a picture is 2 m and its width is $1\frac{2}{5}$ m. Find the area of the picture. Express your answer as a decimal.

$2 \times 1\frac{2}{5} = 2\frac{4}{5}$
$= 2.8\,\text{m}^2$

The area of the picture is $2.8\,\text{m}^2$.

5 Jacob bought 5 pieces of material to make pillowcases. Each piece of material was $1\frac{7}{8}$ m long.

a What was the total length of material he bought?
b One metre of the material cost £6. How much did he pay for all the material?

a $5 \times 1\frac{7}{8} = 9\frac{3}{8}$

He bought $9\frac{3}{8}$ m of material.

b $9\frac{3}{8} \times £6 = £56.25$

He paid £56.25 for all the material.

6 Mrs Kent's family eats $12\frac{3}{4}$ kg of potatoes a month. The cost of 1 kg of potatoes is £2. Find the cost of the potatoes her family eats in a year.

$12 \times 12\frac{3}{4} = 153\,\text{kg}$

Her family eats 153 kg of potatoes in a year.

$153 \times £2 = £306$

The cost of potatoes her family eats in a year is £306.

Solve these word problems. Show your workings clearly.

4 Mr Green had $\frac{2}{5}$ of a cake. He divided the cake equally among 4 pupils. What fraction of the cake did each pupil get?

Method 1

Method 2

$$\frac{2}{5} \div 4 = \frac{\cancel{2}}{5} \times \frac{1}{\cancel{4}_2}$$
$$= \frac{1}{10}$$

From the model we see that each pupil got $\frac{1}{10}$ of a cake.

5 Jake pours $\frac{4}{9}\,\ell$ of milk from a jug equally into 4 cups. Find the amount of milk, in litres:

a in each cup?

b in 3 cups?

a

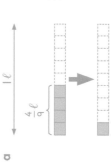

$1\,\ell$

$\frac{4}{9}\,\ell$

$$\frac{4}{9} \div 4 = \frac{\cancel{4}1}{9} \times \frac{1}{\cancel{4}_1}$$
$$= \frac{1}{9}\,\ell$$

From the model we see that the amount of milk in each cup is $\frac{1}{9}\,\ell$.

b $\frac{1}{9} \times 3 = \frac{3}{9} = \frac{1}{3}\,\ell$

The amount of milk in 3 cups is $\frac{1}{3}\,\ell$.

---

2 Divide. Draw models to help you where necessary.

a $\frac{4}{5} \div 2 = \frac{2}{5}$

$\frac{4}{5} \div 2 = \frac{2}{5}$

b $\frac{6}{7} \div 3 = \frac{2}{7}$

$\frac{6}{7} \div 3 = \frac{2}{7}$

c $\frac{3}{4} \div 2 = \frac{3}{8}$

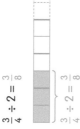

$\frac{3}{4} \div 2 = \frac{3}{8}$

d $\frac{2}{5} \div 3 = \frac{2}{15}$

$\frac{2}{5} \div 3 = \frac{2}{15}$

3 Divide. Express your answer in its simplest form.

a $\frac{4}{5} \div 7 = \frac{4}{35}$

$\frac{4}{5} \times \frac{1}{7} = \frac{4}{35}$

b $\frac{5}{8} \div 9 = \frac{5}{72}$

$\frac{5}{8} \times \frac{1}{9} = \frac{5}{72}$

c $\frac{8}{9} \div 4 = \frac{2}{9}$

$\frac{{}^{2}\cancel{8}}{9} \times \frac{1}{\cancel{4}_1} = \frac{2}{9}$

d $\frac{10}{11} \div 5 = \frac{2}{11}$

$\frac{{}^{2}\cancel{10}}{11} \times \frac{1}{\cancel{5}_1} = \frac{2}{11}$

Practice 7   Word problems (3)

Solve these word problems. Show your workings clearly. Draw models to help you where necessary.

1 Liam writes 72 pages of a story in a day. He writes $\frac{1}{2}$ of the pages in the morning and $\frac{1}{3}$ of the pages in the afternoon. He writes the rest of the pages in the evening. How many pages of the story does he write altogether in the morning and afternoon?

72 pages

morning   afternoon   evening

6 units → 72 pages
1 unit → 12 pages   or
5 units → 60 pages

$$\frac{1}{2} + \frac{1}{3} = \frac{3}{6} + \frac{2}{6} = \frac{5}{6}$$

$$\frac{5}{\cancel{6}_1} \times \cancel{72}^{12} = 60$$

Liam writes 60 pages of the story altogether in the morning and afternoon.

2 Last Saturday, Ravi spent 6 hours altogether reading, playing games and chatting with his friends. He spent $\frac{2}{5}$ of the time reading and $\frac{1}{2}$ of the time playing games. How many minutes did he spend chatting with his friends?

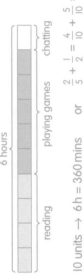

6 hours

reading   playing games   chatting

10 units → 6h = 360 mins   or $\frac{2}{5} + \frac{1}{2} = \frac{4}{10} + \frac{5}{10} = \frac{9}{10}$
1 unit → 36 mins $1 - \frac{9}{10} = \frac{1}{10}$

$$6 \times \frac{1}{10} = \frac{6}{10}\,h = 36\,mins$$

Ravi spent 36 minutes chatting with his friends.

---

6 Max bought $\frac{3}{5}$ kg of pumpkin. He divided the pumpkin into 6 equal portions.
  a Find the mass, in kilograms, of 1 portion of pumpkin.
  b Find the total mass, in kilograms, of 4 portions of pumpkin.

a

1 kg

$\frac{3}{5}$ kg

?

$$\frac{3}{5} \div 6 = \frac{\cancel{3}}{5} \times \frac{1}{\cancel{6}_2} = \frac{1}{10}\,kg$$

From the model we see that the mass of 1 portion of pumpkin was $\frac{1}{10}$ kg.

b $\frac{1}{10} \times 4 = \frac{4}{10} = \frac{2}{5}$ kg
The total mass of 4 portions of pumpkin was $\frac{2}{5}$ kg.

7 Alicia bought a plot of land with an area of $\frac{2}{5}$ km². She divided the land equally into 8 small plots. What was the total area of 3 of the small plots of land?

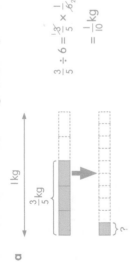

1 km²

$\frac{2}{5}$ km²

?

$$\frac{2}{5} \div 8 = \frac{\cancel{2}^1}{5} \times \frac{1}{\cancel{8}_4} = \frac{1}{20}\,km^2$$

$$3 \times \frac{1}{20} = \frac{3}{20}\,km^2$$

From the model we see that the total area of 3 small plots of land was $\frac{3}{20}$ km².

3 Abby's dad earns £720 a week. He spends $\frac{1}{3}$ of his money on rent and $\frac{3}{4}$ of the remaining money on shopping. How much money does he spend on both rent and shopping?

Method 1

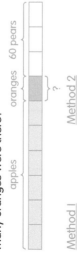

6 units → £720
1 unit → £120
5 units → £600

Method 2

$1 - \frac{1}{3} = \frac{2}{3}$ (remainder)

$\frac{3}{4} \times \frac{2}{3} = \frac{1}{2}$ (shopping)

$\frac{1}{3} + \frac{1}{2} = \frac{2}{6} + \frac{3}{6} = \frac{5}{6}$ (rent & shopping)

$\frac{5}{6} \times £720 = £600$

Abby's dad spends £600 on rent and shopping.

4 A box contained pieces of fruit such as apples, oranges and pears. $\frac{3}{5}$ of the pieces of fruit were apples. $\frac{1}{4}$ of the remaining pieces of fruit were oranges and the rest were pears. If there were 60 pears in the box, how many oranges were there?

[bar model: apples, oranges, 60 pears]

Method 1
3 units → 60
1 unit → 20

Method 2

$1 - \frac{3}{5} = \frac{2}{5}$ (remainder)

$\frac{1}{4} \times \frac{2}{5} = \frac{1}{10}$ (oranges)

$\frac{3}{5} + \frac{1}{10} = \frac{6}{10} + \frac{1}{10} = \frac{7}{10}$ (apples & oranges)

$1 - \frac{7}{10} = \frac{3}{10}$ (pears)

$\frac{3}{10} \to 60$ pears

$\frac{1}{10} \to 20$ oranges

20 pieces of fruit were oranges.

5 Sian opened a 2 kg packet of flour. She used $\frac{4}{9}$ of the flour to make a pizza. Then she used $\frac{2}{7}$ of the remaining flour to make bread. Find the mass of the packet of flour that she had left.
Give your answer to 2 decimal places.

Pizza $\rightarrow \frac{4}{9}$ of the flour

Remaining flour $\rightarrow \frac{5}{9}$ of the flour

$1 - \frac{2}{7} = \frac{5}{7}$

Left $\rightarrow \frac{5}{7}$ of $\frac{5}{9} = \frac{5}{7} \times \frac{5}{9} = \frac{25}{63}$

$\frac{25}{63} \times 2 \approx 0.79$ kg or 793·65 g

She had 0·79 kg (or 793·65 g) of flour left.

6 During a triathlon, Sharon swam $\frac{1}{4}$ of the total route and cycled $\frac{3}{5}$ of the remaining route. She jogged the rest of the route. If she jogged 3600 m, find the total distance of the route.

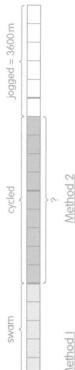

Method 1
6 units → 3600 m
1 unit → 600 m
20 units → 12 000 m
= 12 km

Method 2

$1 - \frac{1}{4} = \frac{3}{4}$ (remainder)

$\frac{3}{5} \times \frac{3}{4} = \frac{9}{20}$ (cycled)

$\frac{1}{4} + \frac{9}{20} = \frac{5}{20} + \frac{9}{20} = \frac{7}{10}$ (swam & cycled)

$1 - \frac{7}{10} = \frac{3}{10}$ (jogged)

$\frac{3}{10} = 3600$ m

$\frac{10}{10} = 12\,000$ m = 12 km

The total distance of the route taken was 12 km.

Maths Journal

1   Ella solved the following word problem in 2 ways.

> Eddie ate $\frac{1}{2}$ of a pie. Rob ate $\frac{1}{2}$ of the remainder.
> What fraction of the pie was left?

Show 2 different ways of solving the word problem. You may draw a model if necessary.

<u>Method 1</u>

Eddie   Rob
($\frac{1}{2}$ of remainder)

From the model we see that $\frac{1}{4}$ of the pie was left.

<u>Method 2</u>

$1 - \frac{1}{2} = \frac{1}{2}$ (remainder)

$1 - \frac{1}{2} = \frac{1}{2}$ (fraction of pie left of remainder)

$\frac{1}{2} \times \frac{1}{2} = \frac{1}{4}$

$\frac{1}{4}$ of the pie was left.

or

$1 - \frac{1}{2} = \frac{1}{2}$ (remainder)

$\frac{1}{2} \times \frac{1}{2} = \frac{1}{4}$ (fraction of the pie that Rob ate)

$\frac{1}{2} \times \frac{1}{4} = \frac{3}{4}$ (fraction of the pie Eddie and Rob ate)

$1 - \frac{3}{4} = \frac{1}{4}$

$\frac{1}{4}$ of the pie was left.

Challenging Practice

1   Fill in the spaces.

How many groups of $3\frac{1}{2}$ in 7?

a $\frac{2}{3} + \frac{2}{3} + \frac{2}{3} + \frac{2}{3} + \frac{2}{3} = \dfrac{5}{} \times \frac{2}{3}$

b $\frac{1}{4} + \frac{1}{4} + \frac{1}{4} + \frac{1}{4} + \frac{1}{8} + \frac{1}{8} = \dfrac{4}{} \times \frac{1}{4}$

2   Lisa was given half of a cake and Nick was given $\frac{1}{3}$ of the other half. The remaining cake was shared equally among 8 pupils. What fraction of the whole cake did each of the 8 pupils get?

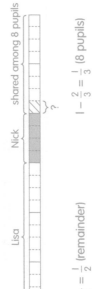

Lisa   Nick   shared among 8 pupils

$1 - \frac{1}{2} = \frac{1}{2}$ (remainder)

$\frac{1}{3} \times \frac{1}{2} = \frac{1}{6}$ (Nick)

$\frac{1}{2} + \frac{1}{6} = \frac{3}{6} + \frac{1}{6} = \frac{2}{3}$ (Lisa & Nick)

$1 - \frac{2}{3} = \frac{1}{3}$ (8 pupils)

$\frac{1}{3} \div 8 = \frac{1}{3} \times \frac{1}{8} = \frac{1}{24}$

Each pupil got $\frac{1}{24}$ of the cake.

Review 2

Date: _____

1 Express each fraction in its simplest form.

a $\dfrac{6}{14} = \dfrac{3}{7}$

b $\dfrac{9}{24} = \dfrac{3}{8}$

c $\dfrac{5}{10} = \dfrac{1}{2}$

d $\dfrac{15}{18} = \dfrac{5}{6}$

2 For each pair of fractions, find the lowest common multiple of the denominators. Then express both fractions with the same denominator.

a $\dfrac{2}{3}, \dfrac{7}{12}$ $\dfrac{\boxed{8}}{\boxed{12}}, \dfrac{\boxed{7}}{\boxed{12}}$

b $\dfrac{1}{3}, \dfrac{5}{8}$ $\dfrac{\boxed{8}}{\boxed{24}}, \dfrac{\boxed{15}}{\boxed{24}}$

3 Shade to find the sum of $\dfrac{1}{3}$ and $\dfrac{3}{5}$ on the model. Then complete the addition sentence.

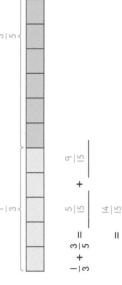

$\dfrac{1}{3} + \dfrac{3}{5} = \dfrac{5}{15} + \dfrac{9}{15}$

$= \dfrac{14}{15}$

Problem Solving

Date: _____

1 Jim and Sheena each had an identical cottage pie. Jim ate $\dfrac{2}{3}$ of his cottage pie and Sheena ate $\dfrac{1}{4}$ of her cottage pie. Jim ate 150 g more cottage pie than Sheena. What was the mass of each cottage pie?

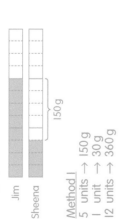

Jim

Sheena

150 g

Method 1

5 units → 150 g

1 unit → 30 g

12 units → 360 g

Method 2

$\dfrac{2}{3} - \dfrac{1}{4} = \dfrac{8}{12} - \dfrac{3}{12} = \dfrac{5}{12}$

$\dfrac{5}{12}$ → 150 g

$\dfrac{1}{12}$ → 30 g

$\dfrac{12}{12}$ → 360 g

The mass of each cottage pie was 360 g.

2 Mr Clark had some pineapples for sale. He sold 24 pineapples in the morning. In the afternoon, he sold $\dfrac{2}{7}$ of the remainder. Then he had $\dfrac{1}{2}$ of the total number of pineapples left. How many pineapples did Mr Clark have at first?

sold 24 pineapples in the morning $\dfrac{1}{2}$ of the total number of pineapples left   sold in the afternoon

$\dfrac{1}{2}$ of the total number of pineapples → 5 units

Total number of pineapples → 10 units

3 units → 24 pineapples

1 unit → 8 pineapples

10 units → 80 pineapples

Mr Clark had 80 pineapples at first.

4 Add. Express your answer in its simplest form where necessary.

a $\frac{3}{4} + \frac{1}{12} = \frac{9}{12} + \frac{1}{12}$
$= \frac{10}{12}$
$= \frac{5}{6}$

b $\frac{3}{5} + \frac{2}{7} = \frac{21}{35} + \frac{10}{35}$
$= \frac{31}{35}$

5 Shade to find the difference of $\frac{4}{5}$ and $\frac{2}{3}$ on the model. Then complete the subtraction sentence.

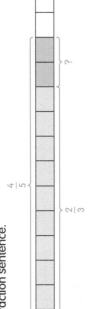

$\frac{4}{5} - \frac{2}{3} = \frac{12}{15} - \frac{10}{15}$
$= \frac{2}{15}$

6 Subtract. Express your answer in its simplest form where necessary.

a $\frac{3}{4} - \frac{1}{12} = \frac{9}{12} - \frac{1}{12}$
$= \frac{8}{12}$
$= \frac{2}{3}$

b $\frac{3}{5} - \frac{3}{9} = \frac{27}{45} - \frac{15}{45}$
$= \frac{12}{45}$
$= \frac{4}{15}$

7 Write each division sentence as a fraction.

a $4 \div 9 = \frac{\boxed{4}}{\boxed{9}}$

b $4 \div 11 = \frac{\boxed{4}}{\boxed{11}}$

8 Write each fraction as a division sentence.

a $\frac{5}{6} = \underline{} \div \underline{}$

b $\frac{7}{12} = \underline{} \div \underline{}$

9 Express each fraction as a decimal. Round your answer to 2 decimal places where necessary.

a $\frac{4}{5} = 0.80$

b $\frac{2}{9} \approx 0.22$

c $\frac{5}{12} \approx 0.42$

10 Divide. Express your answer as a mixed number. Where necessary, express your answer in its simplest form.

a $7 \div 5 = 1\frac{2}{5}$

b $19 \div 4 = 4\frac{3}{4}$

c $22 \div 8 = \frac{22}{8}$
$= \frac{11}{4}$
$= 2\frac{3}{4}$

d $28 \div 6 = \frac{28}{6}$
$= \frac{14}{3}$
$= 4\frac{2}{3}$

11 Express each division sentence as a mixed number and as a decimal correct to 2 decimal places where necessary.

Division Sentence	a Mixed Number	a Decimal
a $8 \div 3$	$2\frac{2}{3}$	$2 \cdot 67$
b $13 \div 4$	$3\frac{1}{4}$	$3 \cdot 25$
c $18 \div 7$	$2\frac{4}{7}$	$2 \cdot 57$
d $23 \div 5$	$4\frac{3}{5}$	$4 \cdot 60$

Solve these word problems. Show your workings clearly.

12 Ron used $\frac{3}{5}$ kg of flour to make bread and $\frac{2}{7}$ kg of flour to make scones. How many more kilograms of flour did he use to make bread than scones?

$\frac{3}{5} - \frac{2}{7} = \frac{21}{35} - \frac{10}{35}$
$= \frac{11}{35}$ kg

He used $\frac{11}{35}$ kg more flour to make bread.

13 Henry cycled $2\frac{1}{4}$ km to the park to meet his friend. Then he cycled $1\frac{2}{5}$ km to the sandwich shop to get some lunch. What was the total distance Henry cycled?

$2\frac{1}{4} + 1\frac{2}{5} = 3\frac{13}{20}$ km

The total distance Henry cycled was $3\frac{13}{20}$ km.

14 Tina used $4\frac{5}{12}$ m of thread to sew a costume. Kelvin used $1\frac{2}{3}$ m of thread to mend his shirt. How many metres of thread did they use altogether?

$4\frac{5}{12} + 1\frac{2}{3} = 5\frac{13}{12} = 6\frac{1}{12}$ m

They used $6\frac{1}{12}$ m of thread altogether.

15 Tom and Aisha had an equal number of eggs at first. Then Tom sold $\frac{1}{3}$ of his eggs and Aisha sold $\frac{3}{4}$ of her eggs. If Aisha sold 250 more eggs than Tom, how many eggs did each person have at first?

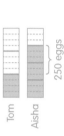
Tom
Aisha
250 eggs

5 units → 250 eggs
1 unit → 50 eggs
12 units → 600 eggs
Each person had 600 eggs at first.

16 Ros poured $1\frac{3}{4}\,\ell$ of orange juice into a container. She added $3\frac{1}{3}\,\ell$ of mango juice into the container. She then poured $2\frac{2}{3}\,\ell$ of the mixed juice into a jug. How many litres of mixed juice were left in the container?

$1\frac{3}{4} + 3\frac{1}{3} = 1\frac{9}{12} + 3\frac{4}{12}$
$= 4\frac{13}{12} = 5\frac{1}{12}\,\ell$

There were $5\frac{1}{12}\,\ell$ of mixed juice.

$5\frac{1}{12} - 2\frac{2}{3} = 5\frac{1}{12} - 2\frac{8}{12}$
$= 4\frac{13}{12} - 2\frac{8}{12} = 2\frac{5}{12}$

$2\frac{5}{12}\,\ell$ of mixed juice were left.

17 Find the value of:

a $\frac{2}{5}$ of $\frac{10}{11} = \frac{2}{5} \times \frac{\cancel{10}^{\,2}}{11} = \frac{4}{11}$

b $\frac{8}{9}$ of $\frac{5}{12} = \frac{\cancel{8}^{\,2}}{9} \times \frac{5}{\cancel{12}_{\,3}} = \frac{10}{27}$

c $\frac{6}{7} \times \frac{5}{8} = \frac{\cancel{6}^{\,3}}{7} \times \frac{5}{\cancel{8}_{\,4}} = \frac{15}{28}$

d $\frac{4}{5} \times \frac{10}{12} = \frac{\cancel{4}^{\,1}}{\cancel{5}} \times \frac{\cancel{10}^{\,2}}{\cancel{12}_{\,3}} = \frac{2}{3}$

18 Find the product.

a $\frac{2}{5} \times \frac{15}{7} = \frac{6}{7}$

b $\frac{9}{5} \times \frac{5}{12} = \frac{3}{4}$

c $\frac{4}{3} \times \frac{7}{6} = 1\frac{5}{9}$

d $\frac{8}{3} \times \frac{9}{12} = 2$

19 Find the product.

a $2\frac{1}{4} \times 16 = 36$

b $27 \times 1\frac{2}{9} = 33$

c $5\frac{3}{6} \times 42 = 231$

d $55 \times 6\frac{3}{11} = 345$

e $2\frac{5}{6} \times 15 = 42\frac{1}{2}$

f $45 \times 2\frac{5}{12} = 108\frac{3}{4}$

20 Divide. Express your answer in its simplest form.

a $\frac{7}{8} \div 5 = \frac{7}{8} \times \frac{1}{5} = \frac{7}{40}$

b $\frac{9}{11} \div 4 = \frac{9}{11} \times \frac{1}{4} = \frac{9}{44}$

c $\frac{4}{7} \div 12 = \frac{\cancel{4}^{\,1}}{7} \times \frac{1}{\cancel{12}_{\,3}} = \frac{1}{21}$

d $\frac{3}{7} \div 6 = \frac{\cancel{3}^{\,1}}{7} \times \frac{1}{\cancel{6}_{\,2}} = \frac{1}{14}$

e $\frac{5}{8} \div 4 = \frac{5}{8} \times \frac{1}{4} = \frac{5}{32}$

f $\frac{2}{9} \div 6 = \frac{\cancel{2}^{\,1}}{9} \times \frac{1}{\cancel{6}_{\,3}} = \frac{1}{27}$

Solve these word problems. Show your workings clearly.

21 Matt bought $\frac{8}{9}$ kg of chicken. He used $\frac{1}{4}$ of it to make chicken soup. How many kilograms of chicken did he use to make the soup?

$\frac{\cancel{8}^{\,2}}{9} \times \frac{1}{\cancel{4}_{\,1}} = \frac{2}{9}$ kg

He used $\frac{2}{9}$ kg of chicken to make the soup.

22 In a race, Joshua covered a total distance of $\frac{11}{12}$ km. He ran $\frac{4}{5}$ of the distance and walked the rest of the way. How many kilometres did he run?

$\frac{11}{\cancel{12}^{3}} \times \frac{\cancel{4}^{1}}{5} = \frac{11}{15}$ km

He ran $\frac{11}{15}$ km.

23 On a picnic, 12 children each got $3\frac{1}{4}$ sandwiches. How many sandwiches did the children get altogether?

1 child → $3\frac{1}{4}$ sandwiches

12 children → $12 \times 3\frac{1}{4}$

= 39 sandwiches

The children got 39 sandwiches altogether.

24 Mr Ali used $4\frac{3}{8}$ kg of meat to prepare a pot of soup. He cooked 12 identical pots of soup. How many kilograms of meat did he use altogether?

1 pot → $4\frac{3}{8}$ kg

12 pots → $12 \times 4\frac{3}{8}$

= $52\frac{1}{2}$ kg

He used $52\frac{1}{2}$ kg of meat altogether.

25 Ella poured $\frac{3}{8}$ ℓ of jelly mix equally into 9 jelly moulds. Find the volume of jelly mix in 2 of these moulds.

$\frac{3}{8} \div 9 = \frac{\cancel{3}^{1}}{8} \times \frac{1}{\cancel{9}_{3}}$

$= \frac{1}{24}$ ℓ

$2 \times \frac{1}{\cancel{24}_{12}} = \frac{1}{12}$ ℓ

The volume of jelly mix in 2 jelly moulds was $\frac{1}{12}$ ℓ.

26 Sally sold 135 cabbages in a day. She sold $\frac{1}{3}$ of the cabbages in the first hour and $\frac{2}{5}$ of the cabbages in the second hour. How many cabbages did she sell altogether in the two hours?

$\frac{1}{3} + \frac{2}{5} = \frac{5}{15} + \frac{6}{15} = \frac{11}{15}$

$\frac{11}{15} \times 135 = 99$ cabbages

Sally sold 99 cabbages in the two hours.

27 $\frac{1}{7}$ of a school's garden was used to grow vegetables. $\frac{1}{3}$ of the remaining garden was used to grow flowers. What fraction of the garden was used to grow flowers?

vegetables

flowers

$1 - \frac{1}{7} = \frac{6}{7}$

$\frac{1}{3} \times \frac{6}{7} = \frac{2}{7}$

$\frac{2}{7}$ of the garden was used to grow flowers.

28 Jan's family spent £840 on a holiday. They spent $\frac{2}{3}$ of the amount on the accommodation and $\frac{1}{2}$ of the remaining amount on food. How much did they spend on the accommodation and food altogether?

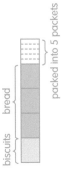

accommodation

food

$1 - \frac{2}{3} = \frac{1}{3}$ (remainder)

$\frac{1}{2} \times \frac{1}{3} = \frac{1}{6}$ (food)

$\frac{2}{3} + \frac{1}{6} = \frac{4}{6} + \frac{1}{6} = \frac{5}{6}$

$\frac{5}{6} \times £840 = £700$

They spent £700 on the accommodation and food.

29 Matthew used $\frac{1}{5}$ of a box of sugar for biscuits and $\frac{3}{4}$ of the remainder to make bread. The rest of the sugar was packed equally into 5 packets. What fraction of the total amount of sugar was in each packet?

biscuits   bread

packed into 5 packets

$\frac{1}{5} \div 5 = \frac{1}{5} \times \frac{1}{5} = \frac{1}{25}$

$\frac{1}{25}$ of the total amount of sugar was in each packet.

30 Saleem travelled $\frac{1}{4}$ of a journey by bus. He jogged $\frac{1}{2}$ of the remaining distance and walked the rest of the journey. If he walked 800 m, what was the total distance he travelled?

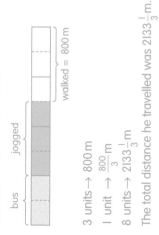

bus   jogged

walked = 800 m

3 units → 800 m

1 unit → $\frac{800}{3}$ m

8 units → $2133\frac{1}{3}$ m

The total distance he travelled was $2133\frac{1}{3}$ m.

31 Serena's mum filled up $\frac{7}{8}$ of her petrol tank for a trip. She used $\frac{6}{11}$ of the petrol by the end of the trip. The capacity of her petrol tank was 70 ℓ. How much petrol did she use for the trip?

Express your answer as a decimal correct to 1 decimal place.

$\frac{7}{\underset{4}{8}} \times \frac{\overset{3}{6}}{11} = \frac{21}{44}$

$\frac{21}{44} \times 70 = 33\frac{9}{22} \approx 33.4\,\ell$

She used 33.4 ℓ of petrol for the trip.

32 $\frac{3}{10}$ of the seats on a train were first class seats. The rest were standard seats. $\frac{4}{5}$ of the standard seats were occupied. What fraction of all seats were unoccupied standard seats?

Method 1

$1 - \frac{3}{10} = \frac{7}{10}$

$\frac{7}{10}$ of the seats standard seats.

$1 - \frac{4}{5} = \frac{1}{5}$

$\frac{1}{5}$ of the standard seats were unoccupied.

$\frac{7}{10} \times \frac{1}{5} = \frac{7}{50}$

$\frac{7}{50}$ of all the seats were unoccupied standard seats.

Method 2

$\frac{4}{5} \times \frac{7}{10} = \frac{28}{50} = \frac{14}{25}$

$\frac{7}{10} - \frac{14}{25} = \frac{35}{50} - \frac{28}{50}$

$\qquad = \frac{7}{50}$

33 Kerry had some boxes of vegetables for sale. She sold 35 boxes on Monday. She sold $\frac{1}{5}$ of the remaining boxes of vegetables on Tuesday. Then she had $\frac{1}{3}$ of the total number of boxes of vegetables left. How many boxes of vegetables did she have at first?

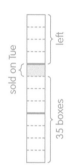

sold on Tue

35 boxes   left

7 units → 35 boxes

1 unit → 5 boxes

12 units → 60 boxes

She had 60 boxes of vegetables at first.

34 Alisha uses $\frac{1}{4}$ of a packet of flour to make bread. She uses $\frac{1}{9}$ of the remainder to make pizza. What fraction of the packet of flour does she have left?

$$1 - \frac{1}{4} = \frac{3}{4}$$

$$1 - \frac{1}{9} = \frac{8}{9}$$

$$\frac{8}{9} \times \frac{3}{4} = \frac{2}{3}$$

Alisha has $\frac{2}{3}$ of the packet of flour left.

35 300 people attended a party. After one hour, $\frac{1}{3}$ of the number of people left the party. After another hour, $\frac{3}{10}$ of the remaining people left the party. How many people were left at the party in the end?

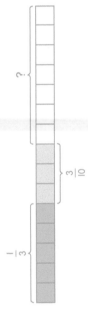

15 units → 300 people

1 unit → 20 people

7 units → 7 × 20 = 140 people

140 people were left at the party in the end.

Unit 5: Area of a Triangle

Week	Learning Objectives	Thinking Skills	Resources
3	**(1) Base and height of a triangle** Pupils will be able to identify the base and corresponding height of a triangle.	• Spatial visualisation • Inductive reasoning	• Pupil Textbook 5A, pp 133 to 136 • Practice Book 5A, pp 133 to 134 • Teacher's Guide 5A, pp 221 to 224
4	**(2) Finding the area of a triangle** Pupils will be able to: • state that the area of a triangle is half that of its related rectangle • state the area of a triangle in terms of its base and corresponding height • find the area of a triangle given its base and corresponding height *Maths Journal* This journal enables pupils to express their understanding that triangles with equal (or common) bases and a common height will have equal areas.	• Spatial visualisation • Inductive and deductive reasoning	• Pupil Textbook 5A, pp 137 to 144 • Practice Book 5A, pp 135 to 139 • Teacher's Guide 5A, pp 225 to 232

Unit 5: Area of a Triangle

Week	Learning Objectives	Thinking Skills	Resources
4	*Let's Explore!* Pupils will be able to calculate the areas of different triangles and conclude that triangles with equal bases and equal heights have the same area. *Let's Wrap It Up!* Emphasise the key concepts, skills and processes that have been taught in the unit. Discuss the worked example with pupils to assess whether they have mastered these concepts, skills and processes.	• Spatial visualisation • Deduction	• Pupil Textbook 5A, pp 145 to 146 • Teacher's Guide 5A, pp 233 to 234
4	*Put On Your Thinking Caps!* Pupils will be able to apply their knowledge that triangles with equal bases and a common height have the same area to solve the problem posed.	• Spatial visualisation Heuristic for problem solving: • Look for a pattern	• Pupil Textbook 5A, p 147 • Practice Book 5A, pp 140 to 142 • Teacher's Guide 5A, pp 235

Area of a Triangle

Learning objective: Base and height of a triangle

Pupils will be able to identify the base and corresponding height of a triangle.

Key concept

Any side of a triangle can be the base and for each base, there is a corresponding height.

Thinking skills

- Spatial visualisation
- Inductive reasoning

What you will need

Acute-angled triangle ABC (see Photocopy master 7 on p 325)

Teaching sequence

1

- Revise the parts of a triangle with pupils. Show pupils examples of different triangles, e.g. acute-angled, obtuse-angled and right-angled. Ask pupils to discuss the similarities and differences between them.
- Similarities: All of them have three sides and three angles.
- Differences:
  (1) One has a right angle and two angles less than 90°.
  (2) One has three angles less than 90°.
  (3) One has an angle greater than 90° and two angles less than 90°.

2

- To introduce the terms **base** and **height**, show the acute-angled triangle ABC provided on Photocopy master 7.
- Draw a perpendicular line from A to BC and name it AD. Explain to pupils that the side BC is called a base and for this base, AD is the height of triangle ABC. Repeat the procedure for bases AB and AC.
- Emphasise that **any side of a triangle can be a base. For a given base, the height is the perpendicular line from the opposite corner (vertex) to the base.**

Unit 5 Area of a Triangle

Let's Learn!

Base and height of a triangle

1 ABC is a triangle.

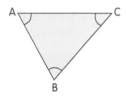

 Let's recall the parts of a triangle. It has three sides and three angles.

The three sides are AB, BC and CA.

2 In triangle ABC:

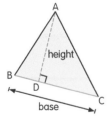 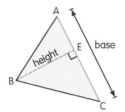 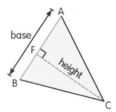

AD is perpendicular to BC. BC is called the **base** and AD is called the **height**.

BE is perpendicular to AC. In this case, AC is the base and BE is the height.

CF is perpendicular to AB. In this case, AB is the base and CF is the height.

133

- Obtuse-angled triangle PQR and right-angled triangle DEF (see Photocopy master 8 on p 326)
- Ruler

Teaching sequence

- Show the obtuse-angled triangle PQR provided on Photocopy master 8.
- Draw the perpendicular line from P to QR (extended) and name it PS. Explain to pupils that when QR is the base, the height is PS. Highlight to pupils that in this case, the base has to be extended (or produced) in order to draw the height.
- Repeat the procedure for bases PR and PQ.
- Show the right-angled triangle DEF. Ask pupils to identify the three bases and their corresponding heights.

- Ask pupils to work on this question as practice.

Unit 5 Area of a Triangle

③ PQR is another triangle.

If the base is QR, the height is PS.

If the base is PR, the height is QT.

If the base is QP, the height is RU.

> Any side of a triangle can be the base.

> The height is always perpendicular to the base.

④ Each of these triangles is named XYZ.

ZW is perpendicular to XY.
In each case, ZW is the height and XY is the base.

134

Teaching sequence

5 and **6**

- Ask pupils to work on these questions as an informal assessment.

5 Name the base for the given height in each triangle.

a

If the height is BE, the base is AC.

b

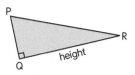

If the height is QR, the base is PQ.

c

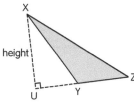

If the height is XU, the base is YZ.

6 Name the height for the given base in each triangle.

a

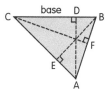

If the base is CB, the height is AD.

b

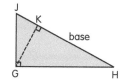

If the base is JH, the height is GK.

c

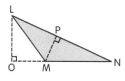

If the base is MN, the height is LO.

d

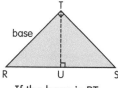

If the base is RT, the height is ST.

135

Unit 5: Area of a Triangle   223

What you will need

- Ruler
- Set square

Independent work

- *Let's Practice!*
- Practice I in Practice Book 5A, pp 133 to 134.

Note

Besides noting that each height is perpendicular to its corresponding base, pupils may also notice that the three heights of a triangle pass through a common point. For an obtuse-angled triangle, the heights have to be extended to meet at a common point. The point where the three heights meet is called the orthocentre. It is inside an acute-angled triangle, at the right angle vertex of a right-angled triangle and outside an obtuse-angled triangle.

Teaching sequence

- This activity reinforces the concept that the heights of a triangle are always perpendicular to the respective bases.

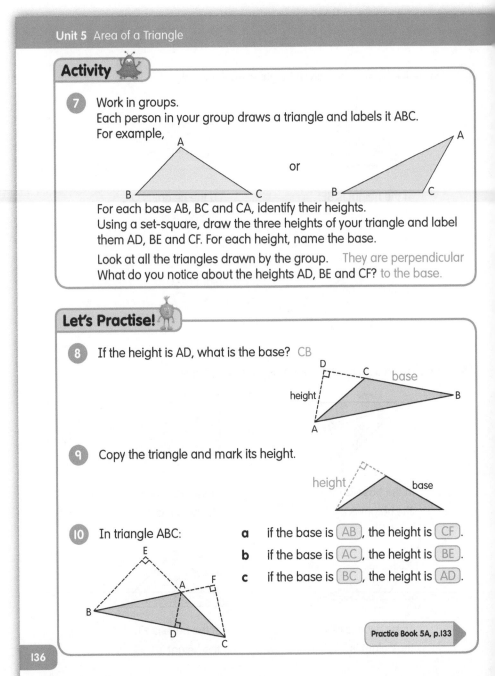

Unit 5 Area of a Triangle

Activity

7   Work in groups.
    Each person in your group draws a triangle and labels it ABC.
    For example,

    or

    For each base AB, BC and CA, identify their heights.
    Using a set-square, draw the three heights of your triangle and label them AD, BE and CF. For each height, name the base.

    Look at all the triangles drawn by the group.   They are perpendicular
    What do you notice about the heights AD, BE and CF? to the base.

Let's Practise!

8   If the height is AD, what is the base? CB

9   Copy the triangle and mark its height.

10 In triangle ABC:

    a   if the base is AB, the height is CF.
    b   if the base is AC, the height is BE.
    c   if the base is BC, the height is AD.

    Practice Book 5A, p.133

136

224   **Unit 5:** Area of a Triangle

Learning objectives: Finding the area of a triangle

Pupils will be able to:

- state that the area of a triangle is half that of its related rectangle
- state the area of a triangle in terms of its base and corresponding height
- find the area of a triangle given its base and corresponding height

Key concepts

- The area of a triangle is half that of its related rectangle.
- Area of a triangle
$$= \frac{1}{2} \times \text{base} \times \text{height}$$

Thinking skills

- Spatial visualisation
- Inductive and deductive reasoning

What you will need

Right-angled triangle ABC (see Photocopy master 9 on p 327)

Let's Learn!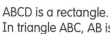

Finding the area of a triangle

1 What is the area of triangle ABC?

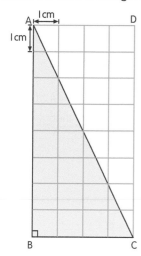

> Triangle ABC is half of rectangle ABCD.

> Recall that:
> Area of a rectangle = Length × Width.

ABCD is a rectangle.
In triangle ABC, AB is perpendicular to BC.
BC is the base when AB is the height.
The base BC = 4 cm and the height AB = 8 cm.

Area of triangle ABC $= \frac{1}{2} \times$ area of rectangle ABCD

$$= \frac{1}{2} \times 4 \times 8 = 16 \text{ cm}^2$$

> How are the lengths 4 cm and 8 cm of rectangle ABCD related to triangle ABC?

> They are the base and height of triangle ABC.

137

Teaching sequence

1

- Help pupils to recall their work on finding the area of a rectangle from Unit 12 in Pupil Textbook 4B.
- Show the right-angled triangle ABC provided on Photocopy master 9, with AB = 8 cm and BC = 4 cm. Set BC as the base. Ask pupils to identify the corresponding height and then explain to pupils that the shaded portion of rectangle ABCD is the area of the triangle.

- Ask pupils: *"What fraction of the rectangle ABCD is the triangle ABC?"* $\left(\frac{1}{2}\right)$ The shape could be cut out to illustrate that the area of triangle ABC = half the area of rectangle ABCD.

- Encourage pupils to observe that:
Area of △ABC
$$= \frac{1}{2} \text{ of rectangle ABCD}$$
$$= \frac{1}{2} \times 4 \text{ cm} \times 8 \text{ cm}$$
$$= \frac{1}{2} \times \text{BC} \times \text{AB}$$
$$= \frac{1}{2} \times \text{base} \times \text{height}$$

Unit 5: Area of a Triangle 225

Additional activity

Ask pupils to work in groups of four. Ask them to find another method to find the area of triangle ABC. Pupils should be able to discuss the problem and see that they can subtract the areas of triangles FBA and ACE from the area of rectangle FBCE.

What you will need

Acute-angled triangle ABC (see Photocopy master 10 on page 328)

Teaching sequence

- Show the acute-angled triangle ABC provided on Photocopy master 10. The height AD = 4 cm, BD = 2 cm and BC = 6 cm. Shade the area of triangle ABC and highlight the rectangle BCEF as shown.

- Guide pupils to recognise that the area of triangle ABC is half that of rectangle BCEF.

- Area of triangle ABC

$$= \frac{1}{2} \times 6\,\text{cm} \times 4\,\text{cm}$$

$$= \frac{1}{2} \times BC \times AD$$

$$= \frac{1}{2} \times \text{base} \times \text{height}$$

- Show another acute-angled triangle with a different base and height and repeat the teaching procedure.

- Guide pupils to conclude that:

Area of a triangle

$$= \frac{1}{2} \times \textbf{base} \times \textbf{height}$$

- The diagram below can also be used to illustrate the argument.

 What is the area of triangle ABC?

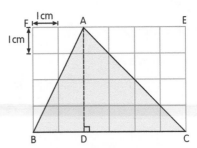

In triangle ABC, the base BC = 6 cm and the height AD = 4 cm.

Area of triangle ABC = area of triangle ABD + area of triangle ADC

Area of triangle ABD $= \frac{1}{2} \times$ area of rectangle FBDA

$$= \frac{1}{2} \times 2 \times 4$$

$$= 4\,\text{cm}^2$$

Area of triangle ADC $= \frac{1}{2} \times$ area of rectangle ADCE

$$= \frac{1}{2} \times 4 \times 4$$

$$= 8\,\text{cm}^2$$

So area of triangle ABC = 4 + 8

$$= \boxed{12\,\text{cm}^2}$$

Now area of rectangle FBCE = 6 × 4

$$= 24\,\text{cm}^2$$

Half of its area = $\boxed{12\,\text{cm}^2}$

So area of triangle ABC $= \frac{1}{2} \times$ area of rectangle FBCE

$$= \frac{1}{2} \times 6 \times 4$$

$$= \frac{1}{2} \times \text{base BC} \times \text{height AD}$$

The lengths 6 cm and 4 cm of rectangle FBCE are the base and height of triangle ABC.

Triangle ABC is half of rectangle FBCE.

What you will need

Obtuse-angled triangle ABC
(see Photocopy master II on
page 329)

3 What is the area of triangle ABC?

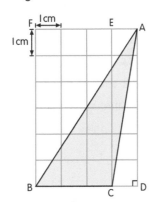

In triangle ABC, the base BC = 3 cm and the height AD = 6 cm.

Area of triangle ABC = area of triangle ABD − area of triangle ACD

Area of triangle ABD = $\frac{1}{2}$ × 4 × 6
$$= 12 \text{ cm}^2$$

Area of triangle ACD = $\frac{1}{2}$ × 1 × 6
$$= 3 \text{ cm}^2$$

So area of triangle ABC = 12 − 3
$$= \boxed{9 \text{ cm}^2}$$

How are the lengths
3 cm and 6 cm of
rectangle BCEF related
to triangle ABC?

Now area of rectangle BCEF = 3 × 6
$$= 18 \text{ cm}^2$$
Half of its area = $\boxed{9 \text{ cm}^2}$

So area of triangle ABC = $\frac{1}{2}$ × area of rectangle BCEF

$$= \frac{1}{2} × 3 × 6$$

$$= \frac{1}{2} × \text{base BC} × \text{height AD}$$

139

Teaching sequence

3

- Show the obtuse-angled
  triangle ABC provided
  on Photocopy master II
  and guide pupils to the
  conclusion that:

Area of a triangle
$$= \frac{1}{2} × \textbf{base} × \textbf{height}$$

What you will need

- Ruler
- Square grid paper

Additional activity

- Ask pupils to cut a rectangle from a piece of square grid paper (p 330). Next ask pupils to cut the rectangle into three pieces to try to make a triangle. Ask pupils: *"Can it be done?"*
- Ask pupils to measure the length and width of the rectangle before cutting. Can they find the area of the triangle without measuring its base and height?

Teaching sequence

- An alternative approach to derive the formula for the area of a triangle is given in this activity. Pupils are required to transform the triangle into a rectangle and notice that the area of the triangle is equal to the area of this rectangle GBCH. Observe that $GB = \frac{1}{2} EB$ so:

Area of triangle ABC
$$= \frac{1}{2} \times \text{base} \times \text{height}.$$

Activity

(4) In triangle ABC, BC is the base and AD is the height.

1 Copy Diagram I on a piece of square grid paper.
2 Cut out triangles AKL and ALM.
3 Rotate triangle AML through a half-turn about point M.
4 Rotate triangle AKL through a half-turn about point K.
5 The position of the triangles should now match Diagram 2.

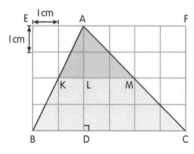

Diagram I

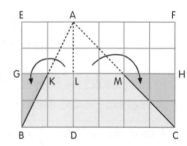

Diagram 2

Area of triangle ABC = area of rectangle ▢ GBCH

$$= \frac{1}{2} \times \text{area of rectangle } \boxed{} \text{ EBCF}$$

$$= \frac{1}{2} \times BC \times EB$$

$$= \frac{1}{2} \times BC \times \boxed{AD}$$

$$= \frac{1}{2} \times \text{base} \times \boxed{} \text{ height}$$

What you will need

- Ruler
- Square grid paper

Activity

5 In triangle PQR, QR is the base and PS is the height.

1 Copy Diagram I on a piece of square grid paper.

2 Cut out triangles PVX and VRX.

3 Rearrange the two triangles as shown in Diagram 2.

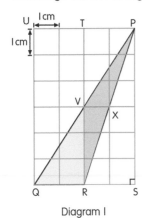

Diagram I

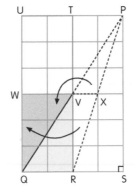

Diagram 2

Area of triangle PQR = area of rectangle ⬡ WQRV

$\quad\quad = \frac{1}{2} \times$ area of rectangle ⬡ UQRT

$\quad\quad = \frac{1}{2} \times QR \times TR$

$\quad\quad = \frac{1}{2} \times QR \times \boxed{PS}$

$\quad\quad = \frac{1}{2} \times base \times$ ⬡ height

Area of a triangle = $\frac{1}{2} \times$ Base $\times$ Height

141

Teaching sequence

5

- An alternative approach to derive the formula for the area of a triangle is given in this activity. Pupils are required to transform the triangle into a rectangle and notice that the area of the triangle is equal to the area of this rectangle.

What you will need

- Ruler

Additional activity

Ask pupils to work in pairs. Tell them that the area of an unknown triangle is 72 cm². Ask pupils to find as many triangles as possible, with different bases and heights, that have an area of 72 cm².

Teaching sequence

- Demonstrate to pupils how to apply the formula for the area of a triangle.

- In this activity, pupils should calculate the area of a right-angled triangle using each side as the base to verify that any side of the triangle can be the base.

6 Find the area of triangle PQR.

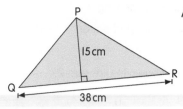

Area of triangle PQR $= \frac{1}{2} \times$ base $\times$ height

$= \frac{1}{2} \times 38 \times 15$

$= \boxed{} 285$ cm²

Activity

7

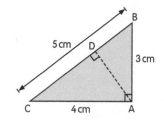

Work in pairs.

ABC is a triangle. ∠BAC is a right angle and AD is perpendicular to BC.

1 Measure the height AD in centimetres to 1 decimal place. 2·4 cm

2 In turn, take each side of the triangle, AB, AC, BC as the base.

3 Work out the area of triangle ABC. Do you get the same area? Yes

142

Independent work

Let's Practise!

8 Find the area of each shaded triangle.

a 136 cm² 17 cm 16 cm

b 182 cm² 7 cm 52 cm

c 475 cm² 20 cm 18 cm 25 cm

d 483 m² 28 m 14 m 23 m

e 868 cm² 35 cm 31 cm 56 cm

f 90 m² 8 m 12 m 17 m 15 m 25 m

Let's Practise!

9 Find the area of each shaded triangle.

a 28 cm² 14 cm 4 cm

b 96 cm² 12 cm 16 cm 20 cm

c 290 cm² 9 cm 11 cm 29 cm

d 182 m² 13 m 15 m 28 m

143

8

- Ask pupils to work on these questions as practice.

Objective of activity

This journal enables pupils to express their understanding that triangles with equal (or common) bases and a common height will have equal areas.

Thinking skills

- Spatial visualisation
- Deduction

Independent work

Practice 2 and *Maths Journal* in Practice Book 5A, pp 135 to 139.

Teaching sequence

14 *Maths Journal*

- From the model of the triangle, pupils should deduce that triangles BED and ECD have the same area, as they have the same height and the lengths of their bases are the same.

Let's Practise!

10 In triangle ABC, BC = 44 cm and AD = 27 cm. Find the area of triangle ABC. 594 cm²

11 In the diagram, QR = 26 cm, QS = 20 cm and PS = 26 cm. Find the area of triangle PQR. 338 cm²

12 In triangle ABC, BD = 9 m, DC = 10 m and AD = 18 m. Find the area of triangle ABC. 171 m²

13 In the diagram, LM = 18 cm, KM = 16 cm and KN = 14 cm. Find the area of triangle KLM. 126 cm²

> Practice Book 5A, p.135

Maths Journal

14

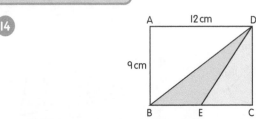

ABCD is a rectangle and BE = EC.
What can you say about the areas of triangles BED and ECD? Why?

The lengths of the bases are the same and they have the same height. So their areas are the same.

144

Objective of activity

Pupils will be able to calculate the areas of different triangles and conclude that triangles with equal bases and equal heights have the same area.

Thinking skills

- Spatial visualisation
- Deduction

Let's Explore!

15

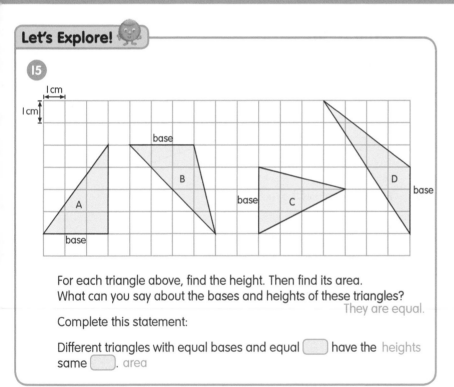

For each triangle above, find the height. Then find its area.
What can you say about the bases and heights of these triangles?

They are equal.

Complete this statement:

Different triangles with equal bases and equal ⬚ have the heights
same ⬚. area

Let's Wrap It Up!

You have learnt:

- to identify the three sides of a triangle
- that any side of a triangle can be the base
- that the height of a triangle is always perpendicular to the base
- **Area of a triangle = $\frac{1}{2}$ × Base × Height**.

Teaching sequence

15 *Let's Explore!*

- Ask pupils to work in groups of four. Each pupil in the group finds the height and works out the area of one of the four given triangles.
- Guide pupils to realise that the triangles have equal bases and equal heights.
- Ask pupils to compare the areas of the four triangles. Guide pupils to realise that different triangles can have equal bases and heights and therefore the same area.

Let's Wrap It Up!

- Emphasise the key concepts, skills and processes that have been taught in the unit.

145

Teaching sequence

Let's Wrap It Up!

- Discuss the worked example with pupils to assess whether they have mastered these concepts and skills and to provide further help on any difficulties that pupils may still have.

Let's Wrap It Up!

Let's Revise!

ABCD is a rectangle of perimeter 48 cm. AB = 6 cm and CD = DE.

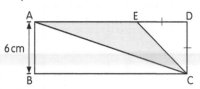

a Find the length of the rectangle.

Perimeter = 48 cm
AB + BC   = 48 ÷ 2
          = 24 cm
Length BC = 24 − 6
          = 18 cm

b Find the area of the shaded triangle ACE.

Method 1

DE = CD = 6 cm
AD = BC = 18 cm
Area of △CDE = $\frac{1}{2}$ × 6 × 6
             = 18 cm²
Area of △ACD = $\frac{1}{2}$ × 18 × 6
             = 54 cm²
Area of shaded triangle ACE = Area of △ACD − Area of △CDE
                            = 54 − 18
                            = 36 cm²

Method 2

Area of shaded triangle ACE = $\frac{1}{2}$ × AE × CD
                            = $\frac{1}{2}$ × (18 − 6) × 6
                            = $\frac{1}{2}$ × 12 × 6
                            = 36 cm²

146

234   **Unit 5:** Area of a Triangle

Objective of activity

Pupils will be able to apply their knowledge that triangles with equal bases and a common height have the same area to solve the problem posed.

Thinking skill

Spatial visualisation

Heuristic for problem solving

Look for a pattern

Independent work

Challenging Practice and *Problem Solving* in Practice Book 5A, pp 140 to 142.

Put On Your Thinking Caps!

16. ABCD is a rectangle. BE = ED.

Find the area of the shaded triangle ABE.

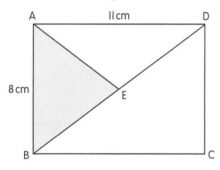

Area of triangle ABD = $\frac{1}{2}$ × 8 × 11 = 44 cm²

Area of triangle ABE = 44 ÷ 2 = 22 cm²

Practice Book 5A, p.140 >   Practice Book 5A, p.142 >

147

Teaching sequence

16 *Put On Your Thinking Caps!*

- This problem is an application of the concept that triangles with equal bases and a common height will have equal areas.

- Guide pupils to deduce that triangles ABE and ADE have equal areas since their bases are equal and they have a common height.

Unit 5 Area of a Triangle

Date: _____

Practice 1 Base and height of a triangle

1) In each triangle, a base or a height is given. Name the related height or base.

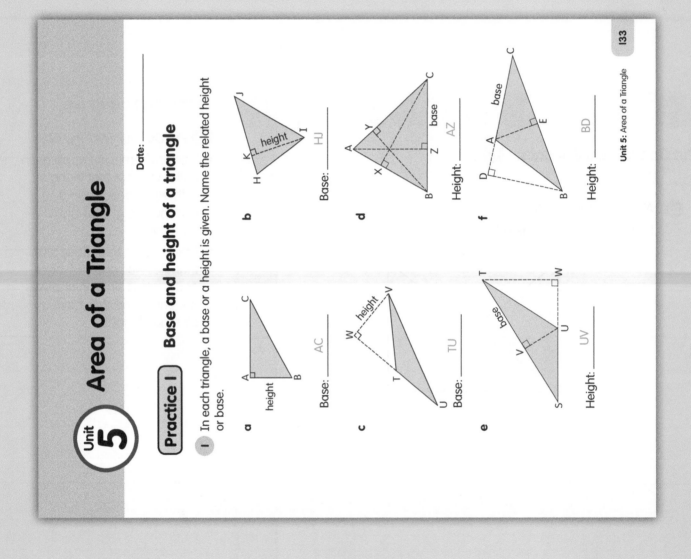

a

height

Base: AC

b

height

Base: HJ

c

height

Base: TU

d

base

Height: AZ

e

base

Height: UV

f

base

Height: BD

Practice 2 Finding the area of a triangle

1 Find the area of each shaded triangle. Write down each step and give your answers in the correct units.

a

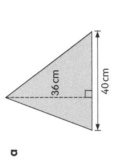

$$\text{Area of triangle} = \frac{1}{2} \times \text{Base} \times \text{Height}$$
$$= \frac{1}{2} \times 40 \times 36$$
$$= \underline{\hspace{2cm}} 720 \text{ cm}^2$$

b

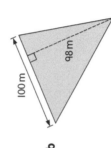

$$\text{Area of triangle} = \frac{1}{2} \times 100 \times 98$$
$$= \underline{\hspace{2cm}} 4900 \text{ m}^2$$

c

$$\text{Area of triangle} = \frac{1}{2} \times 4 \times 20$$
$$= \underline{\hspace{2cm}} 40 \text{ cm}^2$$

d

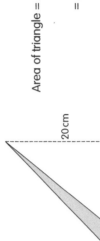

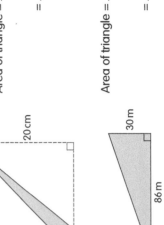

$$\text{Area of triangle} = \frac{1}{2} \times 86 \times 30$$
$$= \underline{\hspace{2cm}} 1290 \text{ m}^2$$

2 For each triangle, the base is given. Label the height. Use a set-square to draw the height where necessary.

a

b

c

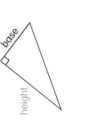

d

e

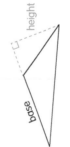
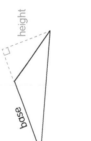

f

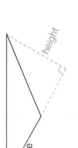
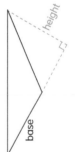
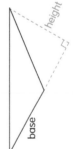
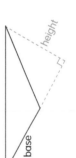

g

h

Page 137

2 Find the area of each shaded triangle.

a
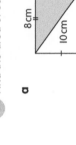
8cm, 6cm, 10cm

$\text{Area} = \frac{1}{2} \times \underline{8} \times \underline{6}$

$= \underline{24}\,\text{cm}^2$

b

10cm, 24cm, 26cm

$\text{Area} = \underline{120}\,\text{cm}^2$

c
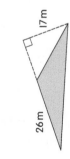
5m, 4m, 3m

$\text{Area} = \underline{6}\,\text{m}^2$

d

10cm, 8cm, 15cm

$\text{Area} = \underline{60}\,\text{cm}^2$

3 Find the area of each shaded triangle.

a
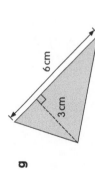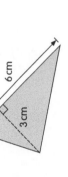
12cm, 8cm, 10cm

$\text{Area} = \frac{1}{2} \times \underline{12} \times \underline{8}$

$= \underline{48}\,\text{cm}^2$

b
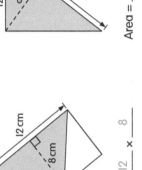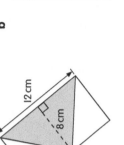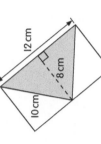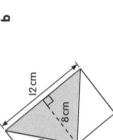
12cm, 9cm, 20cm

$\text{Area} = \underline{90}\,\text{cm}^2$

Page 136

e
23cm, 15cm

$\text{Area of triangle} = \frac{1}{2} \times 23 \times 15$

$= 172\cdot5\,\text{cm}^2$

f
26m, 17m

$\text{Area of triangle} = \frac{1}{2} \times 26 \times 17$

$= 221\,\text{m}^2$

g
6cm, 3cm

$\text{Area of triangle} = \frac{1}{2} \times 6 \times 3$

$= 9\,\text{cm}^2$

h
54cm, 72cm

$\text{Area of triangle} = \frac{1}{2} \times 72 \times 54$

$= 1944\,\text{cm}^2$

i
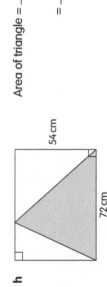
45m, 70m, 32m

$\text{Area of triangle} = \frac{1}{2} \times 38 \times 45$

$= 855\,\text{m}^2$

Maths Journal

1 Four pupils worked out the area of the shaded triangle on the right.

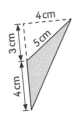

The following are their workings.

Zack: $4 \times 4 = 16$ cm²
Patrick: $\frac{1}{2} \times 5 \times 4 = 10$ cm²
Becky: $\frac{1}{2} \times 7 \times 4 = 14$ cm²
James: $\frac{1}{2} \times 3 \times 4 = 6$ cm²

Explain the mistakes they have made. Then write the correct answer.

Zack: He did not multiply by $\frac{1}{2}$.

Patrick: He used the wrong height.

Becky: She used the wrong base.

James: He used the wrong base.

The area of the shaded triangle is: $\frac{1}{2} \times 4 \times 4 = 8$ cm²

2 The area of the shaded triangle is 15 cm².
Explain why the area of the rectangle is 30 cm².

Area of related rectangle = 2 × Area of triangle

Total area of the 2 unshaded triangles = Total area of the shaded triangle

Therefore area of the rectangle = 2 × Area of shaded triangle
= 2 × 15
= 30 cm²

---

c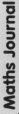

Area = 24 cm²

d (28 cm, 18 cm, 25 cm)

Area = 252 cm²

4 Find the area of each shaded triangle.

a (5 cm, 6 cm, 5 cm)

Area = $\frac{1}{2}$ × 5 × 5
= 12·5 cm²

b (8 cm, 4 cm, 2 cm)

Area = 8 cm²

c (7 cm, 5 cm, 4 cm)

Area = 14 cm²

d (25 cm, 15 cm, 6 cm, 20 cm)

Area = 105 cm²

Date: _____

Challenging Practice

1 ABCD is a square with 10 cm sides and BE = EC. Find the area of the shaded triangle.

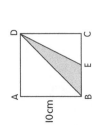

BE = 10 ÷ 2 = 5 cm
Area of shaded triangle = $\frac{1}{2} \times 5 \times 10 = 25\,\text{cm}^2$

2 ABCD is a rectangle 18 cm by 8 cm. AE = ED and AF = FB. Find the area of the shaded triangle.

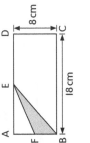

FB = 8 ÷ 2
= 4 cm
AE = 18 ÷ 2
= 9 cm
Area of shaded triangle = $\frac{1}{2} \times 4 \times 9$
= 18 cm²

3 ABCD is a rectangle with an area of 48 cm². The length of CD is 3 times the length of DF. BC = 4 cm.

a Find the length of the rectangle.
b Find the area of the shaded triangle.

a Length = 48 ÷ 4
= 12 cm
b DF = 12 ÷ 3
= 4 cm
Area of triangle = $\frac{1}{2} \times 4 \times 4$
= 8 cm²

4 ABCD is a rectangle 12 cm by 5 cm. BE = 4 cm. Find the area of the shaded region, ABED.

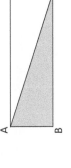

Area of shaded region, ABED
= area of rectangle ABCD − area of △DEC
= $(12 \times 5) - (\frac{1}{2} \times 8 \times 5)$
= 60 − 20
= 40 cm²

5 ABCD is a square with 8 cm sides. AE = AF = 4 cm. Find the area of the shaded triangle, CEF.

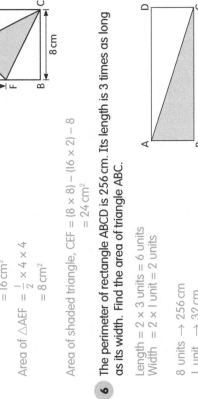

Area of △EDC = Area of △BCF
= $\frac{1}{2} \times 8 \times 4$
= 16 cm²

Area of △AEF = $\frac{1}{2} \times 4 \times 4$
= 8 cm²

Area of shaded triangle, CEF = $(8 \times 8) - (16 \times 2) - 8$
= 24 cm²

6 The perimeter of rectangle ABCD is 256 cm. Its length is 3 times as long as its width. Find the area of triangle ABC.

Length = 2 × 3 units = 6 units
Width = 2 × 1 unit = 2 units

8 units → 256 cm
1 unit → 32 cm
3 units → 96 cm

Area of triangle = $\frac{1}{2} \times 96 \times 32$
= 1536 cm²

Date: _____

Problem Solving

1 Look at the pattern of triangles below.

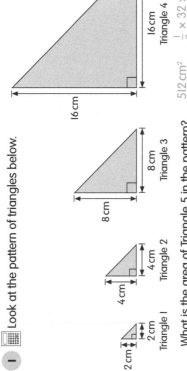

2 cm

2 cm
Triangle 1

4 cm

4 cm
Triangle 2

8 cm

8 cm
Triangle 3

16 cm

16 cm
Triangle 4

What is the area of Triangle 5 in the pattern? ___512 cm²___ Triangle 8

$\frac{1}{2} \times 32 \times 32 = 512 \text{ cm}^2$

Which triangle in the pattern will have an area of 32 768 cm²? ___Triangle 8___

Guess and check with a calculator, Triangle 6 = $\frac{1}{2} \times 64 \times 64 = 2048 \text{ cm}^2$

Triangle 7 = $\frac{1}{2} \times 128 \times 128 = 8192 \text{ cm}^2$

Triangle 8 = $\frac{1}{2} \times 256 \times 256 = 32768 \text{ cm}^2$

2 ABCD is a square with 20 cm sides.
AX = XB, BY = YC, CZ = ZD, AW = WD. WY and XZ are straight lines.
Find the total area of the shaded parts.

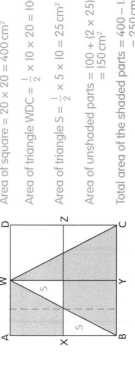

Area of square = $20 \times 20 = 400 \text{ cm}^2$

Area of triangle WDC = $\frac{1}{2} \times 10 \times 20 = 100 \text{ cm}^2$

Area of triangle S = $\frac{1}{2} \times 5 \times 10 = 25 \text{ cm}^2$

Area of unshaded parts = $100 + (2 \times 25)$
$= 150 \text{ cm}^2$

Total area of the shaded parts = $400 - 150$
$= 250 \text{ cm}^2$

Week	Learning Objectives	Thinking Skills	Resources
5	**(1) Finding ratio** Pupils will be able to: • understand the concept of ratio as a way to show the relative sizes of two quantities • understand that a given ratio does not indicate the actual sizes of the quantities involved • draw a comparison model to represent two quantities given the ratio • solve simple word problems involving ratio using model drawing *Let's Explore!* This task is an investigation activity to reinforce the concept of ratio.	• Comparing • Visualisation	• Pupil Textbook 5A, pp 148 to 154 • Practice Book 5A, pp 143 to 146 • Teacher's Guide 5A, pp 246 to 252
5	**(2) Equivalent ratios** Pupils will be able to: • express equivalent ratios given two quantities • write a given ratio $x : y$ in its simplest form • find the missing number(s) in equivalent ratios	• Comparing • Visualisation	• Pupil Textbook 5A, pp 155 to 161 • Practice Book 5A, pp 147 to 148 • Teacher's Guide 5A, pp 253 to 259

Week	Learning Objectives	Thinking Skills	Resources
5	**(3) Word problems (I)** Pupils will be able to solve up to 2-step word problems involving ratio of two quantities using: • the concept of equivalent ratios • model drawing and the unitary method *Maths Journal* This activity helps pupils to reflect on what they have learnt in writing ratios and using the unitary method to solve ratio word problems.	• Comparing • Visualisation	• Pupil Textbook 5A, pp 162 to 168 • Practice Book 5A, pp 149 to 152 • Teacher's Guide 5A, pp 260 to 266
6	**(4) Comparing three quantities** Pupils will be able to: • use ratio to show the relative sizes of three quantities • express equivalent ratios given three quantities • write a given ratio $x : y : z$ in its simplest form • find the missing number(s) in equivalent ratios	• Comparing • Visualisation	• Pupil Textbook 5A, pp 169 to 172 • Practice Book 5A, pp 153 to 154 • Teacher's Guide 5A, pp 267 to 270

Unit 6: Ratio

Week	Learning Objectives	Thinking Skills	Resources
6	**(5) Word problems (2)** Pupils will be able to solve up to 2-step word problems involving ratio of three quantities using: • the concept of equivalent ratios • model drawing and the unitary method *Maths Journal* This activity helps pupils to reflect on the methods they have learnt to write ratios and simplify the ratios using division. *Let's Explore!* This activity involves getting pupils to make as many ratios as possible using all the given numbers irrespective of whether they can be simplified.	• Comparing • Visualisation	• Pupil Textbook 5A, pp 173 to 177 • Practice Book 5A, pp 155 to 160 • Teacher's Guide 5A, pp 271 to 275

Unit 6: Ratio

Week	Learning Objectives	Thinking Skills	Resources
6	*Let's Wrap It Up!* This section summarises the two strategies to write equivalent ratios and the method to simplify them. *Put On Your Thinking Caps!* This problem gets pupils to practise the making a systematic list strategy in conjunction with the ratio concept.	• Comparing • Visualisation Heuristic for problem solving: • Making a systematic list	• Pupil Textbook 5A, pp 177 to 178 • Practice Book 5A, pp 161 to 162 • Teacher's Guide 5A, pp 275 to 276
	Review 3		• Practice Book 5A, pp 163 to 172
	Revision 1		• Practice Book 5A, pp 173 to 186

Summative assessment opportunities

Assessment Book 5, Test 3, pp 27 to 32
For extension, Assessment Book 5, Challenging Problems 2, pp 33 to 34
Assessment Book 5, Check-up 2, pp 35 to 46

Ratio

Learning objectives:
Finding ratio

Pupils will be able to:

- understand the concept of ratio as a way to show the relative sizes of two quantities
- understand that a given ratio does not indicate the actual sizes of the quantities involved

- draw a comparison model to represent two quantities given the ratio
- solve simple word problems involving ratio using model drawing

Thinking skills

- Comparing
- Visualisation

Key concept

Ratio is a way of comparing the relative sizes of two quantities or sets of items.

Teaching sequence

- Illustrate and explain the concept of ratio using the example in the question.
- There are 2 chocolate muffins and a blueberry muffin. This means there are 2 units of chocolate muffins to 1 unit of blueberry muffin. We say that the ratio of the number of chocolate muffins to the number of blueberry muffins is 2 : 1.
- Emphasise the following:
  - (1) Ratio is a way of comparing the relative sizes of two sets of items.
  - (2) Order is important when writing a ratio. In a ratio, the first and second numbers refer to the first and second quantities respectively.
  - (3) In this example, the ratio units represent the actual units.

- Use this question to informally assess pupils' ability to write a ratio given two sets of items.
- Emphasise that the order of objects is important when we write ratios.

Unit 6 — Ratio

Let's Learn!

Finding ratio

 There are 2 chocolate muffins and 1 blueberry muffin.

> Let's compare the number of chocolate muffins with the number of blueberry muffins.

The **ratio** of the number of **chocolate muffins to** the number of **blueberry muffins** is **2 : 1**.

> We read 2 : 1 as **2 to 1**.

> Here the ratio gives the number of objects in each set.

The **ratio** of the number of **blueberry muffins to** the number of **chocolate muffins** is **1 : 2**.

The ratio of the number of **blue flags** to the number of **yellow flags** is ⬚ 2 ⬚ : ⬚ 5 ⬚.

The ratio of the number of **yellow flags** to the number of **blue flags** is ⬚ 5 ⬚ : ⬚ 2 ⬚.

148

3 Meena has 2 trays of large eggs and 3 trays of small eggs.

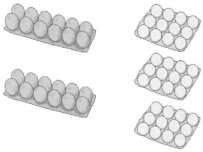

There is an equal number of eggs on each tray.

2 trays to 3 trays is 2 : 3.

The ratio of the number of large eggs to the number of small eggs is 2 : 3.

The ratio of the number of small eggs to the number of large eggs is 3 : 2.

I tray contains 12 eggs. Here the ratio does not give the actual numbers of large and small eggs.

4

The ratio of the number of boxes of orange juice to the number of boxes of apple juice is (3) : (5).

The ratio of the number of boxes of apple juice to the number of boxes of orange juice is (5) : (3).

Note

Highlight to pupils that **3** shows that a given ratio may not always indicate the actual size of the quantities involved (i.e. number of items in each set).

Teaching sequence

3

- Guide pupils to understand that a ratio can also be written in terms of equal sets/groups of items using the example in the question.
- Explain to pupils that in this example, each tray contains an equal number of eggs.
- Use the following questions to emphasise this point:
  (a) *"How many trays of large eggs are there?"* (2)
  (b) *"How many trays of small eggs are there?"* (3)
  (c) *"How many large eggs are there altogether?"* (24)
  (d) *"How many small eggs are there altogether?"* (36)
  (e) *"What is the ratio of the number of large eggs to the number of small eggs?"* (2 : 3)
  (f) *"What is the ratio of the number of small eggs to the number of large eggs?"* (3 : 2)

4

- Use this parallel question to informally assess if pupils understand the ratio concept.
- Emphasise that you can use the number of groups of trays as units when there are equal number of cartons in each group.

Unit 6: Ratio **247**

Teaching sequence

- Explain that ratio does not only involve comparing items in terms of quantity size but also in terms of the size of other attributes such as mass, length, volume or capacity etc.
- In the given example, emphasise that to compare two quantities as a ratio, they must be in the same unit. Here, both masses are in the same unit – kg. However, if one mass were in g and the other mass in kg, we would not be able to compare them as a ratio.

- Use this example to help pupils understand that a given ratio does not indicate the actual size of quantities involved.
- The ratio of the number of big leaves to the number of small leaves is 3 : 4. However, that does not mean that there are 3 big leaves and 4 small leaves.

Unit 6 Ratio

⑤ Tim bought 2 kg of onions and 9 kg of potatoes.

To compare as a ratio, the masses must be in the same unit.

The ratio of the mass of potatoes to the mass of onions is ⑨ : ② .

The ratio of the mass of onions to the mass of potatoes is ② : ⑨ .

⑥

I unit = 2 leaves
So a ratio does not necessarily give the actual quantities compared.

I unit

I unit

The ratio of the number of big leaves to the number of small leaves is 3 : 4.

The ratio of the number of small leaves to the number of big leaves is ④ : ③ .

Additional activity

Tell pupils that the ratio of the age of Pupil A to the age of Pupil B is 4 : 9. Then ask pupils to draw a possible model to represent this ratio.

Teaching sequence

7

- Assess pupils' ability to write the ratio of the length of B to the length of A based on the model provided.

8

- Work through the word problem and relate it to the part-whole concept in subtraction. After finding the length of the longer piece of wood, pupils can then find the ratio of the shorter piece of wood to the longer piece of wood.

7

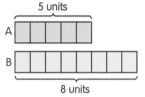
A
B
5 units
8 units

5 units to 8 units

The ratio of the length of A to the length of B is 5 : 8.

The ratio of the length of B to the length of A is ⬚ 8 ⬚ : ⬚ 5 ⬚.

8 Alison cuts a piece of wood, 24 cm long, into two. The shorter piece is 7 cm long. Find the ratio of the length of the shorter piece to the length of the longer piece.

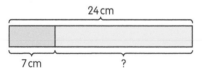
24 cm
7 cm   ?

Length of shorter piece of wood = 7 cm

Length of longer piece of wood = 24 − 7

= 17 cm

The ratio of the length of the shorter piece to the length of the longer piece is 7 : 17.

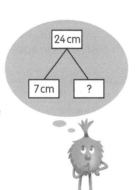
24 cm
7 cm   ?

151

Objective of activity

This task is an investigation activity to reinforce the concept of ratio.

What you will need

10 cubes for each pair of pupils

Teaching sequence

- Ask pupils to solve the word problem as an informal assessment. The concept involved here is also the part-whole concept. Ask pupils to state which are the parts and which is the whole.

10 *Let's Explore!*

- Ask pupils to work in pairs. Provide each pair with 10 cubes.
- Guide pupils to see that there are many different ways of grouping the cubes to make different ratios.
- There are two parts to this investigation. Ask pupils to compare the similarities and differences between the two parts of the activity.

Unit 6 Ratio

9 Matt had 15 kg of rice. He sold 7 kg of the rice. What was the ratio of the mass of rice sold to the mass of rice left?

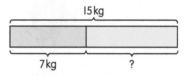

Mass of rice sold = [7] kg

Mass of rice left = [15] – [7]

= [8] kg

The ratio of the mass of rice sold to the mass of rice left is [7] : [8].

Let's Explore!

10 Work in pairs.

You will need 10 cubes.

1 First separate the 10 cubes into two groups. Count the number of cubes in each group.

2 Record your answers in a table as shown below.

Group A	Group B	Ratio A : B
1	9	1 : 9
2	8	2 : 8
⋮	⋮	⋮

3 Next join the cubes in 2s. Then put them in two groups. Count the units of cubes in each group.

4 Record your answers in the same way as in **2**.

Group A	Group B	Ratio A : B
2	8	2 : 8
4	6	4 : 6
⋮	⋮	⋮

5 Discuss the ratios obtained in the two tables.

152

Let's Practise!

11 The table shows the masses of seafood sold by a fishmonger.

Seafood	Mussels	Prawns	Lobsters	Crabs	Crayfish
Mass	2 kg	5 kg	3 kg	11 kg	8 kg

Copy and complete the table below. Then write as many ratios as you can from the data given above. An example is shown.

	Ratio
Mass of mussels to mass of prawns	2 : 5
Mass of lobsters to mass of crayfish	3 : 8
⋮	⋮
Mass of crabs to total mass of seafood	11 : 29

Answers vary

12 Draw models to show the following ratios.

Example

A : B = 2 : 5

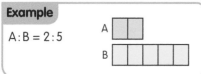

a A : B = 4 : 9   **b** A : B = 11 : 7

c A : B = 8 : 3   **d** A : B = 12 : 5

13 Look at the pictures below. Write two ratios to compare the number of eggs in Set A and in Set B.

A : B = 2 : 5
B : A = 5 : 2

Set A   Set B

153

Independent work

Practice I in Practice Book 5A,
pp 143 to 146.

Let's Practise!

14 Look at the picture below. Write two ratios to compare the items shown.

I unit

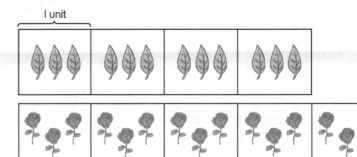

12 : 15, 15 : 12, 4 : 5 and 5 : 4   Accept any two answers.

15 A huge chequered table cloth is 3 m wide and 7 m long. Find the ratio of the length of the table cloth to its width. 7 : 3

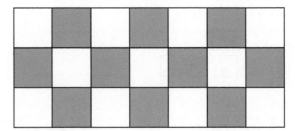

16 Mr Bell has £88. He gives £35 to his son and the rest to his daughter. Find the ratio of the amount of money his son gets to the amount of money his daughter gets. 35 : 53

Practice Book 5A, p.143

154

Learning objectives:
Equivalent ratios

Pupils will be able to:

- express equivalent ratios given two quantities
- write a given ratio $x:y$ in its simplest form
- find the missing number(s) in equivalent ratios

Key concepts

- Finding the common factor of the terms of the ratio of two quantities
- Dividing the terms of a ratio of two quantities by the common factor to express a ratio in its simplest form

Thinking skills

- Comparing
- Visualisation

What you will need

4 red apples or counters and 8 green apples or counters

Let's Learn!

Equivalent ratios

 Ella has 4 red apples and 8 green apples. The ratio of the number of red apples to the number of green apples is 4:8. Ella puts 2 apples of the same colour on each tray.

2 trays of red apples

4 trays of green apples

= I unit

There are 2 trays of red apples and 4 trays of green apples.

The ratio of the number of red apples to the number of green apples is 2:4.

155

Teaching sequence

1

- Illustrate and explain the concept of equivalent ratios using 4 red apples and 8 green apples. Show pupils that 4 red apples and 8 green apples can be grouped in many ways. For each way, the ratio can be written in terms of groups and not in terms of the number of apples.

- The ratio of the number of red apples to the number of green apples is 4:8.

- Next rearrange the red and green apples on trays, in groups of two. There will be 2 trays of red apples and 4 trays of green apples. So the ratio of the number of red apples to the number of green apples is 2:4.

Continued on p 254

What you will need

18 counters of two colours for every four pupils

Additional activity

Ask pupils to work in groups of four. Give each group 18 counters. Ask pupils to divide the counters into two groups in as many ways as possible. Then invite one of the groups to present the different ratios they made with their counters.

Teaching sequence

- Finally rearrange the red and green apples on trays, in groups of four. There will be one tray of red apples and two trays of green apples. The ratio of the number of red apples to the number of green apples is now 1 : 2.
- Explain that 4 : 8, 2 : 4 and 1 : 2 are **equivalent ratios**. These ratios all compare the same number of red apples to the number of green apples.
- Emphasise that 1 : 2 is the ratio in its **simplest form**.

Unit 6 Ratio

Next she puts 4 apples of the same colour on each tray.

= 1 unit

1 tray of red apples

2 trays of green apples

There is 1 tray of red apples and 2 trays of green apples.

The ratio of the number of red apples to the number of green apples is 1 : 2.

The three ratios 4 : 8, 2 : 4 and 1 : 2 compare the same number of red apples and green apples.

These ratios are **equivalent ratios**:

4 : 8 = 2 : 4 = 1 : 2

1 : 2 is a ratio in its **simplest form**.

Which ratio shows the actual number of red apples and green apples? 4 : 8

2

The ratio of the number of pencils to the number of board pins
is (6) : (12).

3 ◯ groups of pencils   6 ◯ groups of board pins

The ratio of the number of pencils to the number of board pins
is (3) : (6).

 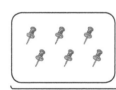

| ◯ group of pencils   2 ◯ groups of board pins

The ratio of the number of pencils to the number of board pins
is (|) : (2).

The equivalent ratios are (6) : (12) , (3) : (6) and (|) : (2).

In these equivalent ratios, the ratio in its simplest form is (|) : (2).

The ratio which shows the actual number of pencils and
board pins is (6) : (12).

- Give pupils counters. Ask them to work in pairs to show the correct grouping for each ratio.
- Use this question to informally assess whether pupils can use grouping to find equivalent ratios.

What you will need

Coloured counters (e.g. red and yellow unit cubes, beads, magnetic buttons)

You can begin this activity before showing pupils the procedure for ③. Give pupils a set of two numbers. Ask them to find factors of each number and then a common factor for each set of numbers.

Teaching sequence

- Demonstrate and explain the procedure for reducing a ratio to its lowest terms:

Step 1: Find a common factor of the terms of the ratio.

$2 \times 2 = 4$
$2 \times 3 = 6$
2 is a common factor of 4 and 6.

Step 2: Divide each term of the ratio by the common factor.

$4 : 6 = 2 : 3$

2 : 3 cannot be simplified any further. It is a ratio in its simplest form.

- Use this question to informally assess whether pupils can write a ratio in its simplest form.
- Revise the guess and check method to find the common factor of the terms of the ratio. (e.g. 12 : 4)
- Ask pupils to try the following numbers in sequence starting from 2, 3, 4, 5 and 6.
- 12 and 4 can be divided by 2 and the result is 6 : 2. Divide further using 2 and the result is 3 : 1.
- Some pupils may be able to see right away that 12 and 4 can be divided to get 3 : 1.

Unit 6 Ratio

③ What is the ratio 4 : 6 in its simplest form?

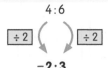

$2 \times 2 = 4$ and $2 \times 3 = 6$.
2 is a common factor of 4 and 6.

Divide 4 and 6 by 2.

4 : 6

÷ 2 〔 〕 ÷ 2

= **2 : 3**

2 and 3 cannot be divided further by a common factor.

The ratio 4 : 6 in its simplest form is 2 : 3.

④ What is each ratio in its simplest form?

a   12 : 4

÷ [4] 〔 〕 ÷ [4]

= [3] : [1]

[4] is a common factor of 12 and 4. Divide 12 and 4 by [4].

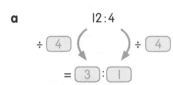

b   9 : 15

÷ [3] 〔 〕 ÷ [3]

= [3] : [5]

First find a common factor of 9 and 15.

158

Arrange pupils into pairs.
Ask them to write statements
for a set of two numbers, e.g. 3
and 12. Next ask pupils to think
of a set of two other numbers
and write similar statements.

E.g. $3 \times 4 = 12$

$12 \div 3 = 4$

So 4 is a common factor.

Ratio **Unit 6**

5 Find the missing number in these equivalent ratios.

$2:5 = 6:\boxed{15}$

Look at the first terms of the equivalent ratios – **2**:5 = **6**:$\boxed{15}$.

Method 1

Method 2

$2 \times 3 = 6$
$5 \times 3 = 15$

$6 \div 2 = 3$

2:5

$\boxed{\times 3}$ $\boxed{\times 3}$

$= \mathbf{6}:\boxed{15}$

So 3 is the
multiplying factor.

$\mathbf{3} \times 5 = \boxed{15}$

6 Find the missing number in these equivalent ratios.

$15:12 = \boxed{5}:4$

Look at the second terms of the equivalent ratios – $15:\mathbf{12} = \boxed{5}:\mathbf{4}$.

Method 1

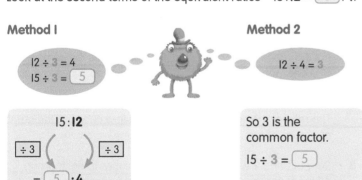

Method 2

$12 \div 3 = 4$
$15 \div 3 = \boxed{5}$

$12 \div 4 = 3$

15:12

$\boxed{\div 3}$ $\boxed{\div 3}$

$= \boxed{5}:\mathbf{4}$

So 3 is the
common factor.

$15 \div 3 = \boxed{5}$

159

Teaching sequence

5

- Show pupils how to find the multiplying factor by using multiplication.
- Look at the first terms of the equivalent ratios:

  2:5 = **6**:?

  $6 \div 2 = 3$

  3 is the multiplying factor.

  $5 \times 3 = 15$

  So the equivalent ratios are $2:5 = 6:15$.

6

- Show pupils how to find the common factor by using division.
- Look at the second terms of the equivalent ratios:

  $15:\mathbf{12} = ?:\mathbf{4}$

  $12 \div 4 = 3$

  3 is the common factor.

  $15 \div 3 = 5$

  So the equivalent ratios are $15:12 = 5:4$.

Objective of activity

This activity helps to reinforce
the concept of equivalent ratios
using the grouping procedure.

What you will need

14 yellow cubes and 28 red
cubes per group

Teaching sequence

- Ask pupils to work on
these questions as an
informal assessment.

- Ask pupils to work in groups
of two or four. Give each
group 14 yellow cubes and
28 red cubes.

- Ask pupils to investigate and
find all possible equivalent
ratios from the different ways
of grouping the cubes.

- However, remind pupils to
follow these conditions when
grouping the cubes:

  (a) Each group must have the
  same number of cubes.

  (b) Yellow and red cubes
  cannot be mixed within
  a group.

- Then ask pupils to do the
same activity using 8 yellow
cubes and 24 red cubes.

- Invite volunteers to present
their answers to the class.
Highlight to pupils that the
number of cubes in each
group is actually a common
factor for the ratios. Although
the answers given for step
2 will vary, the answers will
always simplify to 1:2.

Unit 6 Ratio

7 Find the missing number in these equivalent ratios.

a

$20 \div 4 = \boxed{5}$
$3 \times 5 = \boxed{15}$

b
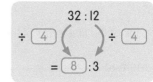

$12 \div 3 = \boxed{4}$
$32 \div 4 = \boxed{8}$

c
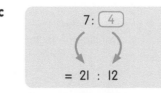

$21 \div 7 = \boxed{3}$
$12 \div 3 = \boxed{4}$

d

$16 \div 2 = \boxed{8}$
$3 \times 8 = \boxed{24}$

Activity

8 Work in groups of two or four.

Each group will need 14 yellow cubes and 28 red cubes.

1 Put the cubes in groups so that each group has the same number
of cubes. You cannot mix yellow cubes and red cubes in a group.

2 Then write the ratio as shown below.
The ratio of the number of groups of yellow cubes to the number
of groups of red cubes is ⬭ : ⬭. Answers vary

3 Repeat **1** and **2** with a new number of cubes in each group.
All the ratios you have obtained are **equivalent ratios**.

4 You can repeat the activity using 8 yellow cubes and 24 red cubes.

160

What you will need

Scientific calculator

Independent work

- *Let's Practise!*
- Practice 2 in Practice Book 5A, pp 147 to 148.

Ratio **Unit 6**

Teaching sequence

12 *Let's Practise!*

- By using a calculator for this question, pupils are able to demonstrate the process of how to find missing parts of equivalent ratios.

Let's Practise!

Answer these questions.

9 Mr Lee had 3 boxes of red chalk and 8 boxes of white chalk. Each box contained 5 pieces of chalk.

    a Find the number of pieces of red chalk Mr Lee had. 15

    b How many pieces of white chalk did Mr Lee have? 40

    c Find the ratio of the number of pieces of red chalk to the number of pieces of white chalk. 15 : 40

    d Find the ratio of the number of boxes of red chalk to the number of boxes of white chalk. 3 : 8

    e What can you say about the ratios in **c** and **d** ?
        They are equivalent ratios.

10 Express each of the following ratios in its simplest form.

    a $4 : 14 = \boxed{2} : \boxed{7}$ **b** $18 : 8 = \boxed{9} : \boxed{4}$

    c $8 : 32 = \boxed{1} : \boxed{4}$ **d** $42 : 12 = \boxed{7} : \boxed{2}$

11 Complete the equivalent ratios.

    a $4 : 7 = 12 : \boxed{21}$ **b** $3 : 8 = \boxed{12} : 32$

    c $27 : 15 = \boxed{9} : 5$ **d** $6 : 42 = 2 : \boxed{14}$

12 Complete the equivalent ratios.

    a $3 : \boxed{5} = 48 : 80$ **b** $\boxed{68} : 51 = 4 : 3$

    c $70 : \boxed{140} = 2 : 4$ **d** $\boxed{4} : 7 = 128 : 224$

Practice Book 5A, p.147

161

Unit 6: Ratio   259

Learning objectives: Word problems (I)

Pupils will be able to solve up to 2-step word problems involving ratio of two quantities using:

- the concept of equivalent ratios
- model drawing and the unitary method

Key concept

Applying equivalent ratio concept, part-whole concept, taking away concept and comparison concept to solve up to 2-step word problems involving ratio of two quantities

Thinking skills

- Comparing
- Visualisation

Teaching sequence

1 and **2**

- Ask pupils to identify the two sets of items in each problem and write a ratio that corresponds to them.
- Then ask pupils to reduce the ratio to its lowest terms by dividing the terms by the highest common factor.
- These two word problems help pupils to see relationships between the items in the word problems and ratio. Given a set of two quantities, they are expected to write a ratio of two items in symbolic form.

Unit 6 Ratio

Let's Learn!

Word problems (I)

1 There are 6 goats and 18 cows on Joseph's farm. Find the ratio of the number of goats to the number of cows on his farm.

The ratio of the number of goats to the number of cows is 6 : 18.

6 : 18

÷ 6 ( ) ÷ 6

= **1 : 3**

> Write the ratio 6 : 18 in its simplest form. Divide 6 and 18 by the common factor, 6.

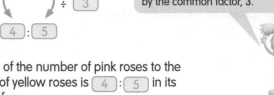

The ratio of the number of goats to the number of cows on the farm is 1 : 3.

2 There are 12 pink roses and 15 yellow roses in Amit's garden. Find the ratio of:

a the number of pink roses to the number of yellow roses

b the number of yellow roses to the number of pink roses

12 : 15

÷ ③ ( ) ÷ ③

= ④ : ⑤

> Write the ratio 12 : 15 in its simplest form. Divide 12 and 15 by the common factor, 3.

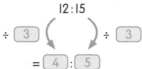

a The ratio of the number of pink roses to the number of yellow roses is ④ : ⑤ in its simplest form.

b The ratio of the number of yellow roses to the number of pink roses is ⑤ : ④.

162

Additional activity

Arrange pupils in pairs. Ask each pupil to think of a real-life situation similar to **3** and write a similar word problem. Pupils swap their word problems with their partner's and solve them.

3 48 children attend a party. 16 of them are girls. Find the ratio of the number of girls to the number of boys at the party.

$48 - 16 = 32$

There are 32 boys at the party.

$16 : 32 = 1 : 2$

$16 : 32$

$= 1 : 2$

The ratio of the number of girls to the number of boys at the party is $1 : 2$.

4 On a rainy day, Mr Jones sold 56 umbrellas and raincoats altogether. He sold 24 raincoats on that day.

a Find the ratio of the total number of umbrellas and raincoats sold to the number of raincoats sold.

b Find the ratio of the number of umbrellas sold to the number of raincoats sold.

a $\boxed{56} : \boxed{24} = \boxed{7} : \boxed{3}$

The ratio of the total number of umbrellas and raincoats sold to the number of raincoats sold is $\boxed{7} : \boxed{3}$.

b Number of umbrellas sold $= \boxed{56} - \boxed{24}$

$\qquad\qquad\qquad\qquad\quad = \boxed{32}$

$\boxed{32} : 24 = \boxed{4} : \boxed{3}$

The ratio of the number of umbrellas sold to the number of raincoats sold is $\boxed{4} : \boxed{3}$.

163

Teaching sequence

3

- Guide pupils to see that this is a 2-step word problem.
- Pupils should be able to relate it to the 'part-whole' concept.
- Explain the steps to solve the problem:

  Step 1: Use the 'part-whole' concept in subtraction to find the number of items in the second set (the number of boys from the whole).

  Step 2: Write the required ratio in its simplest form.

4

- Use this word problem to informally assess pupils' ability to use the 'taking away' concept in subtraction to find the number of items left, and to write the required ratio in its simplest form.

Arrange pupils in pairs and
ask each pair to write a word
problem that explains the
following equations:

$72 - 12 = 60$

$50 : 60 = 5 : 6$

Teaching sequence

- In this question, pupils have to first use the 'taking away' concept in subtraction to find the number of plums left. They then need to write the ratio of the number of grapes to that of plums in its simplest form.

- To solve this word problem, pupils need to:
  (1) Use the 'adding on' concept to find the number of apple pies in the end.
  (2) Then write the required ratio of the number of apple pies to the number of strawberry tarts in its simplest form.

Unit 6 Ratio

 There are 25 plums and 40 grapes in a basket. Millie eats 5 grapes. What is the ratio of the number of plums to the number of grapes left in the basket now?

$40 - 5 = 35$ grapes
There are 35 grapes in the basket now.

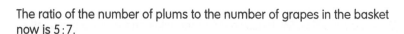

$$25 : 35$$

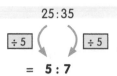

$$= \ 5 : 7$$

The ratio of the number of plums to the number of grapes in the basket now is $5 : 7$.

 Roy bakes 30 apple pies and 16 strawberry tarts. He then bakes another 18 apple pies. Find the ratio of the number of apple pies to the number of strawberry tarts in the end.

$30 + \boxed{18} = \boxed{48}$ apple pies
There are $\boxed{48}$ apple pies in the end.

$\boxed{48} : 16 = \boxed{3} : \boxed{1}$

The ratio of the number of apple pies to the number of strawberry tarts in the end is $\boxed{3} : \boxed{1}$.

Teaching sequence

7

(7) A farm has 96 chickens and ducks altogether. 60 of them are chickens. What is the ratio of the number of chickens to the number of ducks?

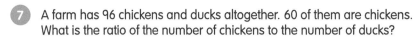
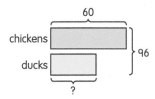
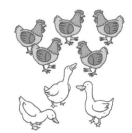

Number of ducks = 96 − 60 = 36

60 : 36 = 5 : 3

The ratio of the number of chickens to the number of ducks is 5 : 3.

- Explain and show pupils how to use the model approach and the unitary method to solve this problem.
- Guide pupils using the following steps:

  Step 1: Draw a comparison model to represent the given information in the word problem. 96 represents the total number of chickens and ducks altogether. 60 represents the number of chickens.

  Step 2: Find the number of ducks.

  Step 3: Write the required ratio in its simplest form.

8

(8) Sam collected a total of 252 wooden and plastic figures. 56 of them were plastic figures. What is the ratio of the number of wooden figures to the number of plastic figures?

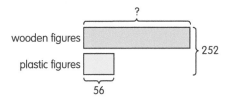

Number of wooden figures = 252 − 56 = 196

196 : 56 = 7 : 2

The ratio of the number of wooden figures to the number of plastic figures is 7 : 2 .

- Assess pupils informally to see if they can follow the strategy above to solve a similar word problem.
- By using a calculator in this question, pupils are being tested on the process of how to find missing parts of equivalent ratios.

165

Ask pupils to write a word
problem that explains
the following:

3 : 8 = 12 : ?

Then ask pupils to solve the word
problem. Invite a volunteer to
present their word problem and
solution to the class.

Teaching sequence

- Explain and show pupils how
to solve this word problem
using two different methods.

Method 1: Pupils first
translate the problem to
symbolic form as shown
in the textbook. Then they
find the unknown value by
multiplying by the common
factor.

Method 2: Pupils draw a
model representing the
information provided in the
question and use the
unitary method to find the
unknown value.

Unit 6 Ratio

 A fishmonger divides a box of prawns into two portions. The ratio
of the mass of the bigger portion to the mass of the smaller portion is
5 : 2. The mass of the bigger portion is 15 kg. Find the mass of the
smaller portion.

Method 1

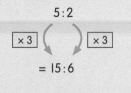

$$5 : 2$$

$$\boxed{\times 3} \quad \boxed{\times 3}$$

$$= 15 : 6$$

$$5 \times 3 = 15$$
$$2 \times 3 = 6$$

$$15 \div 5 \times 2 = 6$$

The mass of the smaller portion of prawns is 6 kg.

Method 2

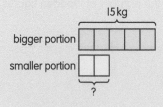

15 kg

bigger portion

smaller portion

?

We can also solve this
problem using a model
to represent the ratio
5 : 2 as 5 units to 2 units.

5 units ⟶ 15 kg
1 unit ⟶ 15 ÷ 5 = 3 kg
2 units ⟶ 2 × 3 = 6 kg

The mass of the smaller portion of prawns is 6 kg.

10 Charlotte has two bottles of milk. The ratio of the volume of milk in Bottle A to the volume of milk in Bottle B is 3 : 4. The volume of milk in Bottle A is 120 ml. Find the total volume of milk in both bottles.

Method 1

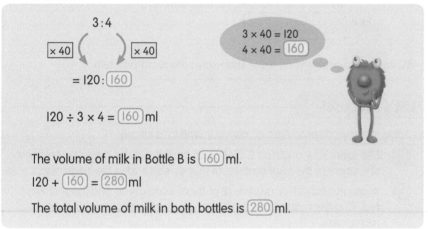

3 : 4

×40   ×40

3 × 40 = 120
4 × 40 = 160

= 120 : 160

120 ÷ 3 × 4 = 160 ml

The volume of milk in Bottle B is 160 ml.

120 + 160 = 280 ml

The total volume of milk in both bottles is 280 ml.

Method 2

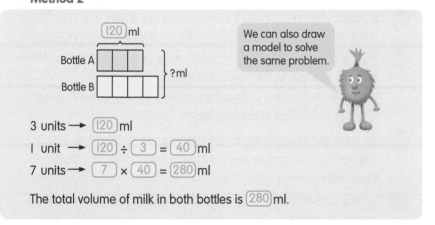

120 ml

Bottle A

Bottle B

? ml

We can also draw a model to solve the same problem.

3 units ⟶ 120 ml

1 unit ⟶ 120 ÷ 3 = 40 ml

7 units ⟶ 7 × 40 = 280 ml

The total volume of milk in both bottles is 280 ml.

167

- Informally assess pupils to see if they can follow the strategy above to solve a similar word problem.

Objective of activity
This activity helps pupils to reflect on what they have learnt in writing ratios and using the unitary method to solve ratio word problems.

Independent work
- *Let's Practise!*
- Practice 3 in Practice Book 5A, pp 149 to 152.

Teaching sequence

11 *Maths Journal*

- Accept any answer that is logical based on the model given.
- In the process of solving the problem, the following skills are practised:
  (a) Comparing and analysing
  (b) Relating units and numbers
  (c) Creating a question statement

Unit 6 Ratio

Maths Journal

11 Look at the model below.

Isabel

Tania

£24

Write a word problem on ratio. Then solve the word problem.

Let's Practise!

Solve these word problems. Show your workings clearly.

12 Ella spent £24 and had £11 left. Find the ratio of the amount of money she spent to the total amount of money she had in the beginning. 24 : 35

13 A box contained 42 apples. 12 of them were green and the rest were red. Find the ratio of the number of green apples to the number of red apples. 2 : 5

14 Peter mixed flour and sugar in the ratio 5 : 2. If he used 125 g of flour, what was the mass of sugar he used? 50 g

15 Mr White cuts a coil of wire into two pieces in the ratio 3 : 4. If the length of the longer piece of wire is 32 cm, what is the total length of the wire? 56 cm

16 The ratio of the number of pupils at the park in the morning to the number of pupils at the park in the afternoon was 13 : 7.
143 pupils were at the park in the morning. What was the number of pupils at the park in the afternoon? 77 pupils

17 Vanessa cuts a piece of rope into two, in the ratio 19 : 4.
The length of the longer piece is 266 cm. What is the length of the shorter piece of rope? 56 cm

18 The total time that Emily and Bob worked in two weeks was 91 h. If Emily worked 52 h, what was the ratio of Emily working hours to Bob's working hours? 4 : 3

168

Practice Book 5A, p.149

Comparing three quantities

Pupils will be able to:

- use ratio to show the relative sizes of three quantities
- express equivalent ratios given three quantities
- write a given ratio $x : y : z$ in its simplest form
- find the missing number(s) in equivalent ratios

Key concept

Ratio is a way of comparing the relative sizes of three quantities or sets of items.

Thinking skills

- Comparing
- Visualisation

What you will need

Red, yellow and pink counters

Ratio **Unit 6**

Let's Learn!

Comparing three quantities

1. Mrs Wolfe had 4 red roses, 8 pink roses and 12 yellow roses. The ratio of the number of red roses to the number of pink roses to the number of yellow roses is 4 : 8 : 12.

Method 1

= 1 unit

She puts 4 roses into each box.

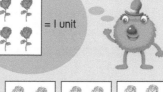

| 1 box of red roses | 2 boxes of pink roses | 3 boxes of yellow roses |

The ratio of the number of red roses to the number of pink roses to the number of yellow roses is 1 : 2 : 3.

Method 2

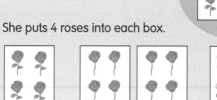

4 : 8 : 12

$\div 4$ $\div 4$ $\div 4$

= 1 : 2 : 3

4 is a common factor of 4, 8 and 12.

4 : 8 : 12 is 1 : 2 : 3 in its simplest form.

The ratio of the number of red roses to the number of pink roses to the number of yellow roses is ⬛ 1 ⬛ : ⬛ 2 ⬛ : ⬛ 3 ⬛.

169

Teaching sequence

1

- Here the ratio concept is extended to three quantities. Illustrate and explain the concept of ratio using three sets of items, e.g. red, yellow and pink counters.
- Using the example in the textbook, when there are 4 red roses, 8 pink roses and 12 yellow roses, the ratio is written as 4 : 8 : 12.
- Then explain the two methods to simplify the ratio.

  Method 1: Rearrange the roses into groups of four: 1 group of 4 red roses each, 2 groups of 4 pink roses each and 3 groups of 4 yellow roses each. We write the ratio 4 : 8 : 12 in its simplest form, which is 1 : 2 : 3.

  Method 2: Find a common factor of the terms of the ratio. 4 is a common factor of 4, 8 and 12. Simplify the ratio by dividing the three terms of the ratio by the common factor.

Additional activity

Ask pupils to explain and correct the mistake made in the simplification of the following ratio:

$12:24:42 = 4:8:12 = 1:2:3$

Teaching sequence

- Use this question to assess pupils' ability to reduce ratios of three quantities to their lowest terms.
- If pupils have problems thinking of a common factor, ask them to guess a number and check if all three numbers are divisible by that number and proceed from there. They can start from 2 and try subsequent numbers.

- Explain how to find the missing values of equivalent ratios by using multiplication and division.

Method 1:
$3 \times 4 = 12$
$2 \times 4 = 8$
$5 \times 4 = 20$

Method 2: Look at the second terms of the equivalent ratios.

$2:3:5 = ?:12:?$

$12 \div 3 = 4$

4 is the multiplying factor, so
$2:3:5 = 8:12:20$.

Unit 6 Ratio

2 What is each ratio in its simplest form?

a $15:12:18$

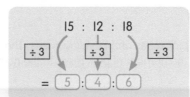

> Divide 15, 12 and 18 by the common factor, 3.

b $12:8:20$

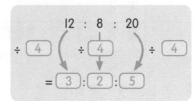

> First find the common factor of 12, 8 and 20.

3 Find the missing numbers in these equivalent ratios.

$2:3:5 = \boxed{8}:12:\boxed{20}$

Look at the second terms of the equivalent ratios –

$2:\mathbf{3}:5 = \boxed{8}:\mathbf{12}:\boxed{20}$.

First find the multiplying factor. Then multiply the first and third terms by the multiplying factor.

Method 1

$3 \times 4 = 12$
Multiply by 4 throughout.

$2:\mathbf{3}:5$

$= \boxed{8}:\mathbf{12}:\boxed{20}$

Method 2

$12 \div 3 = 4$

So 4 is the multiplying factor.

$4 \times 2 = \boxed{8}$

$4 \times 5 = \boxed{20}$

170

4 Find the missing numbers in these equivalent ratios.

$3:5:7 = 9:\boxed{15}:\boxed{21}$

Look at the first terms of the equivalent ratios – **3** : 5 : 7 = **9** : $\boxed{15}$: $\boxed{21}$.

First find the multiplying factor. Then multiply the second and third terms by the multiplying factor.

Method 1

$3 \times \boxed{3} = 9$

Multiply by $\boxed{3}$ throughout.

$$\begin{array}{ccccc} \mathbf{3} & : & 5 & : & 7 \\ \times \boxed{3} & & \times \boxed{3} & & \times \boxed{3} \\ = \mathbf{9} & : & \boxed{15} & : & \boxed{21} \end{array}$$

Method 2

$9 \div 3 = \boxed{3}$

So $\boxed{3}$ is the multiplying factor.

$3 \times 5 = \boxed{15}$

$3 \times 7 = \boxed{21}$

5 Find the missing numbers in these equivalent ratios.

$18 : 12 : 9 = \boxed{6} : \boxed{4} : 3$

Look at the third terms of the equivalent ratios –

$18 : 12 : \mathbf{9} = \boxed{6} : \boxed{4} : \mathbf{3}$

First find the common factor. Then divide the first and second terms by the common factor.

$$\begin{array}{ccccc} 18 & : & 12 & : & \mathbf{9} \\ \div \boxed{3} & & \div \boxed{3} & & \div \boxed{3} \\ = 6 & : & 4 & : & \mathbf{3} \end{array}$$

$9 \div 3 = 3$

So $\boxed{3}$ is the common factor.

$18 \div 3 = \boxed{6}$

$12 \div 3 = \boxed{4}$

171

4

- Assess pupils' ability to use multiplication or division to find the missing values of equivalent ratios similar to **3**.

5

- This question is similar to **2** as the given ratio values are greater than the corresponding values.

- Remind pupils that to find the common factor, they should guess a number and check if all three ratio values are divisible by it.

Objective of activity

This activity provides pupils with more practice in writing the ratio of three quantities.

What you will need

- 3 green, 12 blue and 27 yellow counters for each group
- Scientific calculator

Independent work

- *Let's Practise!*
- Practice 4 in Practice Book 5A, pp 153 to 154.

Teaching sequence

- Assess pupils' ability to use division to find the missing values of equivalent ratios similar to **5**.
- They may have to guess a common factor and then work from there.

- Explain to pupils that they will have to use the 'taking away' concept in subtraction for **b** to find the new ratio of the three quantities.

10 *Let's Practise!*

- By using a calculator in this question, pupils are being tested on the process of how to find missing parts of equivalent ratios.

Unit 6 Ratio

6 Find the missing numbers in these equivalent ratios.

a $15:5:20 = \boxed{3}:1:\boxed{4}$ b $7:21:14 = \boxed{1}:\boxed{3}:2$

Activity

7 Work in groups.

Each group will need 3 green counters, 12 blue counters and 27 yellow counters.

a Write down the ratio of the number of green counters to the number of blue counters to the number of yellow counters. $3:12:27 = 1:4:9$

b Take away 1 green counter and 3 yellow counters. Then find the new ratio of the number of green counters to the number of blue counters to the number of yellow counters. $2:12:24 = 1:6:12$

Let's Practise!

Find the missing numbers in the following equivalent ratios.

8 Write each ratio in its simplest form.

a $5:15:20 = \boxed{1}:\boxed{3}:\boxed{4}$ b $4:18:24 = \boxed{2}:\boxed{9}:\boxed{12}$

c $15:75:135 = \boxed{1}:\boxed{5}:\boxed{9}$ d $36:54:108 = \boxed{2}:\boxed{3}:\boxed{6}$

9 Complete each set of equivalent ratios.

a $1:4:5 = 3:\boxed{12}:\boxed{15}$ b $2:3:8 = \boxed{12}:18:\boxed{48}$

10 Complete each set of equivalent ratios.

a $64:112:32 = \boxed{4}:\boxed{7}:2$ b $125:200:50 = \boxed{5}:8:\boxed{2}$

Practice Book 5A, p.153

172

---

270   **Unit 6:** Ratio

Learning objectives: Word problems (2)

Pupils will be able to solve up to 2-step word problems involving ratio of three quantities using:

- the concept of equivalent ratios
- model drawing and the unitary method

Key concept

Applying the equivalent ratio concept, part-whole concept and comparison concept to solve up to 2-step word problems involving ratio of three quantities

Thinking skills

- Comparing
- Visualisation

Let's Learn!

Word problems (2)

1. At a toy shop, Bill bought 3 pink toy cars, 6 blue toy cars, and 9 yellow toy cars. What was the ratio of the number of pink toy cars to the number of blue toy cars to the number of yellow toy cars that Bill bought?

Method 1

Put 3 toy cars into each box.

| 1 box of pink toy cars | 2 boxes of blue toy cars | 3 boxes of yellow toy cars |

The ratio of the number of pink toy cars to the number of blue toy cars to the number of yellow toy cars that Bill bought was $1:2:3$.

Method 2

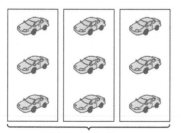

$$3:6:9$$
$$\div 3 \quad \div 3 \quad \div 3$$
$$= 1:2:3$$

3 is a common factor of 3, 6 and 9.

$3:6:9$ is $1:2:3$ in its simplest form.

The ratio of the number of pink toy cars to the number of blue toy cars to the number of yellow toy cars that Bill bought was ⬚1 : ⬚2 : ⬚3.

173

Teaching sequence

1

- Ask pupils to read the word problem and ask them what the difference is between this problem and the ones in Word Problems (1). Pupils should be able to identify that this word problem involves three ratio values whereas the ones in Word Problems (1) involve only two ratio values.

- Emphasise that the methods for solving both types of word problems are the same.

- If necessary, revise the methods used earlier before going through the two methods shown here.

Teaching sequence

2

- Informally assess pupils to check if they can apply the methods used in ❶ to solve a similar word problem.
- Pupils may first simplify the problem by dividing each ratio value by 100 to get 2:8:30.
- Subsequently it will be easier for pupils to find a common factor for 2, 8 and 30.

3

- There are two approaches to solving this problem. The equivalent ratio method has been explained previously.
- The second method is to use model drawing and the unitary method.

  Step 1: Read the question and draw a model to represent the information provided.

  Step 2: Fill in the given value and a '?' for the unknown value.

  Step 3: Based on the model, write an equation to relate the number of units in the model to the given value.

  Step 4: Solve the problem after finding the value for 1 unit.

---

2 During a race, Daniel ran 200 m, Hardeep ran 800 m and Omar ran 3000 m. What was the ratio of the distance Daniel ran to the distance Hardeep ran to the distance Omar ran?

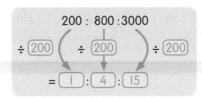

Find the common factor of 200, 800 and 3000.

The ratio of the distance Daniel ran to the distance Hardeep ran to the distance Omar ran was ⬚1⬚:⬚4⬚:⬚15⬚.

3 Rebecca filled three containers, A, B and C, to the brim with orange juice in the ratio 2:3:4. The capacity of the largest container was 12 ℓ. Find the capacity of the smallest container.

Method 1

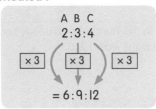

The capacity of the smallest container is 6 ℓ.

Method 2

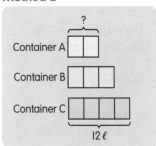

4 units ⟶ 12 ℓ
1 unit ⟶ 12 ÷ 4 = 3 ℓ
2 units ⟶ 2 × 3 = 6 ℓ

The capacity of the smallest container is 6 ℓ.

Teaching sequence

4

- Use this question as an informal assessment to check if pupils can follow the procedures used in the previous question.

- In this question, pupils have to find the total whereas in the previous question, they had to find the parts of the whole.

5

- This question is similar to **3** and **4**. However, pupils may need to use a calculator to aid in computation. If pupils feel they can answer the question without a calculator, they may want to multiply by 15, by multiplying by 10 and then halving this (to multiply by 5), then adding these two answers together.

Ratio **Unit 6**

4 Ray cut a roll of ribbon into three pieces, X, Y and Z, in the ratio of 4:2:1. The length of the longest piece is 28 m. Find the total length of the three pieces.

4 units ⟶ 28 m

1 unit ⟶ 28 ÷ 4 = 7 m

Total length = 4 + 2 + 1 units = 7 units

= 7 × 7 = 49 m

The total length of the three pieces is 49 m.

28 m

X
Y } ?
Z

5 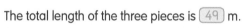 Mr Allen, Miss Brown and Mr Bishop shared a sum of money in the ratio 5:4:6. Mr Bishop's share of the money was £432. How much was the total amount of money?

6 units ⟶ £432

1 unit ⟶ £432 ÷ 6 = £72

Total amount of money

= 5 + 4 + 6 = 15 units

= 15 × 72

= £ 1080

The total amount of money was £ 1080

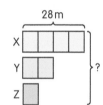

Mr Allen
Miss Brown } ?
Mr Bishop

£432

Let's Practise!

Solve these problems. Show your working clearly.

6 At a stationery shop, Mrs Chase bought 5 rubbers, 15 pens and 40 pencils. What was the ratio of the number of rubbers to the number of pens to the number of pencils that Mrs Chase bought at the stationery shop? 1:3:8

7 Anita mixes 200 ml of cranberry juice, 300 ml of grapefruit juice and 700 ml of lemonade for Angie's birthday party. What is the ratio of the amount of cranberry juice to that of grapefruit juice to that of lemonade? 2:3:7

175

Objective of activity

This activity helps pupils to reflect on the methods they have learnt to write ratios and simplify the ratios using division.

Independent work

Practice 5 and *Maths Journal* in Practice Book 5A, pp 155 to 160.

What you will need

Scientific calculator

Teaching sequence

12 *Maths Journal*

- This journal helps pupils to reflect on the method of finding the common factor for the ratio values, so they can write the ratio in its simplest form.

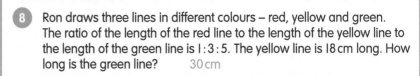

Unit 6 Ratio

Let's Practise!

8 Ron draws three lines in different colours – red, yellow and green. The ratio of the length of the red line to the length of the yellow line to the length of the green line is 1:3:5. The yellow line is 18 cm long. How long is the green line?   30 cm

9 Apple, carrot and orange juice is mixed in the ratio 3:1:2. The volume of apple juice is 720 ml.

    a How much more apple juice is used in the mixture than carrot juice? 480 ml

    b What is the total volume of the juice? 1440 ml

10 Mrs Evans, Mrs Bowden and Miss Harper share a sum of money in the ratio 2:4:15. Miss Harper has £1575.

    a Which girl gets the smallest share? Mrs Evans

    b What is the total sum of money shared by Mrs Evans, Mrs Bowden and Miss Harper? £2205

11 Ethan, George and Amit have some action figures in the ratio 13:5:7. Ethan has 65 action figures.

    a How many action figures does Amit have? 35

    b What is the total number of action figures that Ethan, George and Amit have? 125

> Practice Book 5A, p.155

Maths Journal

12 Miya has 10 white balloons and 20 blue balloons.

Explain how to find the ratio of the number of white balloons to that of the blue balloons in its simplest form. Draw a model if you need to.
Answers vary

176

Objective of activity

This activity involves getting pupils to make as many ratios as possible using all the given numbers irrespective of whether they can be simplified.

Ratio **Unit 6**

Teaching sequence

⑬ *Let's Explore!*

- This activity encourages pupils to discuss how to choose the correct numbers. This helps them to reflect on finding the common factor through guess and check.

Let's Wrap It Up!

- This section summarises the two strategies to write equivalent ratios and the method to simplify them.

Let's Explore!

⑬ **a** Using the following numbers, write sets of equivalent ratios in the form **a** : **b**. You can use each number only once.

2   3   5   6   7   8   9   10   12   14   15   20   21   25   35

| **Example** |
| $2:3 = 6:9 = 8:12$ |

b Using the same numbers in **a**, write as many sets of equivalent ratios in the form **a** : **b** : **c** as you can. You can use each number **only once**.

How many sets of equivalent ratios can you write for **a** and **b**?

How do you choose the numbers for each set of equivalent ratios? Discuss.

Let's Wrap It Up!

You have learnt:

- to use ratio to show the relative sizes of 2 quantities and 3 quantities
- that a given ratio does not necessarily give the actual quantities compared
- to find an equivalent ratio by multiplying the ratio by a common factor

$1:4$

×4   ×4

$= 4:16$

- that a ratio can be reduced to its simplest form by dividing the ratio by the common factor.

$6:18$

÷6   ÷6

$= 1:3$

177

Unit 6: Ratio   275

Objective of activity

This problem gets pupils to practise the making a systematic list strategy in conjunction with the ratio concept.

Thinking skills

- Comparing
- Visualisation

Heuristic for problem solving

Making a systematic list

Independent work

Ask pupils to work through *Challenging Practice, Problem Solving,* Review 3 and Revision 1 in Practice Book 5A, pp 161 to 186.

Teaching sequence

Let's Wrap It Up!

- The worked example reinforces the following skills, concepts and strategies:
  - (a) Application of concept of perimeter of square and rectangle
  - (b) The unitary method
  - (c) Application of ratio concept to solve the problem

14 and 15 *Put On Your Thinking Caps!*

- These two questions require pupils to apply the making a systematic list heuristic and ratio concept to solve the word problems.

Let's Wrap It Up!

Let's Revise!

The ratio of the perimeter of a square piece of paper to the perimeter of a rectangular piece of paper is 2 : 5. If each side of the square piece of paper is 10 cm, find:

a the perimeter of the square piece of paper

10 × 4 = 40 cm

The perimeter of the square piece of paper is 40 cm.

b the perimeter of the rectangular piece of paper

2 units ⟶ 40 cm
1 unit ⟶ 20 cm
5 units ⟶ 100 cm

The perimeter of the rectangular piece of paper is 100 cm.

c the length of the rectangular piece of paper if its width is 15 cm.

Length of the rectangular piece of paper = $\frac{100 - (15 \times 2)}{2}$

$= 35$ cm

The length of the rectangular piece of paper is 35 cm.

Put On Your Thinking Caps!

14 Sam and Tina had some money in the ratio 5 : 2. Sam had £30. If Tina's money consisted only of 20 pence coins, how many 20 pence coins did Tina have? 60 coins

15 Linda had some 50 pence coins and 20 pence coins in the ratio 3 : 2. Linda had four 20 pence coins. How much money did Linda have altogether? £3·80

| Practice Book 5A, p.161 ▶ | Practice Book 5A, p.162 ▶ |

178

---

6 Ratio

Practice I   Finding ratio

1   The table below shows the number of football cards each child has.

a   Find the number of football cards they have altogether.

Child	Number of Football Cards
Farha	8
Peter	3
Jack	5
Omar	11
Total	27

b   Fill in the table below to show the ratios.

The Ratio of …	Ratio
the number of football cards Farha has to the number of football cards Omar has is	8 : 11
the number of football cards Jack has to the number of football cards Peter has is	5 : 3
the number of football cards Peter has to the number of football cards Jack has is	3 : 5
the number of football cards Farha has to the total number of football cards is	8 : 27
the total number of football cards to the number of football cards Omar has is	27 : 11

2 Mr Woods puts some pencils into bundles of 10. He gives Chantal 4 bundles and Lisa 9 bundles of pencils.

a The ratio of the number of pencils Chantal has to the number of pencils Lisa has is __4__ : __9__ .

b The ratio of the number of pencils Lisa has to the number of pencils Chantal has is __9__ : __4__ .

c The ratio of the number of pencils Lisa has to the total number of pencils is __9__ : __13__ .

3 a Some friends went to the supermarket. Find the total volume of milk and total mass of shopping they bought.

Bought by	Volume of Milk	Mass of Shopping
Mr Lee	4 ℓ	8 kg
Miss Brook	9 ℓ	11 kg
Mrs Smith	13 ℓ	15 kg
Mr Bell	5 ℓ	7 kg
Total	31 ℓ	41 kg

b Fill in the spaces below to show the ratios. An example is shown.

i The ratio of the mass of shopping Mrs Smith bought to the mass of shopping Mr Lee bought is __15 : 8__ .

ii The ratio of the volume of milk Miss Brook bought to the volume of milk Mr Bell bought is __9 : 5__ .

iii The ratio of the mass of shopping Mr Bell bought to the mass of shopping Mr Lee bought is __7 : 8__ .

iv The ratio of the total volume of milk bought to the volume of milk Miss Brook bought is __31 : 9__ .

v The ratio of the mass of shopping Mr Lee bought to the total mass of shopping bought is __8 : 41__ .

> When writing two quantities as a ratio, the quantities must be in the same unit.

4 Archie puts some cubes together to form three trains, A, B and C.

a The ratio of the length of A to the length of C is __3__ : __7__ .

b The ratio of the length of C to the length of B is __7__ : __10__ .

c The ratio of the length of A to the total length of A, B and C is __3__ : __20__ .

5 a The ratio of the length of R to the length of P is __7__ : __4__ .

b The ratio of the length of P to the length of Q is __4__ : __3__ .

c The ratio of the length of P to the total length of P, Q and R is __4__ : __14__ . (Accept 2 : 7)

6 Draw models to show the ratios.

a 5 : 9

b 12 : 7

Practice 2 Equivalent ratios

1 Find a common factor, other than 1, of each set of numbers.

a 4 and 6 __2__

b 5 and 15 __5__

c 6 and 18 __2, 3, 6__ Accept any one answer.

d 12 and 32 __2, 4__ Accept either answer.

2 Write ratios to compare the two sets of items.

a

Group A   Group B

The ratio of the number of CDs in Group A to the number of CDs in Group B is __4__ : __8__ .

The ratio of the number of CD holders in Group A to the number of CD holders in Group B is __1__ : __2__ .

__4__ : __8__ = __1__ : __2__ in its simplest form.

b

Group A   Group B

The ratio of the number of pencils in Group A to the number of pencils in Group B is __18__ : __27__ .

The ratio of the number of bundles in Group A to the number of bundles in Group B is __6__ : __9__ .

18 : 27 = 6 : 9 = __2__ : __3__ in its simplest form.

---

7 Grandma Lee gave £15 to Lucy and Charlie. Lucy got £7.

a How much money did Charlie get?

£15 − £7 = £8
Charlie got £8.

b Find the ratio of the amount of money Lucy got to the amount of money Charlie got from Grandma Lee.

7 : 8
The ratio of the amount of money Lucy got to the amount of money Charlie got is 7 : 8.

8 Angus gave bags of fruit to Ben and Kerry in the ratio 8 : 13. He gave them the fruit in 2 kg bags. What was the smallest possible mass of fruit Angus gave to both of them?

Smallest mass of fruit given to Ben = 8 × 2
= 16 kg

Smallest mass of fruit given to Kerry = 13 × 2
= 26 kg

16 + 26 = 42 kg
The smallest possible mass of fruit Angus gave to them was 42 kg.

9 Leanne put 6 counters into a bag. She took out some counters from the bag but not all of them. What is the ratio of the number of counters taken out from the bag to the number of the counters left in the bag? Make a list of all possible ratios using the table below.

Number of Counters Taken Out	Number of Counters Left in the Bag	Ratio
1	5	**1 : 5**
2	4	2 : 4 or 1 : 2
3	3	3 : 3 or 1 : 1
4	2	4 : 2 or 2 : 1
5	1	5 : 1

Practice 3 Word problems (1)

Solve these word problems. Show your workings clearly.

1 Mr Davis bought 24 raisin buns and 18 plain buns for the class party. Find the ratio of the number of raisin buns to the total number of buns Mr Davis bought.

24 + 18 = 42
Mr Davis bought 42 buns altogether.

24 : 42
= 4 : 7
The ratio of the number of raisin buns to the total number of buns Mr Davis bought is 4 : 7.

2 There were 44 chicken and fish pies altogether in a freezer. If there were 12 chicken pies, what was the ratio of the number of chicken pies to the number of fish pies in the freezer?

44 − 12 = 32
There were 32 fish pies.

12 : 32
= 3 : 8
The ratio of the number of chicken pies to the number of fish pies in the freezer is 3 : 8.

3 For each of the following, find the equivalent ratio.

a 3:5 = 9 :15 (×3)

b 7:4 = 28 :16 (×4)

c 4:3 = 24: 18
d 8:3 = 64: 24
e 4:9 = 20 :45
f 6:7 = 42: 49
g 5:8 = 45: 72
h 9:6 = 81 :54

4 Write each ratio in its simplest form.

a 18:12 = 3: 2 (÷6)

b 15:21 = 5: 7 (÷3)

c 12:30 = 2 :5
d 14:28 = 1: 2
e 6:16 = 3 : 8
f 15:35 = 3 : 7
g 4:48 = 1 : 12
h 56:21 = 8 : 3

5 Complete the equivalent ratios.

a 5:4 = 25: 20
b 4:7 = 36: 63
c 3:8 = 39 :104
d 7:9 = 84 :108
e 48:44 = 12 :11
f 60:45 = 12 :9
g 132:96 = 11 :8
h 72:104 = 9 :13

5 In a competition, the ratio of the number of tickets Mrs Elliott collected to the number of tickets Mr King collected was $4:3$. Mr King collected 36 tickets. How many tickets did they collect altogether?

Mrs Elliott

Mr King

36 tickets

3 units → 36 tickets
1 unit → 12 tickets
Total number of tickets = 4 + 3 = 7 units
= 7 × 12
= 84 tickets

Mrs Elliott and Mr King collected 84 tickets altogether.

6 The ratio of the number of monster figures Toby had to the number of monster figures Anna had was $7:3$. Anna had 18 monster figures. How many monster figures did they have altogether?

18 monster figures

Anna

Toby

?

3 units → 18 monster figures
1 unit → 6 monster figures
Total number of monster figures = 7 + 3 = 10 units
= 10 × 6
= 60 monster figures

They had 60 monster figures altogether.

3 There were 12 boys and 18 girls in a class. 3 more boys joined the class and 2 girls left. What is the ratio of the number of boys to the number of girls in the class now?

12 + 3 = 15
There are 15 boys now.

18 − 2 = 16
There are 16 girls now.

15 : 16
The ratio of the number of boys to the number of girls in the class now is 15 : 16.

4 Monica had £42 and Norah had £18 at first. Monica then gave £6 to Norah. Now, what is the ratio of the amount of money Monica has to the amount of money Norah has?

£42 − £6 = £36
Now Monica has £36.

£18 + £6 = £24
Now Norah has £24.

36 : 24
= 6 : 4
= 3 : 2
The ratio of the amount of money Monica has now to the amount of money Norah has now is 3 : 2.

Practice 4 Comparing three quantities

1 Find a common factor, other than 1, of each set of numbers. An example is shown.

	Set of Numbers	Common Factor
a	2, 6 and 8	2
b	5, 10 and 20	5
c	3, 9 and 15	3
d	6, 24 and 27	3

2 For each of the following, find the equivalent ratio.

a
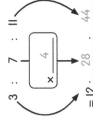

$$2 : 5 : 7$$
$$\times 3$$
$$= 6 : 15 : 21$$

b
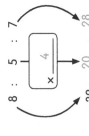

$$3 : 7 : 11$$
$$\times 4$$
$$= 12 : 28 : 44$$

c
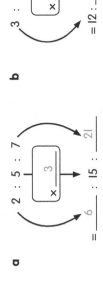

$$4 : 3 : 6$$
$$\times 5$$
$$= 20 : 15 : 30$$

d
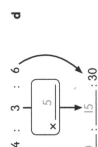

$$8 : 5 : 7$$
$$\times 4$$
$$= 32 : 20 : 28$$

---

7 In a certain month, the ratio of the volume of water used by Household A to the volume of water used by Household B was 13 : 5. Household A used 455 ℓ of water for that month. Find the total amount of water used by the two households for that month.

A 455 ℓ
B ?

13 units → 455 ℓ
1 unit → 35 ℓ
Total amount of water = 13 + 5 = 18 units
= 18 × 35 ℓ
= 630 ℓ

The total amount of water used by Households A and B in that month is 630 ℓ.

8 Some blackcurrant squash and water are mixed in the ratio 4 : 15. The volume of water in the mixture is 1305 ml. What is the total volume of the mixture?

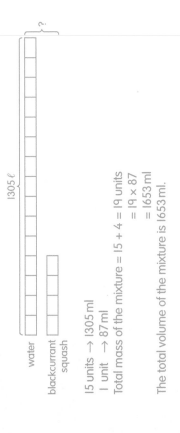

water 1305 ℓ
blackcurrant squash   ?

15 units → 1305 ml
1 unit → 87 ml
Total mass of the mixture = 15 + 4 = 19 units
= 19 × 87
= 1653 ml

The total volume of the mixture is 1653 ml.

Practice 5 Word problems (2)

Solve these word problems. Show your workings clearly.

1 Garry bought 4 tubs of raspberries, 10 tubs of strawberries and 8 tubs of blueberries for a class party. Find the ratio of the number of tubs of raspberries to that of strawberries to that of blueberries.

4:10:8
= 2:5:4
The ratio of the number of tubs of raspberries to that of strawberries to that of blueberries was 2:5:4.

2 Andrew poured 150ml of water into Container A, 400ml of water into Container B and 700ml of water into Container C. Find the ratio of the volume of water in Container A to the volume of water in Container B to the volume of water in Container C.

150:400:700
= 3 : 8 : 14
The ratio of the volume of water in Container A to the volume of water in Container B to the volume of water in Container C was 3:8:14.

---

3 Complete each set of equivalent ratios.

a 1:2:5 = 3 :6: 15

b 8:7:3 = 16 : 14 :6

c 7:4:3 = 28: 16 : 12

d 4:5:9 = 20 :25: 45

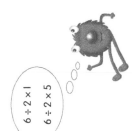

4 Write each ratio in its simplest form.

a 16 : 12 : 8 (÷4) = 4 : 3 : 2

b 21 : 15 : 18 (÷3) = 7 : 5 : 6

c 20 : 30 : 45 (÷5) = 4 : 6 : 9

d 7 : 21 : 35 (÷7) = 1 : 3 : 5

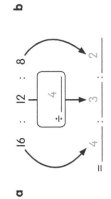
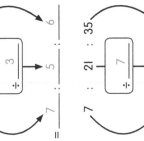

5 Write each ratio in its simplest form.

a 4:16:18 = 2 : 8 : 9

b 27:12:21 = 9 : 4 : 7

c 32:8:20 = 8 : 2 : 5

d 63:18:27 = 7 : 2 : 3

3 Mrs Thomas gave her 3 friends £900 to share among themselves. Miss Chapman received £200, Mr Hughes received £400 and Mr Bailey received the remaining amount. Find the ratio of the amount Miss Chapman received to the amount Mr Hughes received to the amount Mr Bailey received.

Amount Mr Bailey received = £900 − £200 − £400
= £300

200 : 400 : 300
= 2 : 4 : 3
The ratio of the amount Miss Chapman received to the amount Mr Hughes received to the amount Mr Bailey received is 2 : 4 : 3.

4 Mr Gordon made 750 ml of lemonade. He poured 100 ml of lemonade into Glass A, 400 ml of lemonade into Glass C, and the remaining amount into Glass B. Find the ratio of the amount of lemonade in Glass A to the amount of lemonade in Glass B to the amount of lemonade in Glass C.

750 ml − 100 ml − 400 ml = 250 ml
The remaining glass contained 250 ml of lemonade.

100 : 250 : 400
= 2 : 5 : 8
The ratio of the amounts of lemonade in the three glasses is 2 : 5 : 8.

---

5 Ruth cuts a ball of string into three pieces. Their lengths are in the ratio 2 : 3 : 5. The longest piece is 35 cm long. How long is the shortest piece?

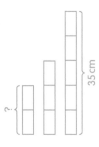

35 cm

5 units → 35 cm
1 unit → 7 cm
2 units → 14 cm
The shortest piece is 14 cm long.

6 The ages of three brothers, David, Robert and Michael, are in the ratio 1 : 2 : 3. David is 7 years old. Find the total age of all three brothers.

7 years

David
Robert
Michael
?

1 unit → 7 years
Total age = 1 + 2 + 3 = 6 units
= 6 × 7
= 42 years

The total age of all three brothers is 42 years.

7 The masses of three dogs, Boxer, Pepper and Milo are in the ratio 6 : 4 : 7. Milo's mass is 21 kg.

  a What is Boxer's mass?

  b What is the total mass of Boxer, Pepper and Milo?

  a 7 units → 21 kg

     1 unit → 3 kg

     6 units → 18 kg

     Boxer's mass is 18 kg.

  b 6 + 4 + 7 = 17 units = 17 × 3 kg

                      = 51 kg

     The total mass of Boxer, Pepper and Milo is 51 kg.

8 Adam, Gemma and Clare collected marbles in the ratio of 10 : 12 : 7. Clare collected 98 marbles. How many marbles did they collect altogether?

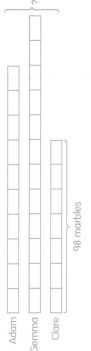

7 units → 98 marbles

1 unit → 14 marbles

10 + 12 + 7 = 29 units

           = 29 × 14

           = 406 marbles

They collected 406 marbles altogether.

9 Amit, Jackie and Tom shared a sum of money in the ratio 13 : 9 : 10. Amit had £65.

  a How much money did Jackie get?

  b What was the total sum of money shared among Amit, Jackie and Tom?

  a 13 units → £65

     1 unit → £5

     9 units → £45

     Jackie got £45.

  b 13 + 9 + 10 = 32 units = 32 × £5

                        = £160

     The total sum of money shared among Amit, Jackie and Tom was £160.

10 The ratio of the heights of three buildings, Building A, Building B and Building C is 2 : 7 : 15. The height of Building C is 330 m.

  a What is the height of Building A?

  b What is the total height of all 3 buildings?

  a 15 units → 330 m

     1 unit → 22 m

     2 units → 44 m

     The height of Building A is 44 m.

  b Total height = 2 + 7 + 15

                 = 24 units

                 = 24 × 22

                 = 528 m

     The total height of all 3 buildings is 528 m.

Challenging Practice

1 A small square with an area of 16 cm² is cut off from a bigger square with a side of 6 cm. Find the ratio of the area of the small square to the area of the remaining part of the bigger square.

6 cm

$6 \times 6 = 36\,cm^2$
$36 - 16 = 20\,cm^2$
$16 : 20 = 4 : 5$
The ratio of the area of the small square to the area of the remaining part of the bigger square is 4 : 5.

2 The ratio of the perimeters of two squares is 2 : 4. The perimeter of the larger square is 16 cm.

a   What is the perimeter of the smaller square?
b   What is the length of one side of the smaller square?

a   4 units → 16 cm
    1 unit → 4 cm
    2 units → 8 cm
    The perimeter of the smaller square is 8 cm.

b   8 ÷ 4 = 2 cm
    The length of one side of the smaller square is 2 cm.

Maths Journal

1 Peter and Miya each drew a model to solve the following word problem.

A chef bought some meat and potatoes. The ratio of the mass of chicken to the mass of burgers to the mass of potatoes he bought was 3 : 1 : 5. He bought 6 kg of burgers. What was the total mass of meat he bought?

Both their models were incorrect. Explain the mistakes each of them made.

Peter's model

chicken
burgers   ?
               6 kg
potatoes

Peter's model is incorrect because
he drew the wrong number of units for
chicken and burgers.
_____
_____

Miya's model

chicken
burgers
        6 kg   ?
potatoes

Miya's model is incorrect because
she misunderstood the question to
be asking for the total mass of meat
and potatoes.
_____
_____

Draw the correct model. Then solve the problem.

chicken
              ?
burgers
        6 kg
potatoes

1 unit → 6 kg
Total mass of meat = 3 + 1 = 4 units
                   = 4 × 6 kg
                   = 24 kg
He bought 24 kg of meat altogether.

Problem Solving

Date: _____

1 The ratio of the number of plants Mr Hill bought to the number of plants Miss Palmer bought was 2 : 5. Mr Hill bought 16 plants. If each plant cost £17, what was the total cost of the plants Mr Hill and Miss Palmer bought?

2 units → 16 plants

1 unit → 8 plants

2 + 5 units = 7 units = 7 × 8 = 56 plants

Mr Hill and Miss Palmer bought 56 plants together.

Total cost = 56 × £17

= £952

The total cost of the plants Mr Hill and Miss Palmer bought was £952.

2 The ratio of the number of boys to the number of girls at a fair is 5 : 8. There are 60 boys at the fair. If the entrance fee for each child to the fair is £3, find the total cost of the entrance fee for the boys and girls.

5 units → 60

1 unit → 12

5 + 8 units = 13 units = 13 × 12 = 156 boys and girls

The total number of boys and girls at the fair is 156.

Total cost = 156 × £3

= £468

The total cost of the entrance fee for the boys and girls is £468.

Review 3

Date: _____

1 Look at the triangle below. Name the related height for each given base.

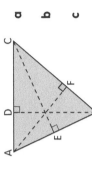

a If the base is AB, the height is ___CE___.

b If the base is BC, the height is ___AF___.

c If the base is AC, the height is ___BD___.

2 Look at the triangle below. Name the related base for each given height.

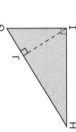

a If the height is LJ, the base is ___GH___.

b If the height is HI, the base is ___GI___.

3 In each shaded triangle, a base or a height is given. Name the related height or base.

a

Height: ___AC___

b

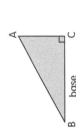

Base: ___EF___

6 Find the area of each shaded triangle.

a

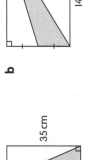

43 cm 35 cm 40 cm

Area = __700 cm²__

b

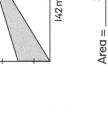

90 m 142 m

Area = __3195 m²__

7 Find the area of the shaded parts.

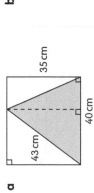

10 cm 24 cm

$24 \times 10 = 240\ cm^2$

$240 \div 2 = 120\ cm^2$

8 PQRS is a rectangle. Find the length of PS.

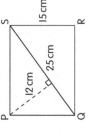

12 cm 25 cm 15 cm

Area of triangle PQS $= \frac{1}{2} \times 25 \times 12$

$= 150\ cm^2$

Area of rectangle PQRS $= 2 \times 150 = 300\ cm^2$

$PS = 300 \div 15 = 20\ cm$

---

c

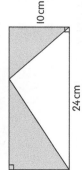

A base B C D

Height: __AD__

d

R U P T S Q base

Height: __RU__

4 In the triangle on the right, draw the three heights for the bases XY, YZ and ZX.

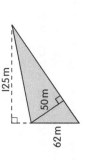

X Z Y

5 Find the area of each shaded triangle.

a

27 cm 150 cm

Area = __2025 cm²__

b

17 cm 16 cm 20 cm

Area = __160 cm²__

c

125 m 62 m 50 m

Area = __3875 m²__

d

15 m 13 m 12 m 4 m 9 m

Area = __24 m²__

9

In the shape, BC = 18 cm and AD = CD. The length of CD is twice the length of BC. Find the area of the shaded triangle ABC.

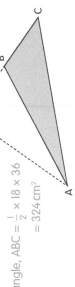

AD = CD
= 2 × 18
= 36 cm

Area of shaded triangle, ABC = $\frac{1}{2}$ × 18 × 36
= 324 cm²

10

ABCD is a rectangle of width 12 cm. Its length is twice as long as its width. AE = 12 cm and AF = BF. Find the area of the shaded triangle CEF.

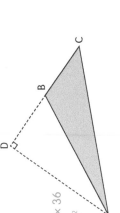

AF = BF
= 12 ÷ 2
= 6 cm

Area of ΔAEF = $\frac{1}{2}$ × 6 × 12 = 36 cm²

Length AD = Length BC
= 2 × 12
= 24 cm

DE = 24 − 12 = 12 cm

Area of ΔCDE = $\frac{1}{2}$ × 12 × 12 = 72 cm²

Area of ΔBCF = $\frac{1}{2}$ × 6 × 24 = 72 cm²

Area of rectangle ABCD = 12 × 24 = 288 cm²

Area of shaded triangle, CEF = 288 − 36 − 72 − 72 = 108 cm²

11

Leah used some wire to make a rectangle ABCD as shown below. The length AD of the rectangle, is twice as long as its width. Find the area of triangle BEC if she used 108 cm of wire.

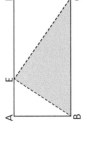

Length: 2 units
Width: 1 unit
Perimeter: 2 × (2 + 1) = 6 units

6 units → 108 cm
1 unit → 18 cm
2 units → 36 cm

Area of triangle BEC = $\frac{1}{2}$ × 36 × 18
= 324 cm²

12

Brian drew a rectangle ABCD. He marked points P and Q on the sides AD and BC and formed two overlapping triangles AQD and BPC as shown. AP = PD and BQ = QC. He then coloured triangle AQD yellow and triangle BPC blue. The overlapping region appeared green in colour. What fraction of the area of the rectangle is the area of the green part?

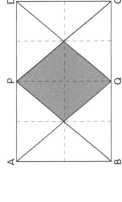

$\frac{1}{4}$

16 A bakery sells custard tarts in boxes of 6. Ethan buys 7 boxes of custard tarts and Paul buys 9 boxes of custard tarts. Find the ratio of:

a the number of custard tarts Ethan has to the number of custard tarts Paul has.
7:9 or 42:54

b the number of custard tarts Paul has to the number of custard tarts Ethan has.
9:7 or 54:42

c the number of custard tarts Ethan has to the total number of custard tarts.
7:16 or 42:96

17 For each of the following, find the equivalent ratio.

a 7:4 = 21: 12
b 5:9 = 35 :63
c 18:21 = 6: 7
d 24:32 = 3 :4

18 For each of the following, find the equivalent ratio.

a 3:8 = 45: 120
b 7:12 = 56 :96
c 12:15 = 84: 105
d 16:12 = 144 :108
e 99:135 = 11: 15
f 108:72 = 9 :6

19 Write each ratio in its simplest form.

a 8:12:24 = 2 : 3 : 6
b 21:9:36 = 7 : 3 : 12

20 Complete each set of equivalent ratios.

a 4:6:9 = 24: 36 : 54
b 48:56:28 = 12 : 14 :7

13 Fill in the spaces.

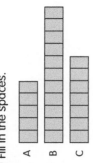

A
B
C

a The ratio of the length of A to the length of B is 5 : 11 .

b The ratio of the length of C to the length of A is 7 : 5 .

c The ratio of the length of B to the total length of A, B and C is 11 : 23 .

14 Christopher had 5 coins in his savings box. He took out a few coins from the savings box but not all of them. What is the ratio of the number of coins taken out to the number of coins left in his savings box? Make a list of all possible ratios using the table below.

Number of Coins Taken Out	Number of Coins Left in Savings Box	Ratio
4	1	4:1
3	2	3:2
2	3	2:3

15 Fill in the spaces.

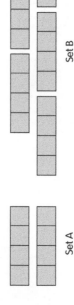

Set A

Set B

a The ratio of the number of groups in Set A to the number of groups in Set B is 2 : 5 .

b The ratio of the number of squares in Set A to the number of squares in Set B is 8 : 20 .

c Write your answer for **b** in its simplest form. 2 : 5 .

Solve these word problems. Show your workings clearly.

21 There were 45 beads in Container A and 79 beads in Container B at first. Sylvie then took 7 beads out of Container A and put them into Container B.

a What is the ratio of the number of beads in Container A to that in Container B at first?

b Find the ratio of the number of beads in Container A to that in Container B in the end. Express your answer in its simplest form.

a 45 : 79

b 45 − 7 = 38
79 + 7 = 86
38 : 86 = 19 : 43

22 Mrs Moore and Mr Morgan bought a camera each. The total cost of the two cameras was £770. Mrs Moore's camera cost £280. What was the ratio of the cost of Mrs Moore's camera to that of Mr Morgan's camera?

Cost of Mr Morgan's camera = £770 − £280
                                              = £490

280 : 490 = 4 : 7
The ratio of the cost of Mrs Moore's camera to that of Mr Morgan's camera is 4 : 7.

23 A company makes yearly donations to Charities A, B and C in the ratio 3 : 7 : 9. It donates £5096 to Charity B in a year.

a How much does it donate to Charity A in a year?

b How much does it donate to the three charities altogether in a year?

a 7 units → £5096
1 unit → £728
3 units → £2184
It donates £2184 to Charity A in a year.

b 3 + 7 + 9 = 19 units = 19 × £728 = £13 832
It donates £13 832 to the three charities altogether in a year.

24 The ratio of the number of boys to the number of girls in a camp is 3 : 7. There are 24 boys in the camp. If the camp fee is £50 per person, find the total amount of fees the girls have to pay.

3 units → 24 girls
1 unit → 8 girls
7 units → 56 girls
There are 56 girls in the camp.

56 × £50 = £2800
The total amount of fees the girls have to pay is £2800.

Revision 1

Date: _____

Section A

**Choose the correct answer.
Write its letter in the box.**

1 What is 3 450 026 in words?

   a three million, four hundred and fifty thousand and twenty-six
   b three million, four hundred thousand and fifty and twenty-six
   c three million, fifty thousand four hundred and twenty-six
   d three million, forty-five thousand and twenty-six

        a

2 Which of the following numbers is the greatest?

   a 15 265   **b** 93 216
   c 320 182   **d** 320 128

        c

3 Which of the following numbers when rounded to the nearest thousand is 23 000?

   a 22 097   **b** 22 499
   c 23 400   **d** 23 501

        c

4 What is the value of $20 + 10 \times 19 - 7$?

   a 140   **b** 203
   c 360   **d** 563

        b

---

25 ▦ The ratio of the number of UK coins to the number of European coins in Mr Cooper's savings box is 9 : 5. He has 640 European coins. If all the UK coins that Mr Cooper has are 50 pence coins, what is the total value of Mr Cooper's UK coins?

5 units → 640 coins
1 unit → 128 coins
9 units → 1152 coins
Mr Cooper collected 1152 UK coins.

Total value = 1152 × £0·50
          = £576
The total value of Mr Cooper's UK coins was £576.

26 ▦ A small square was cut out from a big square with an area of 576 cm². The ratio of the area of the big square to the area of the small square is 64 : 9. Find the length of one side of the small square that was cut out from the big square.

64 units → 576 cm²
1 unit → 9 cm²
9 units → 81 cm²
The area of the small square is 81 cm².

81 = 9 × 9 cm
The length of one side of the small square is 9 cm.

5 What is 1000 less than the product of 32 and 79?

a 111   b 1111

c 1528   d 2528

[c]

6 What is the difference between the values of the digit 6 in 2 300 628 and in 846 150?

a 600   b 5400

c 5522   d 6000

[b]

7 Express $\frac{18}{24}$ in its simplest form.

a $\frac{18}{24}$ b $\frac{3}{4}$

c $\frac{9}{12}$ d $\frac{1}{2}$

[b]

8 Express $\frac{8}{11} \div 4$ in its simplest form.

a $\frac{2}{11}$ b $\frac{8}{44}$

c $\frac{1}{11}$ d $\frac{4}{11}$

[a]

9 What is the value of $\frac{3}{4} - \frac{3}{8}$?

a $\frac{5}{8}$ b $\frac{3}{8}$

c $\frac{1}{2}$ d $\frac{1}{4}$

[b]

10 What is the value of $\frac{3}{4} \times \frac{8}{12}$?

a $\frac{1}{2}$ b $\frac{2}{3}$

c $\frac{5}{12}$ d $\frac{11}{16}$

[a]

11 Which of the following fractions is **not** in its simplest form?

a $\frac{3}{31}$ b $\frac{4}{67}$

c $\frac{7}{98}$ d $\frac{8}{109}$

[c]

12 The difference of $\frac{1}{2}$ and $\frac{3}{11}$ is _____.

a $\frac{5}{22}$ b $\frac{1}{11}$

c $\frac{7}{11}$ d $\frac{17}{22}$

[a]

13 Find the area of triangle ABC.

14 cm, 7 cm, 9 cm

a 126 cm²   b 98 cm²

c 63 cm²   d 49 cm²

[d]

14 What is the missing value in the equivalent ratios?

18 : _____ = 3 : 9

a 6   b 24

c 45   d 54

[d]

15 Rachel filled a box with 24 oranges and 64 apples. The ratio of the number of apples to the number of oranges in the box is _____.

a 3:8   b 3:11

c 8:3   d 8:11

[c]

16 Glass A contained 236 ml of milk and Glass B contained 420 ml of milk. Which of the following shows the ratio of the amount of milk in Glass A to that in Glass B?

a 89:135   b 119:165

c 479:660   d 59:105

[d]

Section B

Read the questions and fill in the answers.

17 $87412 = 80000 +$ ⬭ $+ 400 + 10 + 2$ _____ 7000

18 Using the digits 3, 9, 2, 6, 5, form the smallest 5-digit even number.

_____ 23 596

19 What number is 32 000 when rounded to the nearest thousand?
Write the smallest possible number.

_____ 31 500

20 Arrange the following numbers in order, beginning with the greatest.

35 928   164 239   35 982   916 236

_____ 916 236, 164 239, 35 982, 35 928

21 Find the value of $(2 + 4) \times 7 - 6 + 11$.

_____ 47

22 There were 215 pupils in a school. The school spent £17 on supplies for each pupil. Find the total amount of money that was spent on supplies for all the pupils.

$215 \times £17 = £3655$

_____ £3655

23 Robyn, Sian and Freddie shared a pie in the ratio $1:2:4$. What fraction of the pie did Sian get?

_____ $\frac{2}{7}$

24 A piece of string $\frac{9}{10}$ m long is cut into 3 shorter pieces of the same length.
What is the length of each short piece?

$\frac{9}{10} \div 3 = \frac{\overset{3}{\cancel{9}}}{10} \times \frac{1}{\cancel{3}_1} = \frac{3}{10}\,\text{m} = 30\,\text{cm}$

_____ 30 cm

---

25 On the triangle below, draw the height if the base is AB. Label the height CD.

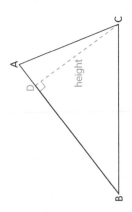

26 Find the area of triangle PQR.

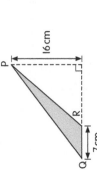

$\frac{1}{2} \times 16 \times 7 = 56\,\text{cm}^2$

_____ 56 cm²

🧮 **You may use your calculator for Questions 27 to 39 .**

27 Express $24\frac{1}{6} - 15\frac{1}{18}$ as a decimal, correct to 1 decimal place.

$24\frac{1}{6} - 15\frac{1}{18} = 9\frac{1}{9} \approx 9.1$

_____ 9.1

28 Find the area of the triangle DEF.

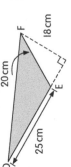

$\frac{1}{2} \times 25 \times 18 = 225\,\text{cm}^2$

_____ 225 cm²

29 Leanne jogged $7\frac{4}{11}$ km on Friday. She jogged $1\frac{3}{8}$ km more on Saturday. How many kilometres did she jog on both days? Give your answer correct to 1 decimal place.

$7\frac{4}{11} + 1\frac{3}{8} = 8\frac{65}{88}$ km

$8\frac{65}{88} + 7\frac{4}{11} = 16\frac{9}{88}$ km

$\approx 16 \cdot 1$ km

16·1 km

30 Find the area of the shaded triangle which is drawn on a cm square grid.

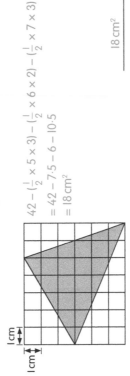

$42 - (\frac{1}{2} \times 5 \times 3) - (\frac{1}{2} \times 6 \times 2) - (\frac{1}{2} \times 7 \times 3)$

$= 42 - 7 \cdot 5 - 6 - 10 \cdot 5$

$= 18$ cm²

18 cm²

31 The ratio of the lengths of three sides of a triangle is $3:4:5$. The shortest side of the triangle is 39 cm. Find the perimeter of the triangle.

Perimeter of the triangle = $3 + 4 + 5 = 12$ units

3 units $\rightarrow$ 39 cm

1 unit $\rightarrow$ 13 cm

12 units $\rightarrow$ 156 cm

156 cm

32 Mr Nelson wants to buy a flat which costs £145 800. He pays £45 000 for the first payment. He pays the rest of the amount in equal instalments for 8 years. Find the amount he has to pay every year.

£145 800 − £45 000 = £100 800

£100 800 ÷ 8 = £12 600

£12 600

33 The table shows the parking charges at a car park.

7:00 a.m. to 5:00 p.m.	£0·50 per $\frac{1}{2}$ h
5:00 p.m. to 12:00 a.m.	£1·00 per hour
12:00 a.m. to 7:00 a.m.	£2·00 per entry

Mrs Brown parked her car at the car park from 3:00 p.m. to 8:00 p.m. on the same day. How much did she have to pay for parking?

From 3:00 p.m. to 5:00 p.m. $\rightarrow$ 2h

$4 \times £0.50 = £2$

From 5:00 p.m. to 8:00 p.m. $\rightarrow$ 3h

$3 \times £1 = £3$

£2 + £3 = £5

34 Box A's mass is $24\frac{1}{2}$ kg. It is $3\frac{3}{8}$ kg lighter than Box B. Find Box B's mass.

$24\frac{1}{2} + 3\frac{3}{8} = 27\frac{7}{8}$ kg

$27\frac{7}{8}$ kg

35 Alisha was training for a marathon. She ran for $18\frac{2}{15}$ km and then walked for $7\frac{1}{18}$ km before stopping for a rest. What was the total distance she covered before resting? Express your answer as a decimal, correct to 1 decimal place.

$18\frac{2}{15} + 7\frac{1}{18} = 25\frac{17}{90}$

≈ 25.2 km

25.2 km

36 The ratio of the masses of flour in two bags is 5:7. The heavier bag contains 1120 g of flour. What is the mass of flour in both bags?

7 units → 1120 g
1 unit → 160 g
5 + 7 = 12
12 units → 1920 g

1920 g

37 Rectangle ABCD and triangle XYZ have the same perimeter. Find the area of triangle XYZ.

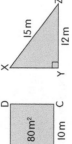

AB = 80 ÷ 10 = 8 m
Perimeter of ABCD = 2 × (10 + 8) = 36 m
Length of XY = 36 − 15 − 12 = 9 m
Area of XYZ = $\frac{1}{2}$ × 12 × 9 = 54 m²

54 m²

38 ABCD and ECFG are rectangles. BC = CF. What is the total area of the shaded parts of the shape?

Area of ΔADE = $\frac{1}{2}$ × 50 × 42 = 1050 cm²
Area of ΔBEC = Area of ΔEFG
Area of ECFG = 50 × 14 = 700 cm²
Shaded parts = 1050 + 700 = 1750 cm²

1750 cm²

39 Look at the pattern of shapes below. Shape 1 is made up of 1 unit square. Complete the table below.

a How many unit squares are there in Shape 4?
b Which shape in this pattern will have 169 small squares?

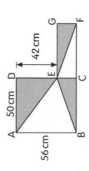

Shape 1   Shape 2   Shape 3   Shape 4

Shape	1	2	3	4	?
Number of Squares	1	4	9	16	169

a ___16___

b ___13___

Section C

Read the questions and write your answers in the spaces. Show your workings clearly.

You may use your calculator in this section.

40 A whole number when divided by 4 gives a remainder of 3. The same whole number when divided by 6 gives a remainder of 1. The number is between 70 and 85. What is the number?

Number Between 70 and 85	÷ 4	÷ 6
75	18 r 3	12 r 3 ✗
79	19 r 3	13 r 1 ✔

41 There are some poles and trees along a 6 km road. The poles are placed at an equal distance apart. There is a tree in between every two poles. The diagram shows the distance between a tree and two poles. Poles are placed at the start and end of the road. How many poles are there?

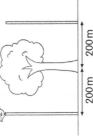

200 m   200 m

6 km ÷ 400 m = 6000 m ÷ 400 m
= 15

There are 15 trees altogether.
Number of poles = 15 + 1 = 16

42 Miss Scott earns £525 more than Mr Byrne each month. They each spend £1250 a month and save the rest. Miss Scott does not have any savings at first. After 11 months, she has £8250 in savings. How much does Mr Byrne earn in a year?

£8250 ÷ 11 = £750
£750 + £1250 = £2000
£2000 − £525 = £1475
Mr Byrne earns £1475 each month.

12 × £1475 = £17 700
He earns £17 700 in a year.

43 Mike caught a total of $7\frac{2}{5}$ kg of fish on a particular day. Of the fish caught, $4\frac{5}{8}$ kg were sea bass and the rest were mackerel. He gave away $1\frac{7}{8}$ kg of mackerel. How many kilograms of mackerel did he have left?

$7\frac{2}{5} - 4\frac{5}{8} = 2\frac{31}{40}$ kg

$2\frac{31}{40} - 1\frac{7}{8} = \frac{9}{10} = 0.9$ kg

He had 0.9 kg of mackerel left.

44. There were $2\frac{4}{11}$ ℓ of milk in Container A and some milk in Container B at first. Lisa then poured $1\frac{2}{5}$ ℓ of milk each into Container A and Container B. In the end, the total volume of milk in the two containers was 10 ℓ. How many litres of milk were there in Container B at first? Express your answer as a decimal correct to 2 decimal places.

$2\frac{4}{11} + 1\frac{2}{5} = 3\frac{42}{55}$ ℓ

$10 - 3\frac{42}{55} = 6\frac{13}{55}$ ℓ

$6\frac{13}{55} - 1\frac{2}{5} = 4\frac{46}{55} \approx 4\cdot84$ ℓ

There were 4·84 ℓ of milk in Container B at first.

45. Helen had to read a book for her school project. On the first day, she read 72 pages of the book. On the second day, she read $\frac{1}{4}$ of the remaining number of pages. In the end, she still had to read $\frac{1}{2}$ of the total number of pages to complete the book. How many pages were there in the book?

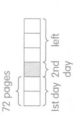

72 pages

1st day   2nd day   left

2 units → 72 pages
1 unit → 36 pages
6 units → 216 pages

There were 216 pages in the book.

46. Mr Wallace's weekly wage is twice that of Miss Taylor. The ratio of Miss Taylor's weekly wage to that of Mr Franklin is 5 : 3. Mr Wallace's weekly wage is £1100. How much is Miss Taylor and Mr Franklin's total weekly wage?

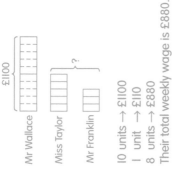

Mr Wallace   £1100
Miss Taylor
Mr Franklin   ?

10 units → £1100
1 unit → £110
8 units → £880

Their total weekly wage is £880.

47. The ratio of the volume of water in Container A to the volume of water in Container B to the volume of water in Container C is 2 : 3 : 8. Container B contains 900 ml of water.
a What is the volume of water in Container C?
b Find the total volume of water in the 3 containers.

a 3 units → 900 ml
1 unit → 300 ml
8 units → 2400 ml
The volume of water in Container C is 2400 ml.

b 2 + 3 + 8 = 13 units
= 13 × 300
= 3900 ml
The total volume of water in the 3 containers is 3900 ml.

48 Look at the shaded part in the square of which each side is 15 cm. P is the mid-point of the square. Find the area of the shaded figure.

15 cm

$\frac{1}{2} \times 15 \times 15 = 112\cdot5 \text{ cm}^2$

$15 \div 2 = 7\cdot5 \text{ cm}$

$\frac{1}{2} \times 15 \times 7\cdot5 = 56\cdot25 \text{ cm}^2$

$112\cdot5 - 56\cdot25 = 56\cdot25 \text{ cm}^2$

The area of the shaded figure is $56\cdot25 \text{ cm}^2$.

49 In the diagram below, KE = EL, AE = ED and BC is 3 times the length of KB. The area of rectangle ABCD is 90 cm^2 and the area of triangle KGB is 6 cm^2. Find the area of triangle KEL.

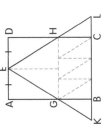

Area of GBCH = 6 × area of KGB
       = 6 × 6 = 36 cm^2

Area of AGHD = 90 − 36 = 54 cm^2

Area of GEH = 54 ÷ 2 = 27 cm^2

The area of triangle KEL = (8 × 6) + 27
             = 75 cm^2

HEURISTICS-BASED QUESTIONS

Noogol

Googol

Koogol

Ooogol

Toogol

Zoogol

Heuristic 1: Draw a model

Example 1

The total of two numbers is 51. Their difference is 9. What are the two numbers?

Solution:

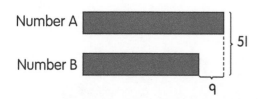

$51 - 9 = 42$
$42 \div 2 = \mathbf{21}$
$21 + 9 = \mathbf{30}$

Alternative Solution:
$51 + 9 = 60$
$60 \div 2 = \mathbf{30}$
$51 - 30 = \mathbf{21}$

The two numbers are 21 and 30.

Example 2

Ella and Tom have 80 marbles altogether. Ella and Alice have 50 marbles altogether. Alice has $\frac{1}{4}$ as many marbles as Tom. How many marbles does Ella have?

Solution:

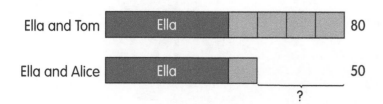

Tom has 4 times the number of marbles as Alice and the difference in the number of units is 3 units.

$80 - 50 = 30$
$30 \div 3 = 10$
$10 \times 4 = 40$ marbles (Tom)
$80 - 40 = 40$ marbles (Ella)

Ella has 40 marbles.

Example 3

The total mass of the Smith family's and the Brook family's suitcases is 90 kg. If the Smith family pack 6 kg more and the Brook family unpack 4 kg, the suitcases of the two families will have the same mass. What is the mass of the Smith family's suitcases in kilograms at first?

Solution:

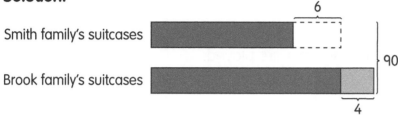

$90 - 4 + 6 = 92$
$92 \div 2 = 46$

$46 - 6 = 40$ kg (the Smith family's suitcases)
$46 + 4 = 50$ kg (the Brook family's suitcases)

The mass of the Smith family's suitcases is 40 kg at first.

Check:
$40 + 50 = 90$ kg
$40 + 6 = 46$ kg (the Smith family pack 6 kg more)
$50 - 4 = 46$ kg (the Brook family unpack 4 kg)

Example 4

Harry is 10 years older than Ava. Their ages add up to 35. How old will Ava be in 15 years' time?

Solution:

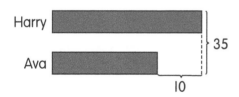

The model above shows that: 2 units ⟶ $35 - 10 = 25$

1 unit ⟶ $25 \div 2 = 12\frac{1}{2}$

Ava is 12 years and 6 months old. In 15 years' time, she will be 27 years and 6 months old.

Heuristic 2: Act it out / draw a diagram

Example 1

There are 7 football teams in a school. Each team will have to play each of the other teams. How many games are played if each plays each of the other teams:

(a)   only once?   (b)   twice?

Solution:

Draw a table or diagram to show how the matches are played.

(a)

	A	B	C	D	E	F	G
A		X	X	X	X	X	X
B			X	X	X	X	X
C				X	X	X	X
D					X	X	X
E						X	X
F							X
G							

(a)   Number of games played = 6 + 5 + 4 + 3 + 2 + 1
                                                  = 21

21 games are played if each team plays each of the other teams only once.

(b)   Number of games played = 2 × 21
                                                  = 42

42 games are played if each team plays each of the other teams twice.

Example 2

The diagram below is made of 24 lolly sticks.

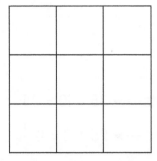

(a)   Remove 6 lolly sticks so that only 3 squares are left.
(b)   Remove 12 lolly sticks so that only 3 squares are left.

Solution:

(a)

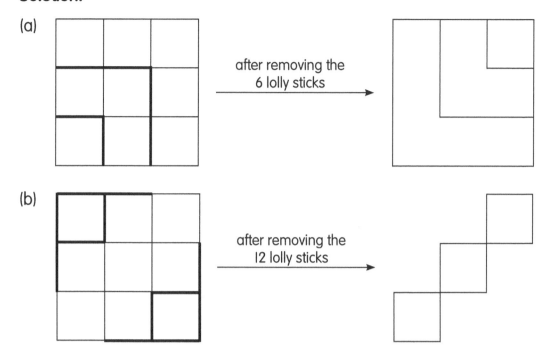

(b)

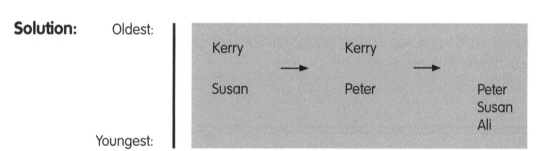

Example 3

Kerry is older than Susan. Peter is younger than Kerry. Susan is older than Ali but younger than Peter. Who is the oldest?

Solution:

Oldest:

Kerry	Kerry	
Susan →	Peter →	Peter
		Susan
		Ali

Youngest:

Kerry is the oldest.

Example 4

Four people are in a room. How many handshakes will there be if all of them shake hands with one another?

Solution:

There will be 6 handshakes.

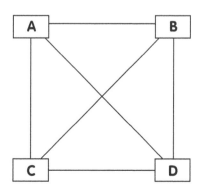

Heuristic 3: Simplify the problem

Example 1

Draw a straight line to cut the diagram on the right into two equal parts.

Solution:

Simplify the diagram and treat it as a square and a rectangle.

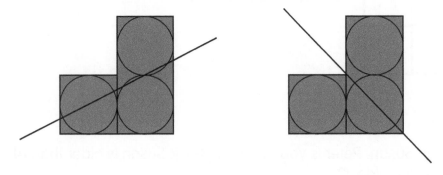

There are multiple ways of dividing the square and rectangle into two equal parts. Two possible ways are shown above. In the solution on the left the straight line passes through the centre of the square and the centre of the rectangle.

Example 2

Fill in the circles with the following numbers so that the sum of the numbers on each side of the triangle is 36.

3, 6, 9, 12, 15, 18

Solution:

Simplify by dividing each number by 3.

$$3, 6, 9, 12, 15, 18 \xrightarrow{\div 3} 1, 2, 3, 4, 5, 6$$

Fill in the circles using the new numbers so that the sum of the numbers on each side of the triangle is $36 \div 3 = 12$.

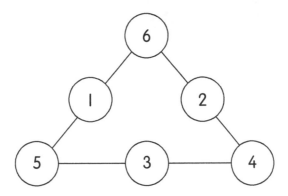

Multiply the number in each circle by 3.

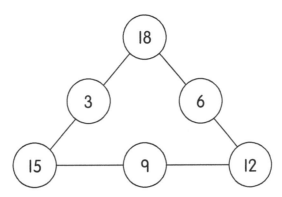

Heuristic 4: Guess and check

Example 1

Ben is 5 years old. His mother is seven times as old as him. In how many years' time will she be 4 times Ben's age?

Solution:

Ben's Age	Ben's Mother's Age	4 Times?
5	35	No
6	36	No
7	37	No
8	38	No
9	39	No
10	**40**	**Yes**

Ben's mother will be 4 times Ben's age in 5 years' time.

Example 2

Fill in the boxes with 1, 2, 3, 4 and 5.

$$
\begin{array}{r}
\boxed{}\ \boxed{}\ \boxed{}\ \boxed{} \\
\times\ \boxed{} \\
\hline
2 \quad 8 \quad 7 \quad 0 \\
\hline
\end{array}
$$

Solution:

The possibilities for the divisor and the last digit of the 4-digit number are:

Last digit of the 4-digit number	5	4	2	5
Divisor	4	5	5	2

Check: 2870 ÷ 4 = 717·5 (So 4 cannot be the divisor.)
2870 ÷ 5 = 574 (So 5 cannot be the divisor.)
2870 ÷ 2 = 1435
1435 × 2 = 2870

The two numbers being multiplied are 1435 and 2.

Example 3

Fill in the boxes with the digits 0, 1, 2, 3, 4 and 5 to find the smallest difference. Use each digit only once.

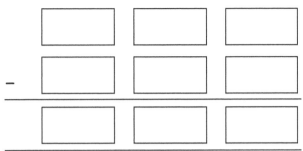

Solution:

For the smallest difference, the hundreds digits must be as follows:

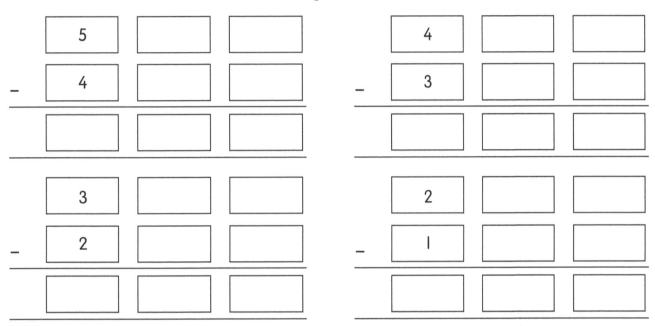

Then from the remaining 4 numbers in each case, the smallest 2-digit number goes on top and the largest 2-digit number goes to the bottom.

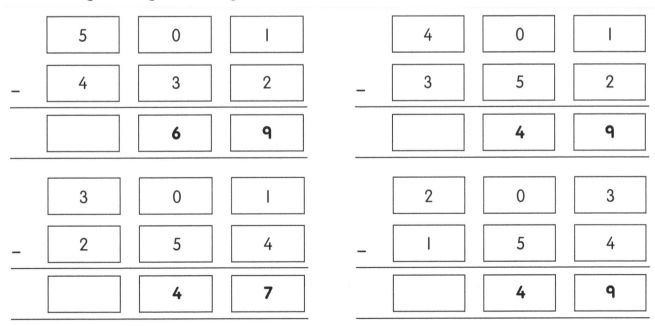

Therefore 301 – 254 gives the smallest difference.

Heuristic 5: Look for patterns

Example 1

Look at the diagram below.

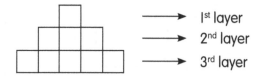

How many blocks are needed to form the 15th layer?

Solution:

The number of blocks in each layer make a number pattern:
1, 3, 5, 7, 9, 11, …, 25, 27, 29.
The 15th number is 29.
So 29 blocks are needed to form the 15th layer.

Example 2

What is the missing number?

3, 8, 15, 24, 35, _____, 63

Solution:

3,   8,   15, 24,   35, _____, 63
  +5   +7   +9   +11   +13   +15

35 + 13 = 48
The missing number is 48.

Example 3

Alice wanted to invite her friends to her birthday party. She called 3 friends on Wednesday. She told each of these 3 friends to call another 3 different friends on Thursday. Each friend who received a call on Thursday called another 3 different friends on Friday. How many friends were called on Friday?

Solution:

The number of friends who were called each day from Wednesday to Friday make a number pattern:
1 × 3 = 3, 3 × 3 = 9, 9 × 3 = 27 friends
27 friends were called on Friday.

Example 4

Diagram 1 has 2 dots.
Diagram 2 has 6 dots.
Diagram 3 has 12 dots.

Diagram 1   Diagram 2   Diagram 3

If the pattern is continued, how many dots are there in:

(a)   Diagram 5?   (b)   Diagram 12?

Solution:

	Number of dots
Diagram 1	$1 \times 2 = 2$
Diagram 2	$2 \times 3 = 6$
Diagram 3	$3 \times 4 = 12$
Diagram 5	$5 \times 6 = 30$
Diagram 12	$12 \times 13 = 156$

There are 30 dots in Diagram 5 and 156 dots in Diagram 12.

Example 5

Find the sum of $3 + 4 + 5 + \ldots + 95 + 96 + 97$.

Solution:

$3 + 97 = 100$
$4 + 96 = 100$
.
.
.
$49 + 51 = 100$

$\left.\right\}$ $49 - 3 + 1 = 47$. So there are 47 pairs of numbers that add up to 100.

$47 \times 100 = 4700$

$4700 + 50 = 4750$

The sum is 4750.

Heuristic 6: Make a systematic list

Example 1

Kristina has a number. When the number is divided by 3, the remainder is 2. When the number is divided by 6, the remainder is 5. Her number is less than 30 but greater than 20. What is her number?

Solution:

	1	2	3	4	5	6	7	8	9
×3	3	6	9	12	15	18	21	24	27
+2	5	8	11	14	17	20	**23**	26	29

	1	2	3	4	5	6	7	8	9
×6	6	12	18	24	30	36	42	48	54
+5	11	17	**23**	29	35				

The possible numbers are 11 and 23.
But 11 is less than 20, so Kristina's number is 23.

Example 2

The composite shape below is made up of a square inside another square. The lengths of the sides of each square are whole numbers. If the area of the shaded part is 56 cm², find the perimeter of the shaded part of the shape.

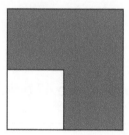

Solution:

Length of side	1	2	3	4	**5**	6	7	8	**9**
Area	1	4	9	16	**25**	36	49	64	**81**

$9 \times 9 = 81 \text{ cm}^2$
$5 \times 5 = 25 \text{ cm}^2$
$81 - 25 = 56 \text{ cm}^2$

The lengths of the sides of the two squares are 9 cm and 5 cm.
Perimeter of the shaded part of the shape = 4 × 9
$$= 36 \text{ cm}$$

Example 3

Catherine saved some £2 coins and £5 notes. Altogether she saved 28 coins and notes in total. If the total value of the coins and notes is £116, how many £2 coins did she save?

Solution:

Value of £2 Coins	Value of £5 Notes	Total Value
14 × 2	14 × 5	28 + 70 = 98
10 × 2	18 × 5	20 + 90 = 110
8 × 2	20 × 5	16 + 100 = **116**

Catherine saved eight £2 coins.

Example 4

The ratio of the number of girls to the number of boys in a class was 3 : 2 at first. There were 30 children altogether. Some children left the class and the ratio became 6 : 5. How many boys left the class?

Solution:

Number of Girls in the Class	Number of Boys in the Class	Ratio of the Number of Girls to the Number of Boys in the Class
18	12	3 : 2 – initial ratio
18	10	9 : 5
16	10	8 : 5
12	**10**	6 : 5
6	**5**	6 : 5

The number of boys decreased from 12 to either 10 or 5.
So either 2 boys or 7 boys left the class.

Heuristic 7: Work backwards

Example 1

I think of a number. When the number is doubled and 3 is added to the result, the answer is 15. What was the original number?

Solution:

15 − 3 = 12
12 ÷ 2 = 6

The original number was 6.

Example 2

A bus reached Bus Stop A and 10 people boarded the bus. At Bus Stop B, $\frac{2}{5}$ of the passengers got off the bus. At Bus Stop C, $\frac{2}{3}$ of the passengers got off the bus. Then 5 people boarded the bus. There were 15 people in the bus when it left Bus Stop C. How many passengers were on the bus when it reached Bus Stop A?

Solution:

Bus Stop C	Bus Stop B	Bus Stop A
15 − 5 = 10 1 unit ⟶ 10 3 units ⟶ 10 × 3 = 30 (number of passengers in the bus when it reached Bus Stop C)	3 units ⟶ 30 1 unit ⟶ 10 5 units ⟶ 10 × 5 = 50 (number of passengers in the bus when it reached Bus Stop B)	50 − 10 = 40 (number of passengers in the bus when it reached Bus Stop A)

40 passengers were in the bus when it reached Bus Stop A.

Heuristic 8: Before and after

Example 1

The original number of boys to the number of girls on a school rounders team was 3:1. After 3 boys and 4 girls joined, the ratio of the number of boys to girls became 2:1. How many boys were on the rounders team at first?

Solution:

Before (3:1)	After		Check Ratio
Boys : Girls	Number of boys + 3	Number of girls + 4	2:1?
3:1	3 + 3 = 6	1 + 4 = 5	6:5
6:2	6 + 3 = 9	2 + 4 = 6	9:6 = 3:2
9:3	9 + 3 = 12	3 + 4 = 7	12:7
12:4	12 + 3 = 15	4 + 4 = 8	15:8
15:5	15 + 3 = 18	5 + 4 = 9	**18:9 = 2:1 ✓**

15 boys were on the rounders team at first.

Example 2

Andy and Ethan went fishing. Andy caught three times as many fish as Ethan. After Andy sold 17 of his fish and Ethan sold 3 of his fish, they both had the same number of fish. How many fish did Andy catch?

Solution:

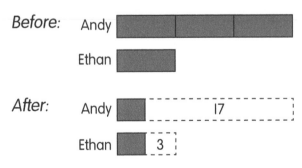

17 − 3 = 14

2 units ⟶ 14
1 unit ⟶ 7
3 units ⟶ 3 × 7 = 21

Andy caught 21 fish.

Heuristic 9: Restate the problem in another way

Example 1

There were twelve teams of 2 and teams of 4 altogether who registered for a spelling competition. On the day of the competition, one member of a team of 4 was ill and had to miss the competition. There were 37 participants altogether at the competition. How many teams of 4 registered for the spelling competition?

Solution:

Restate the problem and assume that all the participants were present on the day of the competition. So, adding 1 more to 37, there were 38 participants.

1st guess : Six teams of 4 and six teams of 2.

$$
\begin{array}{r} 6 \\ \times \ 4 \\ \hline 24 \\ \hline \end{array}
\qquad
\begin{array}{r} 6 \\ \times \ 2 \\ \hline 12 \\ \hline \end{array}
$$

6 → 12 teams

12 → 36 participants

2nd guess : Seven teams of 4 and five teams of 2.

$$
\begin{array}{r} 7 \\ \times \ 4 \\ \hline 28 \\ \hline \end{array}
\qquad
\begin{array}{r} 5 \\ \times \ 2 \\ \hline 10 \\ \hline \end{array}
$$

5 → 12 teams

10 → 38 participants

Seven teams of 4 registered for the spelling competition.

Example 2

5 identical rectangles measuring 5 cm by 2 cm are placed next to each other as shown. What is the perimeter of the shape?

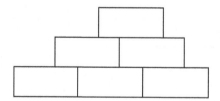

Solution:

Finding the perimeter of the given shape is the same as finding the perimeter of a 15 cm by 6 cm rectangle.

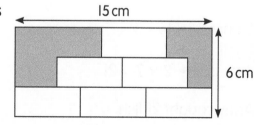

So the perimeter of the shape = (15 + 6) × 2
                                                = 42 cm

PHOTOCOPY MASTERS

Noogol

Googol

Ooogol

Koogol

Toogol

Zoogol

Unit I: Whole Numbers (I)

Let's Learn! (Pupil Textbook 5A, p 2)

Ones	
Tens	
Hundreds	
Thousands	
Ten Thousands	
Hundred Thousands	

Unit I: Whole Numbers (I)

Let's Learn! (Pupil Textbook 5A, pp 6 and I3)

Millions	Hundred Thousands	Ten Thousands	Thousands	Hundreds	Tens	Ones

Unit 2: Whole Numbers (2)

Activity (Pupil Textbook 5A, p 55)

0	1	2	3
4	5	6	7
8	9	+	−
×	÷	(	)

Unit 3 & 4: Fractions (1) & (2)

Let's Learn! (Pupil Textbook 5A, pp 70, 71, 74, 77, 79 and 112)

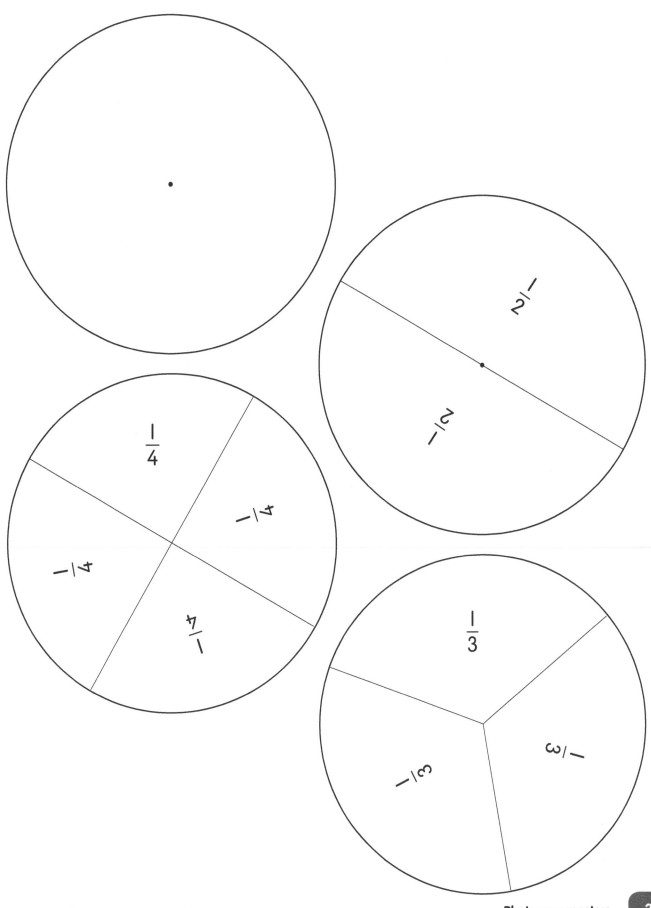

Unit 3 & 4: Fractions (1) & (2)

Let's Learn! (Pupil Textbook 5A, pp 70, 71, 74, 77, 79 and 112)

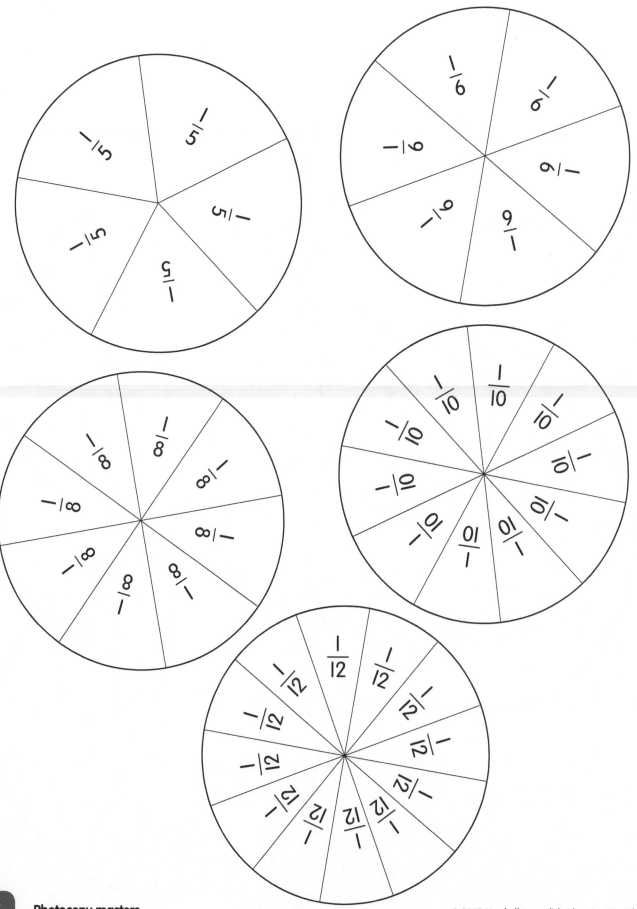

Unit 3: Fractions (I)

Activity (Pupil Textbook 5A, pp 78 and 80)

Unit 4: Fractions (2)

Activity (Pupil Textbook 5A, p 114)

Unit 5: Area of a Triangle

Let's Learn! (Pupil Textbook 5A, p 133)

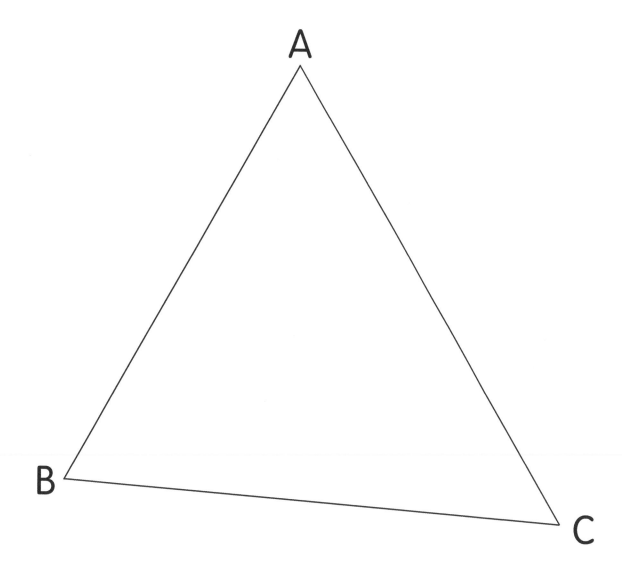

Unit 5: Area of a Triangle

Let's Learn! (Pupil Textbook 5A, p 134)

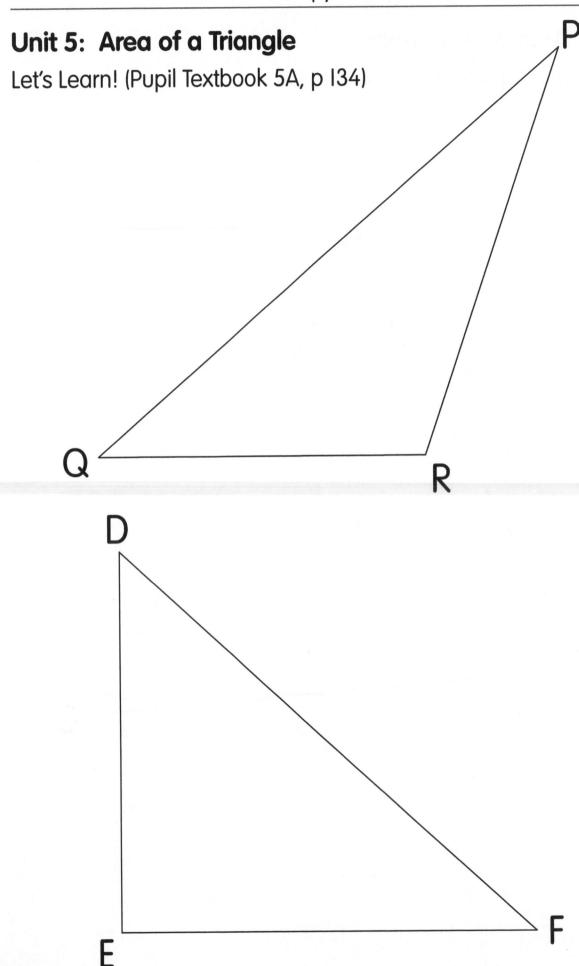

Unit 5: Area of a Triangle

Let's Learn! (Pupil Textbook 5A, p 137)

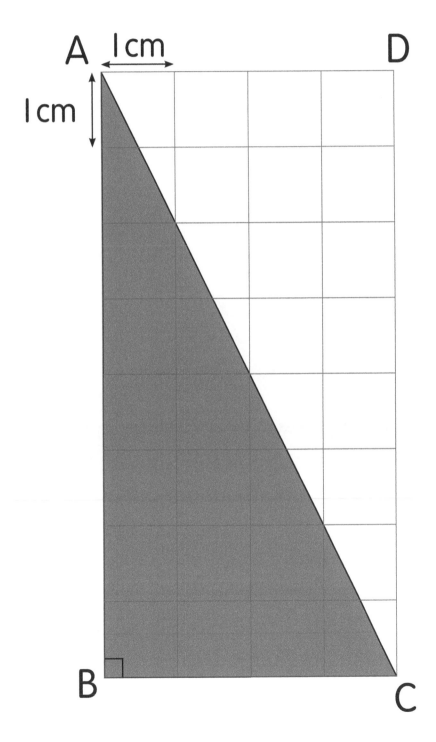

Unit 5: Area of a Triangle

Let's Learn! (Pupil Textbook 5A, p 138)

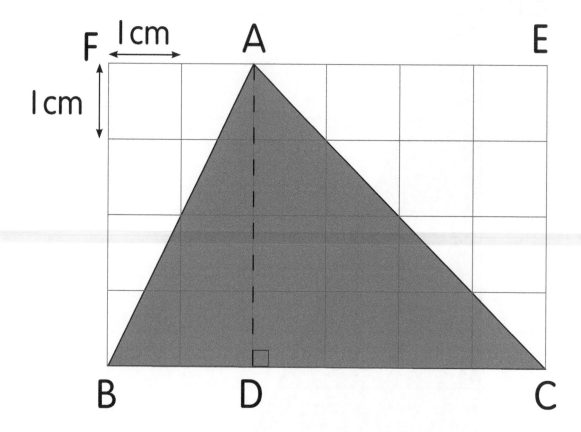

Unit 5: Area of a Triangle

Let's Learn! (Pupil Textbook 5A, p 139)

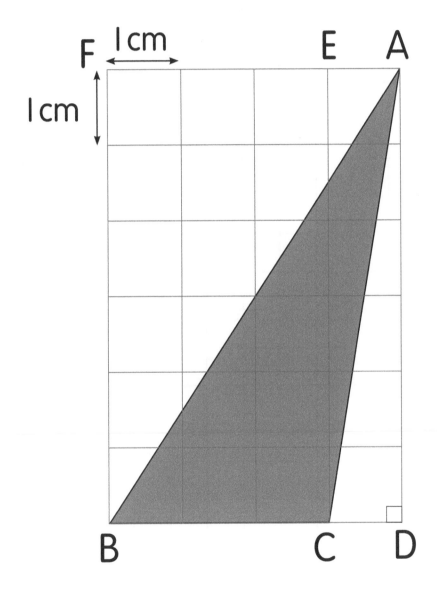

Square grid paper

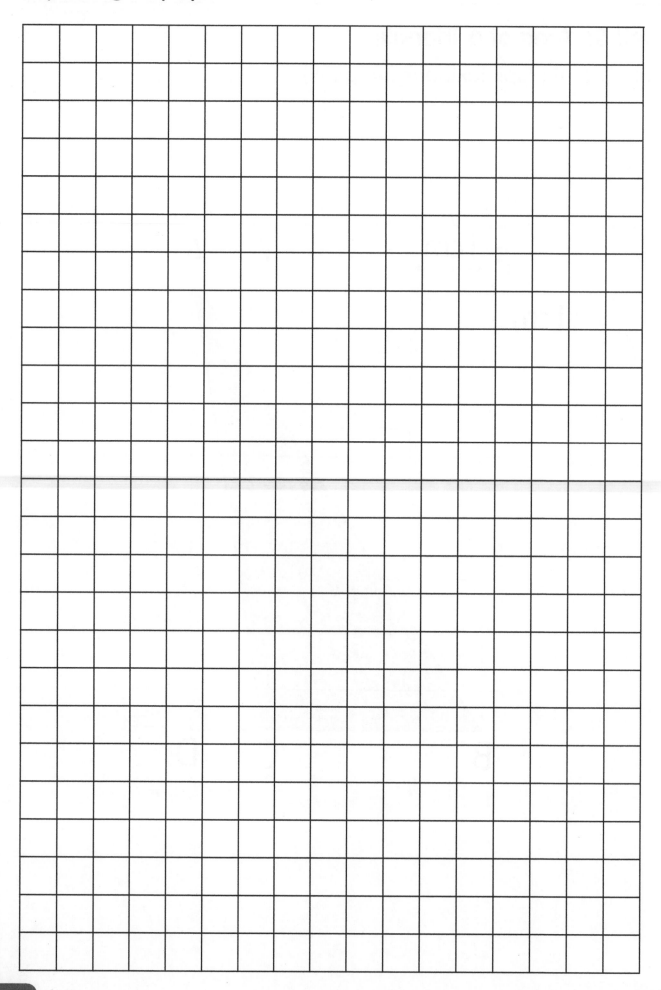

Photocopy masters